SENTICS

DR. MANFRED CLYNES is recognized as one of the keenest and most creative intellects working in science today. He holds degrees in neuroscience (D.Sc.) from the University of Melbourne and a M.S. in music from the Juilliard School of Music in New York, as well as an engineering degree, and did graduate work at Princeton University in the psychology of music. He is also a poet. He was chief research scientist at Rockland State Hospital in Orangeburg, New York, for seventeen years, where he pioneered biocybernetics and discovered the principles of sentics. He has lectured at Harvard, MIT, and Princeton, and is presently Professor of Neuropsychology at the University of Melbourne. Born in Vienna, Clynes was first acclaimed as a pianist in Australia as a teenager, and has successfully toured the major cities of Europe as a concert pianist; his performances today are special cherished events. His teachers in music included Gorodnitzki, Edwin Fischer and especially, Pablo Casals. As a physiologist, he discovered the biologic law of unidirectional rate sensitivity, and among his many inventions is the Computer of Average Transient (CAT), which became a standard tool in virtually all research laboratories for studying brain function. His widely significant research in neurophysiology, culminating in an integration with his work in music and the nature of emotions, has been published in over hundred and ten articles in scientific journals and five books and has been frequently reported by the press. He is a charter member of the International Society for Research on Emotion. An eminent authority on dynamic emotion communication, in music, the arts and in personal life, his book, Sentics, is regarded as a classic today. Sentic cycles, also known as Music of Touch, have helped thousands of people in many parts of the world to insight, greater enjoyment of life and peace.

SENTICS

THE TOUCH OF THE EMOTIONS

DR. MANFRED CLYNES

INTRODUCTION BY YEHUDI MENUHIN

Originally published in 1977 by Doubleday and Co., Inc.

This revised edition published in Great Britain in 1989 by

PRISM PRESS
2 South Street
Bridport
Dorset DT6 3NQ

and distributed in the USA by

AVERY PUBLISHING GROUP INC.
350 Thorens Avenue
Garden City Park
New York 11040

and published in Australia 1989 by

UNITY PRESS
6a Ortona Road
Lindfield
NSW 2070

1 85327 025 3

Printed and bound in the Channel Islands
by The Guernsey Press Limited

Dedication

To the source of essentic form
and to those who get drunk on it

The memory of my father
of Pablo Casals
and of Artur Schnabel
and to three beautiful women
who have lived in me

ACKNOWLEDGMENTS

I thank all those who have contributed to make this book possible: men and women who came to me with their troubles; musicians who gave of themselves; those who helped in scientific work at the Rockland State Hospital in Orangeburg, New York, and at the University of California, San Diego and the Biocybernetic Institute; and above all the thousands who participated in sentic cycles and reported their experience.

I cannot mention them all—but certainly without Pablo Casals, Rudolf Serkin, Darius Clynes, Warren McCullough, Otto Schmitt, Michael Kohn, and Steven Bunnell, this book would not have been born.

Contents

Part Two

SENTIC CYCLES, PERSONAL APPLICATIONS AND EXTENSIONS OF SENTIC THEORY

Part Three

SENTICS, THE INDIVIDUAL, AND SOCIETY

Foreword

Dr. Clynes and I met the first time at the reception desk of the newsroom of the New York *Times* where I was working as a reporter in the newspaper's science department. It was around the time of the congressional hearings on the Nuclear Test Ban Treaty of 1961, and I had been sent to the reception area by the City Desk to interview a person who claimed to have solved the single—seemingly insurmountable, at the time—technical problem standing in the way of a total ban on all tests—in the air, space, water, and underground. That problem was how to distinguish between natural earthquakes and earth tremors touched off by underground nuclear test detonations. The man who it seemed had found the solution was Dr. Manfred Clynes.

I no longer recall the details of Clynes's scheme except that it seemed at the time to be ingeniously simple and quite possibly workable. However, the process of the government's working out the details to the treaty had already progressed too far for any substantial modification: tests would be banned only in space, the atmosphere and under water; underground testing was to be excluded from the ban.

What stayed with me about Dr. Clynes's visit, however, and his (characteristically) mumbled explanation of how to differentiate earthquakes from underground bomb tests was his ingenious and strikingly original style of thought. It was of a quality for which mathematicians reserve the term "elegant," and although I had already met and come to know a great many brilliant men and women of science and medicine—including several Nobel laureates—I had the feeling that I had just encountered my first authentic genius.

Whether, in fact, Manfred Clynes was the *first* genius I had ever met, his membership to that strange and exciting echelon of intuitive mentality has been documented many times over and is done so again here in this book. The reader is in store for the truly thrilling experience of looking at the world from a new perspective—perhaps never to see things quite the same again. Moreover, each reader's experience of this book is likely to be partly a very personal one; mine was, as I went over the original manuscript and found that it evoked discoveries about my own world which were suddenly obvious and, at the same time, completely unexpected.

I believe I can best prepare the reader for the sort of experience I've just promised by suggesting the kinds of thought processes that I believe led Dr. Clynes to the ideas presented in this book. First of all, it is important to realize that Clynes's own world is enormously rich, for he is a concert pianist, neurophysiologist, electronics engineer, biocybernetician, computer inventor, poet, and philosopher. He has the capacity to dip freely into each of those talents and make connections and associations that often produce totally unexpected results.

For example, in 1956 Dr. Nathan Kline, the psychiatrist noted for his work with tranquilizing and antidepressant drugs and director of research at Rockland State Hospital in Orangeburg, New York, suggested that Manfred try to find ways to apply feedback control systems analysis techniques to psychiatric problems. While Manfred thought that this could not be tackled scientifically at that time, he did adapt cybernetic (automatic feedback control) techniques to the study of physiological regulatory mechanisms that control heart rate, blood pressure, body temperature, etc.

One of his experiments at Rockland involved measuring the response of the pupil of the eye to change in illumination. It is well known that the pupil contracts in response to increasing brightness and dilates in diminishing light. However, he surprisingly discovered that when subjects were exposed to brief bursts of darkness (by momentarily extinguishing the light, then turning it back on) their pupils did not dilate in response to the moment of dark but instead contracted to the stimulation of increasing illumination after the moment of darkness. This was, of course, completely unexpected and for a time defied explanation.

Clynes's solution was both ingenious and richly rewarding, for it aided in the discovery of a new biological law—a very rare occurrence in science. His explanation of the unexpected outcome of his experiment was that there must be two information-carrying channels involved in the control of pupil size: one channel responding to decreasing illumination, the other channel responding to increasing illumination. Those two different channels were made distinguishable in the experiment by the fact that the dimming channel responded more slowly than the brightening channel did—too slowly, in fact, for the pupil to dilate in response to diminishing light, so that the other, faster channel supplanted the dilating reaction and caused pupillary constriction in response to subsequent brightening. This is an easy experiment to do, and the reader can try it with another person by simply watching the person's pupils in a lighted room while the light is briefly flicked off and then on again; the pupils will constrict, first, and then redilate.

From that observation—and similar ones involving other physiological regulatory systems such as the dynamic control of heart rate through breathing—Manfred formulated the Biologic Law of Unidirectional Rate Sensitivity. The law concerns the ways in which information can be processed for communication and control functions in living organisms. As such, the law—probably more than any other known law of nature—bears on qualities that distinguish uniquely between living and non-living things. In only a few years after Manfred's first publication of the URS principle, its function in a wide range of biological processes was confirmed by scientists in several laboratories throughout the world.

Simply stated the URS law holds that, first, information about several events in the world outside and within an organism is perceived more acutely (if not actually differently) under changing conditions than under static ones. Thus, we are more sensitive to increasing or to decreasing temperature and lighting than to constant ones—which may even become unnoticeable in time. Secondly, the law states that each of these two kinds of information (increasing or decreasing change) requires its own one-way channel, based on the fact that molecules can arrive only in positive numbers. This channel many be a series of nerve fibers, a selective membrane, a sequence of chemical reactions or hormones, or some other dynamic biological system. For example, information about heating travels in one channel and that about cooling in another. And, as shown in the experiment with the eye's response to changing illumination, two channels that carry information about a "similar" (but actually, opposite) quality —e.g., increasing and decreasing temperature, illumination—may respond at different rates. But other systems have only developed one channel, such as the sensation of smell, which is only sensitive to rate of increase.

From this work, Dr. Clynes began thinking more and more about the relation of our experience of various "standard" qualities of the perceived world. This sort of thought led him to experiments in which he was able, for the first time, to associate specific electrical brain wave patterns with particular events involving certain qualities of the perceived world. Thus, as will be explained in this book, Manfred was able, first, to associate a particular recorded brain wave shape with the perception of redness and later to expand the list to more than one hundred other different visual stimuli (colors, patterns) that were associated with specific shapes of brain waves generated by subjects who perceived the stimuli. It was after he had demonstrated this remarkable feat to his own and others' satisfaction that he made a gigantic—elegant—conceptual leap that resulted in the birth of a whole new field of science—sentics—which this book is about.

In making that leap, Dr. Clynes, in effect, figured that if certain electrical brain wave shapes are characteristic of particular perceived qualities of the environment in the outside world, then there must be brain patterns that are characteristic of qualities of a person's inner world, too. However, while it was completely easy for Dr. Clynes to make the association between stimuli in the outside world and corresponding brain wave shapes, it was quite another thing to find qualities of inner experience that might have associated specific brain patterns and to determine how those patterns might be extracted reliably from all the other activity of the brain.

Clynes's solution to this formidable problem was inspired by his rich musical background. He recalled having read a book by the German musicologist Gustav Becking, in which it was noted that whenever an experienced musician was asked to follow a musical composition by moving his forefinger in the air—as if to conduct the music—the finger "drew" shapes that seemed to be consistent among different compositions by the same composer.

Dr. Clynes decided to use music as the source of qualities of inner experience (one can *think* a melody) and to study the shape of the movement—or in his method, pressure—as a representation of those particular brain waves associated with the music. His notion was that the expressive shape of the finger's pressure was, in effect, a mechanical transduction of the electrical wave shapes generated specifically and characteristically in the brain in association with the inner experience of a particular piece of music's "inner pulse," or qualitative signature!

As he explains in the book, experiments with this concept—involving several notable musicians—supported his hypothesis perfectly. Indeed, the insight into the fundamental nature of music that Clynes's theory and experiments provide makes the very essence of music comprehensible in ways never before possible.

His next elegant leap was to recognize that the qualities he was studying in music could be thought of as corresponding to the qualities inherent in human emotions. And, as he will explain, he was able to show that several different emotions have characteristic expressive "shapes" (no doubt reflecting their generative brain wave shapes), just as different musical compositions do.

I found this realm of Dr. Clynes's work especially evocative because of my own interest in music, experimental psychology, and personality types. He writes in his chapter on music that the shape of a particular piece of music's "inner pulse" is similar to the shapes of the composer's other works because the basic shape reflects the composer's own personality—it is his *personal signature*, a kind of "presence." This concept led me to make a little leap of my own one Sunday while listening to a recording of pianist Joshua Rifkin playing some of the works of the great ragtime composer Scott Joplin.

I was doing some routine paper work while the recording played, but I was surprised suddenly to find myself feeling so deeply moved that my eyes filled with tears! The paper work certainly was not deeply moving, so it had to be the music—but why, particularly, when I wasn't really listening to it?

Then I had an idea. I happen to be of a certain type of personality or temperament. It occurred to me that, just perhaps, Scott Joplin—

a favorite of mine since childhood—and Joshua Rifkin were the same types as I, and that the signature of our common temperamental nature was carried in the inner pulse of Joplin's music, to be rendered to its best by Rifkin to my maximum enjoyment.

I went to the record jacket and found quite extensive notes on both Joplin and Rifkin. Reading them and other notes left little doubt in my mind that my suspicion was correct; Joplin, Rifkin, and Osmundsen were all three cut from the same temperamental cloth.

In terms of my hypothesis, then, what had happened was the following. Black composer Joplin had translated the neurophysiological engram of his basic temperamental nature—his personality signature—from his brain to musical notation on paper in the inner pulse of the music he wrote in New Orleans and Chicago between 1899 and 1909. While the music has wide appeal, it could strike the most responsive chords in those whose fundamental nature was most like Joplin's, as reflected in the similarities of their neurophysiological engrams. Thus, Rifkin, a young music professor and pianist of Joplin's same personality type, was able both to find Joplin's compositions highly appealing and to render them with a high degree of fidelity to the composer's original intent. Finally, while Rifkin's performance of Joplin's works was highly appealing to the general public because his interpretation was so nearly perfect, his recordings of the piano rags were especially moving to persons of like temperament, such as myself.

This is all—or mostly—pure speculation, of course. The only circumstantial support of this interpretation consists of three factors: Manfred's findings in the new science of sentics, my having favored Joplin's music since I was a boy but not liking any performance of it nearly as much as I do Rifkin's, and, lastly, my making a prediction, based upon my hypothesis (and on Manfred's sentics theory), which I believe proved out.

What I am trying to show in this digression is that the reader may expect to gain new and unexpected insights from Manfred's lines of reasoning which should be great fun and possibly very rewarding to explore.

Dr. Clynes's sentic theory may also be seen to apply to the teaching and practice of the martial arts. In the instruction of such disciplines as karate, kiai-jutsu, shoriniji kempo but particularly aikido, tai-chi-ch'uan and wing chun, much is made of the *shapes* of movement. The more nearly perfect one shapes movements—in merely exercises or in actual combat—the more effective will the practitioner be. In fact, martial artists who perfect their techniques—including controlled breathing, concentration, and shaped movement—can develop abilities to perform seemingly supernatural feats. Apparently, the disciplines practiced in certain of the martial arts enable the practitioner to "tap into" a reserve or reservoir of the essence of human being (which clearly exists in everyone, inasmuch as anyone with sufficient determination and application can develop these capabilities).

Now precisely what that "essence" may be—intrinsic energy, ki, chi, or whatever one wants to call it—is not known. One cannot help wondering, however, if the application of Manfred Clynes's new science of sentics to an analysis of the occult aspects of the martial arts might not bring us within reach of the answer to that ultimate question: what are we that we can become?

But I daresay, the reader will come up with many other questions to which sentics might be fruitfully applied—and may even encounter a few unexpected answers along the way, as well. There is "something for everyone" in this book simply because the science of sentics touches on so many aspects of the human condition, from creative expression in science and the arts, to the very core of individual being, to practical matters of physical and mental health. I hope in some small way I have helped prepare the reader for the adventures ahead in this important book.

John A. Osmundsen

New York, 1975

Foreword

Dr. Manfred Clynes' great achievement is to have made emotions and their communication respectable, recognizably rendered into graphs, analysable and measurable. These most intimate, basic and powerful of human drives are no longer imprisoned within the realm of conjecture and blind groping with more or less working hypotheses, but have been released for study, respect and compassion. It is obvious that this signal breakthrough could only have been achieved by a musician: Dr. Clynes is a very distinguished pianist; a scientist who remains a musician at heart. In the same way that painting and drawing furthered our understanding of the human body and of our anatomy, so is music the true and only revelation of emotion, whether as pure music or as the music of language or dance. When, as in Manfred Clynes' case, the music is allied to a penetrating intellect and scientific insight, miracles may happen.

Dr. Clynes' contribution to the interrelationship of emotions, to our crying need for personal expression, and for the cleansing of our minds and souls, illuminates the good sense of our tribal ancestors with their games and gestures and oral traditions, for they knew the supreme importance of sound and contact. Perhaps his gift to humanity will serve to lead us to a more balanced existence, to a coordinated and reciprocal strengthening of mind and heart. Perhaps it will lead to greater harmony and fewer wars. I welcome this sentic science, for the god of love has finally put on the guise of science to lead us into the truly humane — for we, having lost our intuition, and often employing our intellect merely to enhance our brutality, and having lost our faith in feeling and conscience, may rediscover ourselves through the only avenue we acknowledge, that of science.

I pray, however, that just as every thing may be used to both good and evil ends, this new science may be pursued to good, compassionate and wholesome purposes only.

YEHUDI MENUHIN
New York

Preface

This book is about emotion communication. We are discovering—rather to our surprise—that nature has made the communication of emotions elegantly simple. To find out how nature's dynamic communicative forms function in man with precision and power, this is the branch of science called *sentics*.

Western man has long lived as an uneasy guest within nature. In trying to discover natural order, he put himself outside the order he was discovering—as an observer, if not always a dispassionate observer. He could not fit his passions and emotions into the order, but had to regard them as epiphenomena. The existential attributes of emotions could not compare with those of atoms and molecules—they did not seem to belong to the world at all as entities. Many psychologists even doubted their existence, since there was nowhere an emotion could be shown to be located.

Spinoza had long ago regarded emotions as part of nature to be contemplated with the same interest and enjoyment as other natural phenomena, but later centuries progressively divided Western man's attitude into the objective and subjective in an attempt to rid mankind of superstition and prejudice. Having accomplished this task in good measure, man found himself paying the price of having driven a painful wedge into his being, dividing him from himself as well as from his fellow beings and natural environment.

The work that is presented in this book may help to reunite man's divided nature. Research in the developing science of *sentics*—the study of genetically programmed dynamic forms of emotional expression—is leading us to discover the simple elegance of nature's plan within us. Finding experimentally how emotions are grounded precisely in natural order, and how the keys to the communication of emotion are designed according to specific laws, we can discover a new sense of our belonging to nature and recognize our common brotherhood. Sentic studies are uncovering a natural basis of emotion communication universal among humans.

In the chapters that follow we shall describe the precise dynamic forms that are characteristic of each emotion. We call them *essentic forms*. These forms operate like keys in the locks of our nervous system. People touch one another emotionally through these expressive space-time forms. Without them we would live in emotional isolation. Nature has provided for emotion communication and contagion between individuals—the arc of communication—through precise spatio-temporal forms, genetically programmed as specifically as the form of a kidney is programmed. This book describes how these elementary biologic forms were found.

To measure essentic form, new instruments—*sentographs*—had to be developed. These instruments are used for discovering the precise nature of essentic form and for diagnosing aspects of personality. Chapter Four of this book will describe the methods by which the sentograph can be used to measure emotional expression and Chapter Eleven will relate how it can be helpful in discovering a subject's emotional relationships with key figures in his life and with his environment.

Essentic forms are not idiosyncratic to each individual—although when and how he may want to use them may well be. They represent the natural "words" of emotion communication, "words" that were developed before speech arose. Some of these we share with animals—a dog often understands our tone of voice as well as a child. Throughout this book we have tried to look at these "words," carefully and lovingly, to see a glimpse of their exquisite nature and of the laws of their power.

The power of communication of each "word" of essentic form, as expressed in any expressive action (a laugh, a pat on the back, an angry scowl, etc.), depends on its faithfulness to the characteristic shape that it expresses. This biologic solution to the design problem of how individuals may communicate qualities to one another has also made it necessary to develop a new mathematics for dealing with the power of emotion communication. For thousands of years artists have used the remarkable potentiation of realizing precise form to communicate and generate emotion and qualities. The biologic basis for this power is now being discovered through the experimental isolation of pure essentic forms.

The neurophysiologic function of these forms in communicating and generating emotions has largely remained outside the field of psychoanalysis as well as that of traditional psychology. Neither these nor psychiatry has systematically investigated the biologic dynamic functions of essentic forms. Yet, the study of their function leads to methods for using them for therapeutic purposes. The individual's experience of generating specific emotions through repeatedly producing essentic form in accordance with their biologic timing, and being able to be in touch with virtually the entire spectrum of emotions in a controlled manner which these methods provide give the individual a powerful preventive and normative tool. In Part Two of this book, we shall describe the discovery and development of "sentic cycles," which involves the experience of seven basic emotion states in a specific order over the period of a half hour. Practicing this method of "active meditation" has led many subjects to a feeling of peace, increased emotional fluidity and release of blocked emotions, and other beneficial effects. It provides a feeling of grounding in one's inner self. The Buddhist practice of contemplation of feelings presages this experience. The therapist may use it as a tool that produces insight into the personality structure, permits the experience of emotion, and can lead to peace for the person seeking therapy.

How does the practice of sentic cycles and sentic training relate to other forms of therapy? The theory of psychoanalysis presently seems too self-contained to engender a systematic extension linking it with sentic theory. One may hope that a way will be found to provide an integration of the two systems of thought. The Jungian concept of archetypes may constitute a partial bridge. The findings and theories of sentics are also in accord with much of the Gestalt school of psychotherapy and psychology. Some of the phenomena described and measured in sentics may be recognized by those experienced in Gestalt therapy. The importance of closing the Gestalt, the experience of wholes, clearly relates to the experience of essentic form.

In recent years, biofeedback methods have been developed to teach a person to control bodily functions that are not normally subject to conscious control. To achieve this, instruments are used that inform him of the effectiveness of his control over these processes. But in discovering essentic forms within himself, a person does not have to use instrumental biofeedback techniques—the feeling itself *is* an inherent biologic feedback. A person knows through his own feeling when he has expressed the true essentic form. Practice of essentic form is self-centering.

Since sentics is very much involved in the study of fantasy emotions, it also strikes a responsive chord in all disciplines where fantasy emotion is of importance. This, of course, includes the arts and music—sentics has much to say concerning the communication of qualities by artists and musicians. The biologic elements of emotion communication are nowhere better employed than in the arts.

But perhaps the most important application of sentics should be in education. Its methods can allow children, or adults, to learn to be in touch with their emotions, to discriminate between them, and to enjoy their controlled use. For people of all ages, a greater awareness of the emotional processes they share (and specifically the shared experience of doing sentic cycles) may provide a direct way for people of different races and backgrounds to experience their common basis in humanity. In terms of sentics all people are equal. Through sentic education practically all individuals can achieve a high degree of empathy and sensitivity. At present it is largely through chance that such functions develop. But through the practice of sentics in education, they could be developed as systematically as reading and writing.

Like any "hard science" theory, sentics is also capable of making predictions—predictions of new possible experience and about properties of communication processes. Recently we were able to predict the existence of a new form of laughter which could be readily verified experimentally. Finding this new, voiceless laughter (which shall be described in the last chapter of this book) is as exciting, in its way, as the actual discovery in physics of a new particle that previously has been predicted to exist. It is perhaps for the first time that it has been possible to predict precisely new modes of experience before anyone has ever actually experienced them.

It has been conjectured that unique modes of experience may accompany certain stable, "instinctive" animal behavior patterns. Indeed, the behavior of animals associated with some innate release mechanisms, such as the mating posture of the female rat, or the burying of eggs of turtles, is resistant to behavior modification techniques. So also we have found that a Skinnerian approach attempting to change essentic form is unsuccessful; essentic form is not arbitrary. Behavior modification techniques do not alter the programmed neurophysiologic nature of these basic dynamic elements of communication. It is not possible, fortunately, to retrain an individual to experience and communicate love through the essentic form of anger, for example, and vice versa. But as we shall see, it is clearly possible to alter the degrees of inhibition, the readiness to express, and the selection of particular motor functions of the body for expression.

In sum, the research described in this book has led to a new theory of emotion communication.* Precise, genetically programmed brain processes have been found to exist which determine the way we perceive and express emotions. As a result, the developing science of sentics has yielded significant insights into both the way people communicate and the way music and the arts communicate. And a new method of meditation and therapy involving sentic cycles has produced results in preventing and relieving psychosomatic problems and reversing alienation.

Thus it seems that the evolution of sentics may have the capacity to affect the future considerably: by bringing greater enjoyment of being; by preventing violent, irrational aggression; and by teaching man to induce in himself receptive states that increase his creative powers and help him to solve problems. The following chapters will explain the principles upon which sentic theory is based and will show how some of these discoveries came to be made. As sentics grows, much more remains to be discovered. It is our hope that the ideas elaborated throughout this book will introduce the reader to a fascinating branch of scientific inquiry—the study of emotion communication—and act to inspire his own original thinking about these pervasive functions of being human.

* This book is a synthesis of our sentic studies—including some material never before published. For additional details the reader is referred to the author's references in Appendix V.

Introduction

It is man's predicament that he feels the necessity to create a self-conscious vision of himself in the universe in order to feel at home in it. It is not enough that such a world view be intellectual; it is necessary that he develop a feeling of belonging. His role is not defined for him; he feels he needs to define it and discover it for himself. In part, his unique position and problem is posed to him by his gift of language. To re-create his experience in word images is almost too difficult a challenge for him. His resulting social institutions do not clearly reflect his nature. And so he moves like a spiral growing between the poles of verbalization and differentiated direct experience—trying to grasp the transitory and to discover the timeless that reveals itself forever anew in each moment.

"Trying to grasp": in that phrase man's predicament is summed up. That phrase, with its double physiological and psychological meaning, points to man's condition and to the contribution of language to his dilemma. That he may "grasp" more, man's reach should indeed exceed his "grasp." And so, embarked on his quest, he discovers how to ask questions.

Only man can ask a question. Discovery of questions was man's first chain reaction: every good question generates others. (We are now experiencing a Malthusian question explosion perhaps even greater than the population explosion.) A new question leads—it does not follow. Where does it arise then? If it comes by chance, what is chance that it can create new questions? We could begin by saying that questions arise from curiosity. *And thus, the nature of man's quest is linked to his emotional nature.*

A man can be curious and search in different ways, involving different kinds of emotions. One particular way involves a specific emotion that is a kind of intellectual fervor, a "present openness" to whatever ideas may be received by one's brain. This implies a true readiness to receive; not the joy of discovery, but a passionate openness and trust that a new idea could be in the right direction. This state of emotion, which we have called "Being Apreene" and will be more fully discussed in a later chapter, may be observed in some individuals at various times. It has not been given a name previously, though it has clear bodily concomitants. The head may be lifted slightly, the face assumes a characteristic expression, and one feels a certain pleasant tension across the forward and upper part of the head, while at the same time the body seemingly becomes light. There is no anxiety and one seems disconnected from the sensual. Can one find questions that lead, without this emotion? May this emotion be induced and communicated?

As will become more apparent as this book unfolds, emotions and specific knowledge are not as unrelated as has often been thought.

Let us consider the identity of natural forms. Habitually we tend to regard only forms *in space* as "solid" and "real." Yet, there are forms *in time* which belong to the order of the universe and are in every sense as "solid" and "real" as the solidity of spatial form—forms which occur not as accidental processes but arise from ordered programmed relationships. The frequency of a photon of light is an example of a characteristic time form of basic reality. Such time forms exist also in the higher organized entities that relate directly to the laws of the universe, such as molecules, including of course also the DNA molecule. How do man's time forms relate to his DNA program?

We are still largely unaware how the micro-molecular order shapes the living world around us—how the particular shape of the kidney is programmed genetically, for example. But seldom do we even consider how the form of living movement relates to the invisible order of the genetic code. Yet most of life is concerned with movement and only through movement do we communicate in the present moment.

We can try to distinguish those aspects of man's possible time patterns of behavior and communication which are programmed directly as a consequence of DNA relationships, from those which man acquired or devised arbitrarily. In doing so, as we shall see, it is possible to discover in oneself time forms of expression which are "solid" and "true" in the sense that they are faithful to our biologic programming. And strangely, when these true forms are discovered they provide the means for the most powerful im-mediate communication with others in the present moment. This seems to be so because the production and the perception of these forms is governed by a coordinated biologic design, much as are the separate coordinated functions of speaking and hearing.

Indeed, one of the strangest and yet commonplace natural phenomena is the way in which we communicate qualities and shades of emotion to each other through vision, sound, and touch. With methods to be described, we can now measure and identify some of the extraordinary precision with which these dynamic communications are created and sensed. By producing and measuring the precise time profile, or trajectory of the expressive act, in a new way, we are beginning to be able to analyze the remarkable communicative power that is inherent in the trajectories of these forms and to determine which aspects of these processes appear to be biologically designed and genetically preserved.

It is found, in fact, that the nervous system has design features that allow it both to generate precise elements of communication faithful to specific qualities, and also to recognize these elements when communicated by others. It can do this, moreover, through a large variety of modes of sensory communication. But behind the forms of each particular sensory communication, it appears there lies a true generating form specific for that emotional quality. We call these *essentic forms*.

Consider the evolution of qualities of experience for a moment.*

* Throughout this book, the word "quality" will be used in a specialized sense. By a particular quality we mean an irreducible element of experience (such as thirst, an itch, green, warm, etc. and, as we shall see, emotional qualities such as joy, love, anger, grief, etc.) which is not analyzable in terms of other sensations or experience. This concept will be further elaborated in Chapter One. (These and other concepts integral to sentic theory are depicted in a glossary found in Appendix II.)

As life develops, the ability to find the necessary food evolves also. In the early stages of evolution, already single-cellular bacteria are able to sense the presence of a food stuff they need, such as a particular amino acid, and then move in its direction. They stay in the neighborhood of this food concentration until they have a sufficient amount of it and then move on toward another needed food stuff. (This ability is called "chemotaxis.") Sometime in the evolution of life, selective searching becomes the experience of *hunger*. As humans, if it were not for hunger we would find it almost impossible to teach our children to eat, and of course survival would be impossible.

Sometime in the evolution of organisms, then, the behavior pattern of searching for food became governed by a new entity, hunger, or, as we more commonly experience it, appetite. In hunger there is a great deal of knowledge: it tells us what to eat and how much. It tells us when to eat. The body's needs for survival, already assured in the food-searching behavior of single-cellular bacteria, became transmuted into an experiential entity, a selective and subtle quality of experience.

In another path, sexual qualities of experience developed, governing reproduction of the organism. In both these processes *recognition* plays a key role. As the organism searches, prompted by its need, it recognizes that which it looks for; it then acts according to a particular, specific behavior pattern and may experience what we loosely call "satisfaction." After this, it is ready to proceed to search again as it experiences the next need arising.

We have long hidden our ignorance about these and similar processes and their seemingly mysterious unification under the name "instinct." (Indeed, we vaguely sense, in accord with our language, that the opposite of instinct is "extinct.") But relatively little is known yet concerning how the vast amount of knowledge and differentiated experience inherent in instinctive recognition and behavior function as entities or gestalts.

Recognition, which both hunger and sex imply at all levels of evolution, is an information function. In recognition there is in fact information which permits the form of the pattern to be recognized. This in-formation allows selective, preferred energy transmutation to take place—e.g., a particular food is consumed, or the union between particular mates is consummated.

Unlike hunger, though, with sex the recognition and information are mutual. Here nature first invented communication. Later, more forms and patterns evolved that could be precisely and mutually recognized. The specific patterns had their own experiential entities, and involved various sense organs. Some, like smell or color, allow recognition the moment that they are received. Others, like sounds or movement or touch, are forms in time, and are recognized as entities after their form in time has occurred.

As man found the gift of language he tried to describe these entities of experience with words such as "hunger," "thirst," "pain," "yawn," "itch," or "laughter." But it was much easier to invent words for objects in space, like "tree" or "sky," which are mutually observable, than for the subtleties of inward experience. If, in spite of this, we have a remarkable heritage of words for distinct inward experience, it is a special tribute to the wisdom and ingenuity of language. Yet words for shades of inward experience vary considerably from one language to another, and are in fact often untranslatable (the more languages we know, the richer our ability to communicate, evoke, and portray the qualities of experience).

If one looks at the phenomena of experience more closely, one soon discovers that words can only be a rough guide to the actual qualities of experience. The onset and decay, repression and changes of intensity of feeling with time, and many of its shades and combinations cannot be represented exactly by words. Music, however, using specific expressive dynamic forms, permits a more precise communication of many subtleties of qualities.

We have all heard many inflections of tone of voice in our lives, yet when we hear a new mode of inflection expressing a quality we have not previously encountered (e.g., in poetry reading, or in meeting a new friend), we are able to recognize this quality. And so it is also with music. Qualities in music may be recognized, captivate us, and transform our state, even if we are unable to produce them ourselves.

In another way, our own characteristic perception of qualities is manifest in our view of and relationship with animals. We recognize that each kind of animal possesses a "personality." We realize that this is genetically programmed through a yet unknown language of molecular relationship. The precision which defines the "cat" personality, the "rabbit" personality, etc., has both charmed and eluded us. Beyond the individual variations within each species, we recognize that each species itself has characteristic forms of movement: graceful or plodding, swift or nervous, gentle or ferocious, playful or determined. The movements of a pig never suggest the grace of a cat—nor do the strides of the horse compare with the trot of the rhinoceros. But through their movements we also see reflected, as in our own mirror, qualities programmed in our own brains. A cat may not set much store by its own gracefulness, and to a rhinoceros its mate may not appear uncouth, but we see in these movements reflections of our own sensibilities. There appear to be precise qualities in us that these animals touch and bring to life as one touches the keys of an instrument. To what extent can we trust the universality and significance of these qualities?

Knowledge about the real world is ultimately based on some sensory experience. Physics tries to minimize the number of independent sensoria that it utilizes, but concepts of space and time are meaningful to us only because of our *experience* of them. The validity of physics essentially confirms the truthfulness of aspects of these sensoria.† (If we believe that as observers we can be entirely outside the world of phenomena which we wish to describe, we are making a dangerous error.)

Trust in our observations, and our observation of qualities, is based on two brain processes: memory and sensory experiences. Logical thought is impossible without memory. One must be able to remember that the A of the moment before is the same as the A now, before one can compare A with B. In a world of only ever-changing flux, reasoned thought is impossible. Indeed, thought itself is not possible without memory, at the very least a short-term memory.

That we are able to remember how the color red looked yesterday or the year before is evidence of the timeless, unchanging bases of existence, evidence to which we have not perhaps given due weight. Likewise, in remembering the quality of a scent, for example, as we can over a span of many years, it is not only the stored memory that demonstrates the stability of our mental functions but also those processes that allow us to re-experience that stored memory as a precise quality in the present.

We are used to looking at the unchanging foundations of existence only in events outside ourselves, as we observe the physical laws of the universe unchanging in time and in space. But we have been

† But note: even the direction of time, clear in our experience, is not given by the translation into physics of this sensorium.

too little aware that we too are part of nature—that our being is not an "abstraction." We are more "transducers" than isolated observers: as truth transducers we are part of the system.

The processes of fantasy partake of both the physiologic and psychologic realms—but so do of course all forms of sensation as well. We are beginning to realize that in these processes there exist aspects of extraordinary precision, much as we have observed in the lawful behavior of the world around us.

Goethe at the turn of the eighteenth century was already clearly aware that the phenomenon of color could be understood only if one included all the processes involved: physical, physiologic, and psychologic; he had a "systems view" of the phenomenon. He foresaw the discovery of the ingenious use of interacting inhibition and excitation by the nervous system that produces the sensation of white. It has been shown that inhibition and excitation are biologic design principles basic to the organization of the central nervous system and their balance influences the qualities of our experience as decidedly as the individual color or other receptors themselves.

As we begin to see today that qualities exist with a high degree of natural precision, their experience can no longer be relegated to the so-called "vague subjective," or, as is often said, the "*merely* subjective." The functioning of the subjective can be shown to be subject to the highest degree of order and precision. Distinctions between the subjective and objective have become changed. As we know more of our brain processes, the boundary between those is moved. We may see more clearly that it is not through denying inner experience, but in finding its anchor in reality that we can progress.

Man needs to remain faithful to the quest of increasing discrimination of his direct experience. Beauty and ugliness have a myriad of sounds, faces, and touches. The way in which the central nervous system is organized fashions possibilities of man's experience. He needs to clarify how much of his capacities and potentialities are programmed into his brain's organization biologically, and to what extent he can create as on a *tabula rasa* the plan of his possibilities.

A bird learns to fly without needing to ask himself who he is. Man does not have the same confidence "to become." What has caused him to lose that confidence? Is it possible for him to rediscover it? Have his social works placed an untenable strain on his ability to become? Can the present disintegration of his social institutions be transfigured in time to save his potential?

It should recompense us well to study the qualities of our emotional spectrum, studying them not as a pathologist dissects but as an artist cares for his materials. Or perhaps as one who loves. For the quality of our emotions belongs to ourselves perhaps more than any other aspect of being. To love ourselves, then, means to love these pure qualities. In a strange way purely expressed emotions engender a degree of empathy and love as part of our interrelatedness. "Seeing" them as they are eases the burden and boundary that separate man from man.

Unwittingly contributing to the alienating forces, science has frequently nurtured the bias that only that which is presently measurable is real. Good scientists, of course, have never believed this, yet our educational system induces too many people to exclude mistakenly from their considered thoughts the enormous body of experiential *facts* (facts without a theory) with which science has not been able to deal as yet. They have lost confidence in the validity of their own experience. However, a sunset *is* potentially beautiful even though we have not measured this function. And now that we are finding a way to measure the biologic coherence between the forms of expression and experience and are discovering sentic design principles, we begin to see, as we shall show, that the sphere of qualities of emotions belongs to ordered reality as much as the genetic code.

SENTICS

PART ONE

Sentic States: A Common Basis of Human Being

Here on this island, you find
The order of nature has no inner, has no outer—
Centered nowhere, yet everywhere
. . . Touch it and be touched!

ONE

The Qualities of Experience

Progress in science and knowledge appears to come largely from an interplay of *a priori* thoughts with tests of experience. Such a priori thoughts are not all equivalent, however. We can distinguish concepts that have basis in our own being (like "satisfaction") from others that are created ad hoc (like "chess"). The structure of our nervous system causes us to experience in ways determined by it. Our notions of time and space and other qualities are basically not learned from textbooks but from experience.

Although the concepts "beauty" and "goodness" have given rise to philosophic systems, there are many other vital concepts around which philosophers have not chosen to build systems. It is rather difficult to say why not. Partly, it seems through tradition: in philosophy we have our "hamburgers" and "hot dogs" too. There are many concepts that lend themselves to being thought about and meditated upon so as to clarify what may be real and what may be inexact or false in the way they correspond to actual processes. (Progress in science of course consists in precisely this kind of continuing refinement of concepts and their relationship to experience.) Two such "floating" concepts looking for philosophical systems are those of "quality" and "satisfaction."

In order to think clearly, we need to strive for a one-to-one correspondence between the elements of experience, which the central nervous system's physiologic code provides, and the words we devise to correspond with them. In a great many instances language has done an extraordinarily remarkable job in translating the physiologic code, but also it has left a great many areas of experience untranslated and has made mistakes in the naming of others.* In this chapter we shall look at what underlies various aspects of the concept of quality.

"Red" as an Example of a Quality of Experience

Let us start with the quality of redness. To anyone who has seen red, the experience is unique among all other experiences. It does not matter what name we call it; even without a name a person can remember the experience of red. The name red helps us to imagine the experience when it is not there. We may call red a basic quality, in that we cannot imagine a mixture of qualities which would produce the experience of red. And indeed in terms of physiology red is distinguished through the existence of a red receptor in the retina of the eye. Every person (except some of the color blind) has a red receptor. But this is insufficient to characterize the uniqueness of the quality of red. Although the retina may well be regarded as an extension of the brain's nervous system and although

* Most of us tend to take the notion of *quality* for granted. We use the word as it seems to have developed in natural language, accepting its "meaning" without a thorough special inquiry into the possible specific processes underlying its existence. There is something extraordinarily beautiful about language. In it we sense the accumulation of generations, the breath of multitudes, in a bond that seems bound to creativity itself. Yet language is also a filter with long-term time constants. It is a truth constricter as well as revealer whose characteristics we know only in rather small part. Left to its natural development, language changes extremely slowly, even though it is full of remarkable wisdom. But we can no longer be satisfied to be forced to lie in the Procrustean bed of language (in both senses of the word "lie"!). We need to renew language in accordance with our increasing knowledge of brain function.

we now know that in some organisms nerve messages are sent to the retina as well as received from it, we need to see what happens in the brain itself, i.e., the brain processes associated with the experience of red. In 1966 we were able for the first time to show that in human brains the experience of redness is accompanied by a distinct physiologic code, a sequence of operations directly measurable and characteristic only for red and for no other quality (Clynes 1967; see also John 1967 for other brain responses).

D. H. Hubel and T. N. Wiesel had shown in cats and other animals that there is a definite organization of cells in various layers of the brain structured to process visual information according to specific data processing designs. Independently, we found that in humans for every distinct quality of the visual field, be it color or form, there was a definite physiologic response pattern measured as the electric activity of various parts of the brain. We could say there was a clear one-to-one-to-one correspondence between the visual stimulus, the observations of the space-time patterns of the electric brain response, and what was perceived by the viewer. That is, the quality of red has a distinct physiologic code representation in the brain that displays crucial similarities across all people. This comes close to saying that all people see red similarly (except the color-blind, of course). If it is not quite the same as asserting this with full certitude it does indicate with an exceedingly high probability that this is so. The brain patterns which we observe are clearly similar for all individuals with respect to the sequence and the timing of the response components. The components of the response come from several extensive regions of the brain.† (See Figures 1–3).

So there can be no question that by far the greatest proportion of brain electric activity in relationship to the experience of redness is similar across different individuals. This similarity of data processing

† Other processes of the brain may be involved in the recognition of the patterns which we have not observed and it is possible that considerable dissimilarities could arise in such processes. The probability of this, however, must be small since in all those processes that have been available for measurement, the brain functions operate similarly with respect to the quality of red. If there were processes which have escaped our attention operating in the recognition of red these would necessarily have to be on a much more limited scale electrically than the ones we have observed.

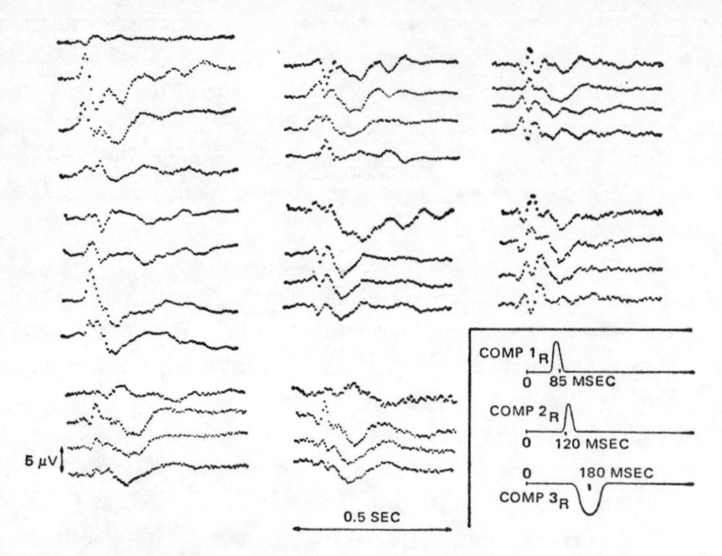

Figure 1. A comparison of responses of eight adult males to the same visual stimulus. Each subject observed an illuminated screen change in color from black to red, and his brain response was measured by four pairs of electrodes attached occipitally in a circular rosette pattern (5 cm. diameter) to the scalp. Each of the four measurements for each subject records the response from each of the four pairs of electrodes. The lower right corner of the figure indicates the three common components that may be distinguished in each of the response groups. The relative magnitude of these components is different for each subject, but their timing is similar for all eight subjects. This figure illustrates various aspects of the one-to-one correspondence found to exist between a specific stimulus and the corresponding space-time pattern evoked in the brain. All traces shown in *Figures 1–3* are averages of 200 responses.

is not learned culturally but is genetically programmed as part of human nature. (Of course we are not talking here about other brain processes that may be associated with perceiving red, concerned with decision-making or evaluating, for example, which of course vary with individuals.)

What then do we know about the *quality* of redness itself? We know that it continues, we know that it is unchanging, and, as we discussed in the introduction, that it can be remembered and imagined. Further, we know that it can also be more intensely "red" up

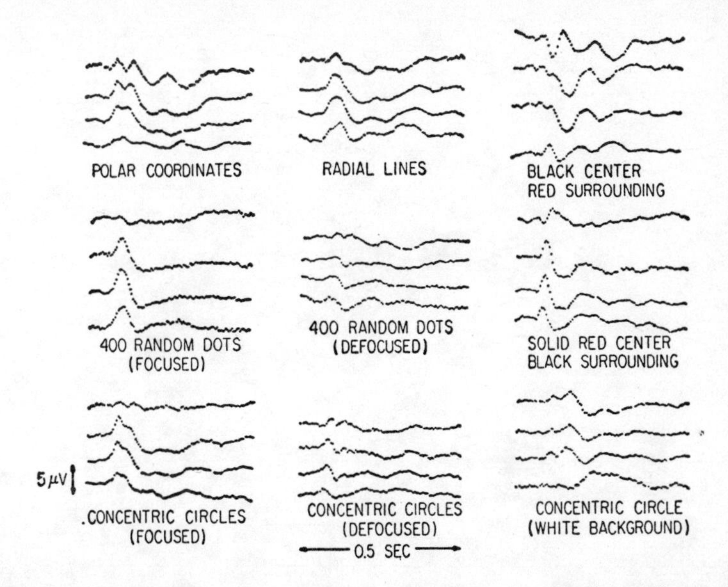

Figure 2. Using the rosette electrode procedure described in *Figure 1*, these measurements record one subject's responses to a variety of visual patterns projected in red on a black background (except for lower right pattern). Note how the amplitude of the responses drops sharply when images are defocused. The bottom right response pattern illustrates how the response to lines is greatly sensitive to the color and intensity of the surrounding field.

to a maximum degree.‡ When mixed with other color qualities it acquires subtly different shades.

The *continuity* of the experience of a quality presents an extraordinary problem. Not only is each quality unique and an entity in itself, but it is experienced continuously, in spite of the fact that in the brain there exist only discontinuous phenomena. The nerve impulses which travel within the brain and nervous system are discontinuous in time. They consist of separate electric impulses that make up trains of nerve firings. Related chemical concentrations of substances represent an aggregate of discontinuous entities in space (i.e., molecules). Yet when we look at a screen illuminated with red light

‡ A degree that can be influenced by psychotropic drugs.

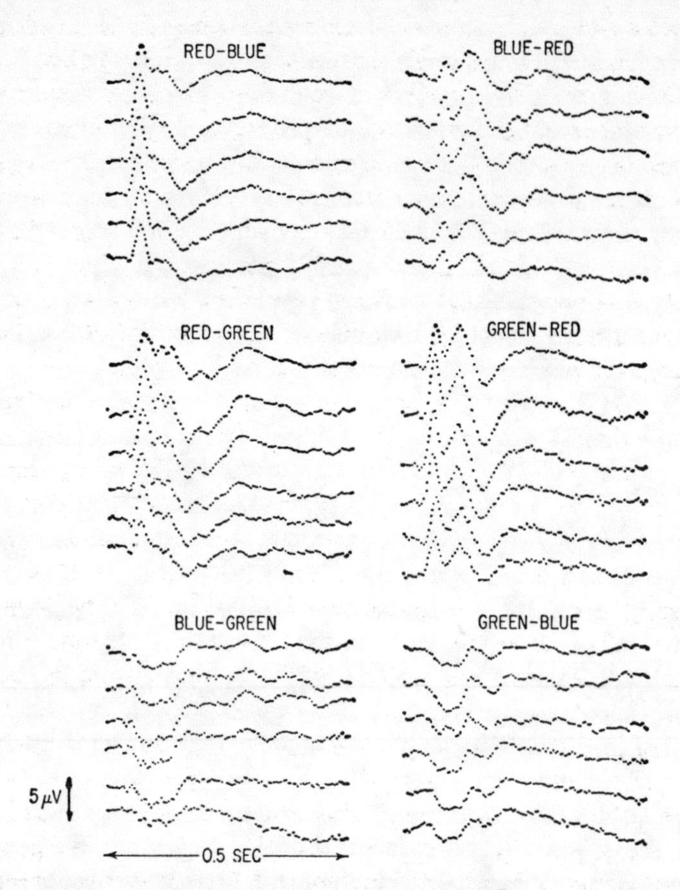

Figure 3. These patterns occur in response to changes of color at the same intensity. Red-Blue indicates that the response was generated by a change from blue to red on the illuminated screen. In this illustration, six pairs of left horizontal occipital electrodes were used, as distinguished from the four electrode pairs of the circular rosette used in the previous figures. (Each pair of electrodes is placed 2 cm. above the other.) Note the stability of each pattern and the gradual shift in balance of the components. Also note the characteristic pattern for each color combination.

we perceive red continuously. (Only when we interrupt the light sufficiently by artificial means do we begin to see a flicker.) This means there must exist an integrating capacity as a brain function which enables the numerous discontinuous events in time and space to be integrated into a single experience and a continuous one.*

Leaving aside the problem of continuity which red shares with every other conscious experience of quality, we may turn next to the extraordinary *stability* of the experience. Red as we see it today does not strike us any differently from red as we saw it when we were many years younger. A child may perhaps like red more than an adult but its "redness" is unchanged throughout a lifetime. It is very likely that two thousand years ago people saw red the same way as we see it today. Indeed if they did not this would indicate a genetic change for which we have no evidence on any grounds.

We have studied the brain responses of color-blind individuals (Clynes and Kohn 1968). (Their brain responses to *changing* color are as one might expect from their perceptual experience.) One can remember the redness of red even if one becomes blind. Other sense experiences display the precise same stability. Beethoven was able to compose with sound images in his brain after he had lost his sense of hearing. A painter may have a clear idea of the form he wishes to paint before he begins, and the most sought-after creators of perfume can imagine a new perfume before they have mixed its ingredients. Indeed, anyone may think of a particular sound with a high degree of precision. There is perhaps no better example of the stability of qualities than our ability to recognize a specific person by the sound of his voice even though that sound may not have been heard for many years. If we consider that the quality of this personal sound becomes unrecognizable through being speeded up or slowed down by only a few per cent as we have found (Clynes 1975), this begins to give one an idea of the high precision of qualities in our experiential personal life.

The quality of red, then, like other qualities displays an extraordinary stability. Can we account for this? We must confess that we are a long way from having refined our understanding to come close to the degree of precision that this phenomenon obviously has, and

* The concept of a field in physics describes the integrating property at a point in space of adding up contributions from various individual particles, so that individual contributions cannot be identified, only their sum.

that it is difficult to propose adequate theories. It seems that the only biologic processes capable of assuring this kind of precision would be ones based on molecular relationships and the precision found in the genetic code. While evidence is clear that the existence of the quality of red as an element of experience is genetically assured, to account for its extraordinary stability over one's lifetime no clear functional mechanism can yet be postulated. The uniqueness of red as a quality depends on a genetic program, as does the uniqueness of a kidney or an arm or a leucocyte.

We may say that the quality of red is an identity and that it involves recognition. Let us proceed to examine the concepts of identity and recognition at different levels of existence.

Identity and Recognition

A quality of experience, being unique, may be said to have an identity. Let us look at the concept of identity.†

A molecule may be said to have an identity. It has a series of properties, which means potential relationships, that are unique to that kind of molecule. These properties are in essence determined by the laws of the universe. But a molecule is made up of atoms, and atoms, in turn, of elementary particles each of which has an identity in the same sense.

If we look at what we regard as being an entity (such as an atom, an elementary particle, a molecule, a tree, the sea, and even the galaxies), it is clear that what we regard as an entity or a basic element depends upon our point of view. We can however see that there are two kinds of objects in the universe: one kind whose form and nature is determined by the laws of the universe like a molecule; and another kind whose form is the result of chance and is not directly prescribed by the laws of the universe like a stone. The orbits and interaction of the elementary particles comprising a molecule occur according to a fixed plan of infinite precision. The properties of a molecule are not accidental; they exist as potentialities inherent in the plan *before* the molecule is formed.

† The terms "identity," "entity," and "oneness" are used interchangeably throughout this book, and for our purposes shall be considered synonymous.

In a sense we can look at the evolution of molecules as the play of a pinball machine, the elementary particles that form a molecule come together by chance but fall into place according to predetermined slots or "holes" in the universal design.

This is also true of the relationship between elementary particles. A photon will recognize an electron differently from a neutron or other particle. Particles recognize one another through a mutual relationship, a relationship that is as basic as their own identities. Our conventional methods of physics usually constrain us to discover the existence of particles before discovering their relationship. But clearly the nature of their relationship is as basic to the universal design as the particles themselves. We can say that *relationship exists*. We shall see that in that sense the recognition of particles by one another represents a proto-phenomenon of "quality."‡

We cannot define identity and quality, only discover them. The relationship of the elementary particles may be regarded as an elementary *recognition* process by which the *identities* of the particle are recognized. The process of recognition occurs at many levels of organization.

To what category, then, do we belong as human living beings? Are our forms accidental like the stone or are we in touch with the design criteria of universal law? We know our form in space is determined by the molecular coding which we call genetic code. Does this code relate forms to natural law or can it create arbitrary, unlimited relationships? This is an important question. Let us see what it really means.

Suppose elsewhere in the universe, perhaps in another galaxy, there were life and a different genetic code, using different types of molecules. Could such a different genetic code in theory create the same type of life forms that ours does? If not, then what constraints does a specific code put on the possible forms of life? Our earthly genetic code can build a bird. Can it build an airplane? What we know about our genetic code tells us what methods it uses for providing in-

‡ If we look at the origins of the word "quality" we see that it comes from the Latin root *quale* meaning "such." Thus the origin of the word "quality" really means "suchness," such as it is—an entirely appropriate formulation as we may agree, as it cannot be defined in any other terms.

structions. Consider the Morse code for a moment. It uses dots and dashes and the sequences of these define the letters and words used. But the dots and dashes themselves have no relation to the actual or possible meanings of the message. These are derived from English or other equivalent language. While we now know the code system of our genetic language remarkably well—the dots and dashes and their sequences—we still have practically no idea how the genetic code programs the shape of the kidney in the precise way that it does. We know the code, but we do not know the language of the message as yet. But clearly there is such a language. At present we can tell only the results of mistakes in spelling, the effects of missing, altered instructions, but not most of the relationship designations that are implicit in a language. In a sense we know the meta-language of the genetic language.

Qualities of Living Forms

The class of all natural forms on earth is enormous. The possible forms generated by the genetic code may seem infinite. However, the class of all possible forms is infinitely greater. With all the possible variety of natural forms, these represent a class apart from inanimate or dead forms. Moreover, our own genetic construction is such that it allows us to recognize natural forms in different ways from the inanimate. The ear, for example, is more sensitive to animate sounds than to inanimate ones. (The nervous system is built to recognize special types of frequency modulation characteristic of animate sounds.) A mother will recognize the cries of an infant even in sleep, and our visual system responds differently to living forms than inanimate ones. *What are the qualities of living forms that make them specially recognizable?* This question goes to the heart of this book. What we shall discuss will be that *the dynamic living qualities are precisely and genetically programmed into our brains*, and that *we communicate these qualities to one another and to ourselves through the production and recognition of their precise forms.*

Recognition plays a key role in genetic processes: the shapes of molecules are recognized with high specificity. The loose chemical bonds used in the processes of building instructions and of replication depend fundamentally on the recognition of specific molecular forms. More recently the importance of vibrational modes, introducing time, has been discovered. Indeed, recognition implies time as well as space: the frequency of a photon is recognized by an electron—forms in time may be programmed by genetic instructions as well as forms in space alone.

In human language we have been far too negligent in *naming* forms in time. The precise reality of forms in time has escaped the language-making processes and words denoting specific time forms are quite rare (e.g., sigh, caress, etc.). But just as spatial forms are precisely programmed genetically, so also can biologic forms in time be programmed through appropriate genetic means. The pattern of response to red, exhibiting the specific spatio-temporal forms of the brain response to red, is the result of a genetic program.

It appears, in sum, that the physiological code gives us a potential spectrum of basic qualities which we may or may not experience. Language properly translates these basic qualities in a one-to-one manner. Where it has failed to do so we need to hasten to correct its omission.

Derived from perhaps a few hundred basic qualities we may experience myriad combinations. But the combinations are not simple additions of qualities. And importantly, qualities seem to be also genetically interrelated in a loosely coupled way, as will be discussed later. It is sufficient to say at this point, however, the number of possible combinations of qualities provides for an abundant, almost limitless variety and creativeness.

We have spoken of qualities and of unique existences as genetically programmed. These unique qualities or entities do not exist in isolation, however, but are in relationship with other brain functions. In particular, there is a class of qualities which is inherently linked to the motor system, so that its uniqueness is complete only with inclusion of the dynamics of the motor system as an integral part of their spatio-temporal existence. It is because of this inherent link to the motor system that these qualities can be communicated. This class of qualities is referred to commonly as *emotions*. In the next chapter and throughout this book we shall be looking at emotions as such a class.

TWO

Emotions

Belonging to a class of qualities inherently linked to the motor system, each emotion, as a unique quality, completes its identity only if the motor dynamic program, part of which we usually call "expression," is included. Emotion and its expression form an existential unit, a system. In order to characterize and understand its function, we need to consider its system properties.

Unfortunately, as psychology as a science developed, emotion and its expression were mostly studied separately. To study emotion without its expression (and vice versa) is like cutting off the hand to study its function. This is one reason why many functions of emotions remained obscure and also why quantitative methods were not found for their study. Indeed, unless our concepts correspond to functioning processes we will not discover their lawful behavior. (Galileo, for example, had to conceive of the concept of acceleration before measurements could correspond to theories.) In studying emotion as a system identity, including the phenomena of expression as part of the system, in a new scientific approach, it becomes possible to evolve new concepts, subject to precise measurements.

This approach is neither exclusively psychological nor exclusively physiological, but considers emotion and its expression as one functional system.

But before we go on to discuss the theories and findings developed from this approach, let us briefly review what we know of the characteristic properties of emotions.

Emotions reflect and affect the quality of life, yet because of our uncertain understanding of the phenomena of emotion we have been far from clear as to how. Thus, some thinkers were even in favor of avoiding or eliminating emotion entirely. They regard emotion as restricting the free use of the mind and blinding man to what is "in his best interests." Others equally strongly assert that life without emotions is not worth living. To navigate between these extremes, a key question seems to be: how to experience emotions constructively rather than being used by them.

The following are some characteristics of the state of emotion, its expression, and its generation:

Emotion states

1. Each basic emotion is a unique experience.
2. To each basic emotion there corresponds a characteristic brain pattern.
3. Each emotional state has a characteristic inertia, in terms of brain and bodily processes. Once it has been established, it will persist for some duration of time.
4. An emotion will tend to confine specific action patterns according to its nature over a period of time.
5. Hormonal and cardiovascular changes occur together with an emotional state. The extent and type of these changes will depend on the nature of the specific emotion and also on the attitude of control by the individual. Hormonal changes, in turn, may predispose a person to experience motion.
6. Memory, unconscious, and autonomic processes influence the control functions relating to emotional states.
7. The experience of emotions is influenced by age, sex, genetic inheritance, and diurnal, seasonal, and other biologic rhythms.

Emotional expression

1. The expression of emotion is an essential aspect of its nature. Emotion needs to be expressed, much as a control system needs to respond to its input until the desired output is obtained.
2. Expression has an effect on the intensity of the state of emotion. It can both charge (increase) and discharge (decrease) the intensity.

Generation of emotion

1. The generation of emotion occurs through perception of and changes in our existential circumstances: our relationships with others, our environment, our losses and our gains, our freedom to pursue our needs, and our self-image.
2. Emotion can also be generated through perceiving emotion in others.
3. Emotion can be generated purely through the imagination—by imagining and remembering persons, forms, qualities, and situations.
4. All these processes can be variously affected by drugs and by specific electrical stimulation of the brain.

Emotions and environment interaction

1. Emotions play a crucial part in our interactions with our social and natural environment.
2. Our drives and mental energy are affected specifically by our emotions.
3. The degree of crowding—and its effect on privacy and intimacy—affects the experience of emotional states.
4. Processes of habituation and adaptation also affect the experience of emotion in a specific environment.

Obviously, emotions have an all-pervasive significance to our life potential. Yet we have great difficulty in studying them systematically. One problem is in the use of vaguely defined words. Thus, "emotion" and "feeling" are used almost interchangeably in psychologic literature as well as in common parlance. In fact, there is no accepted definition that distinguishes the appropriate use of these two concepts. At best, a consensus might be that "feelings" are low-intensity "emotions." Although an emotion may be overpowering and beyond control, or it may be sensed and enjoyed without one's becoming its slave, such an important distinction is not made by our usage of the words "emotion" and "feeling." This is one reason for the need for new terminology. Another is that these words are themselves emotionally charged, which causes further difficulties in discussing them clearly.

Accordingly, we shall call a specific emotional state a *sentic* state. The word "sentic" is derived from the Latin root *sentire* which also is the root of the words "sentiment" and "sensation." We shall use the term specifically to denote the brain state and its corresponding experience generally associated with the word "emotion."

Introduction to Sentic Theory

If we consider how sentic states (e.g., anger) arise spontaneously in our daily life, we may see that reality and fantasy interpenetrate each other in various degrees.

Modes of Experiencing Sentic States

A. *In a real situation* (e.g., a traffic jam causes one to miss a plane; one is insulted or falsely accused).
B. *Through exposure to another's sentic state* (e.g., contagiously experiencing another's anger).
C. *In a fantasy situation imagined by oneself* (e.g., imagining or remembering a real situation, such as being caught in a traffic jam or falsely accused).
D. *Through exposure to a fantasy sentic state generated by another* (e.g., contagiously experiencing the fantasized anger of an actor).

Concerning how the communication of sentic states functions, we may formulate a number of principles that appear to hold, and are in accordance with experience and experiment.

The following sentic principles together delineate some of the system properties of the qualities of sentic states and their communication. The significance of each of these principles, stated didactically here, will become clearer as we consider their function in more specific ways. The latter two principles introduced here for formal reasons will be elucidated in the following chapter.

1. *A sentic state is a single-channel system; only one state can be expressed at any one time.* (Exclusivity Principle)

One can only express one sentic state (which may be basic or compound) with a single act of expression. Any attempt to express different sentic states simultaneously with different parts of the body results in blocking the experience of each state. For example, a person cannot voluntarily express anger with one arm and love with the other at the same time, and experience both simultaneously. (This is also in accordance with the experiments of N. Bull, who found that even under hypnosis two affects could not be simultaneously elicited.)

2. *A sentic state may be expressed by any of a number of different output modalities.* (Equivalence Principle)

The sentic state may be expressed by a variety of motor modes: gestures, tone of voice, facial expression, a dance step, musical phrase, etc. In each mode the emotional character is expressed by a specific, subtle modulation of the motor action involved which corresponds precisely to the demands of the sentic state.

3. *Regardless of the particular motor output chosen to express a sentic state, its dynamic expression is governed by a brain program or algorithm specific for that state which shall be called essentic form.* (Coherence Principle)

Essentic form and its experience are coherently linked. This is not a merely "mechanical" correspondence between the sentic state and its expressive form, but an existential coherence between experienced feeling and the form. There also is an inherent feedback between the act of expression, embodying essentic form, and sentic experience. Thus, the act of expression inherently links the physiologic and the psychologic.

4. *The production and recognition of essentic forms are governed by inherent data processing programs of the central nervous system, biologically coordinated so that a precisely produced form is correspondingly recognized. The recognized form in turn generates a sentic state in the perceiver.* (Complementarity Principle)

This ingenious biologic design allows individuals to recognize the expression of essentic form in other individuals and makes it possible for emotions to be communicated as qualities of experience. The arc of communication between individuals could not be completed without this function.

A similar correspondence may be observed in the production and recognition of speech sounds, phonemes, produced by the vocal cords and perceived by the ear. But symbiosis of the production and recognition of essentic form—their biologic cooperation—is of more primitive evolutionary origin than speech phoneme production and recognition. Animals respond to our tone of voice, and are affected by other forms of our sentic expression, and humans can perceive some of the essentic forms produced by animals.*

Recently this principle was beautifully demonstrated in crickets by the experiment of Bentley and Hoy. They bred a hybrid species of cricket that possessed a new mating song, intermediate between those of its parent species. Without ever having heard it before, females of the new species were attracted by the sound of the new mating song, rather than by those of the parent species. This illustrates that the genetic program for recognizing the mating song was simultaneously transformed with the mutation of the program for producing the song.

To test and prove the sentic principles stated above we conducted experiments prompted by these theories in different cultures. We observed the behavior of the brain and various parts of the body used for expression and a number of physiologic systems as well. These experiments are described in Chapters Four and Five. Before we can understand the specific significance and procedures of these experiments, however, we shall have to examine a further concept—that of the *acton*, an element of voluntary movement.

* One day when visiting the zoo, I saw a bear yawn. Before I knew what I was doing, I found myself yawning, too. But how did I know the bear was *yawning*, and was not hungry or angry? Clearly, it was through perceiving the precise way that he opened his mouth. (And as I dictate this anecdote, I also yawn. The imagined yawn generated a yawn in me also!) A yawn has a clear beginning and end, and a specific timecourse, like other expressive actions.

THREE

Acton Theory

If we consider a simple, single voluntary movement, such as an eye movement or a finger movement, we see readily that it consists of a decision or command, and its execution. The decision embodies the *idea* of the movement. We have named the idea of a quality, together with its specific brain function concomitants, an "idiolog." We may say that there are sensory idiologs (the idea of a sound or smell), affective idiologs (the idea of joy or anger), and motor idiologs (the idea of particular movement). A motor idiolog calls for the execution of a single voluntary motor action. For example, if we have an idea to throw a ball to hit a certain object, we may have a precise motor idiolog. Its execution, in turn, may correspond to this idiolog more or less precisely. Our success with the throw will depend upon the precision of the idiolog and the precision of its execution.

Simple movements initiated by single voluntary decisions (such as the single movement of a finger, or of an arm, or of the eyes) are preprogrammed by the brain before they begin. Every such voluntary movement is carried out cooperatively by two sets of muscles, one set to accelerate the motion and the other to decelerate it. For each movement, a set of "agonist" and "antagonist" muscles work together to create the precise character of the intended movement. The two muscle systems clearly work together with the most remarkable precision in order to start, accelerate, and stop movement as required. This "coordination" is programmed by the brain in the moment it makes the decision.

One may decide to move a finger a distance corresponding to one inch or two inches, or to turn the eyes to look at an object say twenty degrees or thirty degrees to the left. In each case, the muscles start, complete and stop the motion in a fraction of a second (about 0.2 second for most simple movements), according to the specific idea programmed in the decision, that is, according to the motor idiolog. As we have noted, the movement is preprogrammed by the brain before it begins. Once such a short movement has begun the decision is merely executed. Within that fraction of a second it takes to execute there is no feedback that can permit one to modify the programmed decison.

This raises another interesting experiential concept: the length of the "present moment." For a physicist the present moment is infinitely short. Time is conceived as a line along which a point travels from the past toward the future. That point is the present moment. Being a point, it is necessarily infinitely short. Clearly the physicist's time has no experiential reality. An infinitely short time cannot be experienced. Since the present is all that exists, the past having gone and the future not yet being here, such a concept of time is inadequate even for the description of inanimate reality. But it is the best of which we are capable.

In our human experience, however, the present moment has a finite duration. How can we determine this duration? There are a number of interesting experimental approaches. Have you noticed how strange it is that we can see the second hand of a watch moving, but that the minute hand and the hour are seen as stationary? Another being, with a different time consciousness, might well see the minute hand moving also, and yet another may even see the hour hand moving. There could even exist a being for whom day and night would seem a flicker. There is nothing in the essence of our being that preordains the length of the present moment. It is the result of our physiologic design, as is the dynamic character of our other sensations.

Several types of experiments can lead us to a measure of the length of the present moment. One way in which it reveals itself is through finding the velocity at which a slowly moving object (for example, a dot of an oscilloscope) just begins to be seen as moving rather than as stationary. One first determines the shortest distance it can jump and still be recognized to be in a different location (the smallest noticeable increment of position of visual angle). One then measures how fast this small distance must be traversed for the dot to be seen as moving. It turns out that this time is 0.2 second. If the distance is traversed at a slower rate, the dot is seen to be stationary.

Another measure we can use for determining an aspect of the length of the present moment involves the following procedure. Having made a decision, what is the minimum time within which we can make another decision? In experiments to test this, a red light may signify to a subject to press a certain button, while a green light may signify not to press a button or to press another button. The red light is presented to the subject and immediately after, a green light is presented. Can he stop himself from executing the first command? Experiments show that only if the green light is presented 0.2 second or more later can he make a separate decision.

Still another measurement of the function of the present moment consists of presenting consecutive visual images, such as letters, on a screen. At eight to ten letters per second, say, a subject notices the different letters being flashed but only if the succession is slowed to 0.2 second (or five per second) will he be sure of the order of the letters in time. (Similarly, in human speech lengths of perceived and produced speech syllables are about 0.2 second long.)

As we have seen, these measurements all tend to converge to a duration close to 0.2 second for humans (more precisely, 0.18–0.20 second). It seems likely that this duration may be different for other animals, especially those further removed in evolution. Insects and birds appear to be able to make such decisions at a rate faster than the 0.2 second required for humans, and we may guess that if beings were found on other planets or galaxies their time consciousness would probably be very different from ours.

The Acton

Within the duration of the present moment no further decision can be made. A single movement, once begun, must run its course as preprogrammed by the idiolog of the motor action. Such a single movement, consisting of the decision and its execution, has a clear beginning and end. We need to recognize that such a voluntary movement constitutes an existential *entity*. We have named this entity an *acton*. An acton is rooted both in the psychologic and physiologic. To state it as it was defined in 1969:

> A single movement and its decision constitute an existential unit integrally combining the physiologic and conscious aspects. We call such a preprogrammed voluntary movement having a clear beginning and end an "acton." An acton is the combination of the acton's idiolog and its execution. (Clynes 1968; 1969.)

By recognizing such unity where it exists, we may develop theories that correspond more closely to actual processes.

An *expressive* movement which has a clear beginning and end is also an acton, but a special kind of acton. Expressive actons are actons whose dynamic forms (i.e., space-time forms) are modulated by the sentic states seeking expression. The sentic state, through the cerebellum and other brain structures,* influences the preprogrammed course of the acton so as to alter it from the unmodulated, undifferentiated course of the non-expressive acton. For example, a playful toss of a stone differs much from a throw in anger. Moreover, each sentic state has its own characteristic way of modulating the acton. In this way, essentic form is expressed.

The modulation of the acton affects its shape and its total dura-

* Many of the brain's automatic computations that shape the acton are performed by the cerebellum, as has become clear through the work of J. C. Eccles, whose findings have been significant in clarifying the role of the cerebellum in governing specific motor programs.

tion as well. Such sentically modulated actons are called *E-actons,* for "expressive actons." There are specific E-actons for each characteristic sentic state. A smile is an example of such an E-acton. So is a caress or an angry stomp of the foot. An E-acton refers to a single expressive act. And each E-acton begins through a distinct command.

It is important to realize that the modulation of the acton through the sentic state determines its characteristic precise time course, its relative phases of acceleration and deceleration (as well as higher time derivatives)—i.e., the *form* of the motion in time.

Generation of Sentic States Through Repeated E-actons

A remarkable property of E-actons is that they can act to generate the sentic state in the person producing them, as well as in the perceiver—there is a feedback that changes the intensity of the state.† Moreover, when E-actons of the same state are produced repeatedly at appropriate intervals, they can progressively augment the intensity of the sentic state, as we have also found experimentally. The appropriate time intervals are found to be different for each emotion, and must be sufficiently variable not to be predictable or "mechanical." This property of the system behavior of sentic states is crucial in our investigations in generating sentic states.

Aspects of these properties were well known to some psychologists, but were largely ignored. Thus the psychologist G. Maranon writes in the *Journal of Nervous and Mental Diseases* in 1950:

> Emotion is (also produced) by simply seeing in another individual the expressive phenomena, the gestures of emotion. A gesture of terror or of loathing in a person near us, infects us with the terror or the loathing causing us to execute more or less the same gesture and to experience the same vegetative sensation . . .

Furthermore, if we can ourselves execute the gestures of a given emotion, we can come to experience the corresponding visceral

† Most of us may have observed, for example, that repeated sobbing or laughing or "angering" may intensify the sentic state over an initial period of time.

> disturbance and to have the idea of it; in short, we can emotionalize ourselves completely . . .
>
> Gesture is, in short, the expression of a certain emotion; it has in its turn a reverse power over the emotion, and can itself produce the emotion.

He goes on to cite examples of orators—especially Hitler and other demagogues—and actors who by such repeated gestures generate corresponding waves of emotions in spectators. Darwin too, in his treatise on the expression of emotion published in 1872, was aware of the power of repetitive expression in generating emotion.

Such irregular repetition of essentic form does not of course increase the intensity of the sentic state indefinitely. A plateau of intensity tends to be reached after perhaps ten to twenty repetitions. The intensity will then fluctuate, and with continuing repetition the sentic state will be discharged. The duration of this process varies with the specific sentic state.

Thus a single essentic form produced is generally not as effective in generating sentic states as a series of such forms expressed and experienced in succession, though not in completely regular (or "mechanical") succession. We may state this property as the fifth sentic principle:

5. *The intensity of a sentic state is increased, within limits, by the repeated, arrhythmic generation of essentic form through E-actons.*

The ability to generate sentic states in this way is central to the study of sentics and plays a crucial role both in measuring sentic states in the laboratory and in the therapeutic effects of "sentic cycles," which will be discussed in a later chapter.

FOUR

Measuring Essentic Form, the Biologic Basis of Emotion Communication

The multiple expressive modes we use to communicate makes the scientific study of expression quite difficult. Smiles and facial expressions and even gestures have been exceedingly difficult to measure with the necessary subtlety. It also has not been easy to obtain reliably produced, repeated expressions that could be used to validate any measurements. Further, the commonly used expressive modes are culturally conditioned in varying degrees. For all these reasons, it has been impossible until recently to obtain valid data on the precise dynamic forms of expressive action.

The psychologist Paul Ekman has studied facial expression using constructed visual images and found that the recognition of certain elements of expression is universal to all cultures; the range of expressions investigated was limited, however. The school of kinesics, founded mainly by Birdwhistell, has studied many patterns of culturally significant non-verbal expressive communication modes. And specialists in the art of dance, chiefly Laban, have devised systems of notation and theories of "effort" and spatial utilization ("shape") which attempt to delineate specific dance movements. None of these measurements and studies were able, however, to depict the precise dynamic forms and their time derivatives.

It is clear that standardization is required to allow the biologically programmed inner shapes, which we have called essentic forms, to be produced and measured without interference by extraneous factors, as far as possible. In order to arrive at this, let us consider, as noted, that a sentic state can be expressed in a variety of modes—from tone of voice to gestures using many different parts of the body. This is the sentic principle of equivalence, and if valid, it should allow us to select an arbitrary motor output of sufficient degrees of freedom* for the measurement of essentic form. A mode we can choose (and have in fact chosen) that seems to fulfill the requirements is the transient pressure of a finger with the subject placed in an appropriate body position. The dynamic pressure of a single finger on a finger rest has the possibility of being readily repeatable, and can be easily measured, and thus can become a standard means for measuring and comparing various expressive forms.

The subject sits in a chair with a straight back and no armrests. (See Plate 1 in photo insert.) The upper arm—right or left, depending on handedness—is held slightly forward at about a ten-degree angle and the forearm is slightly downward, sloping at about a fifteen-degree angle. The wrist is in line with the arm and the fingers are extended in a relaxed, smooth curve, neither straight nor curled. The middle finger rests on a finger rest one inch high (see Plate 2 in photo insert) so that the other fingers do not touch any objects but are relaxed in a natural position. The finger remains in touch with the finger rest throughout and is not lifted off at any time. Each expressive action is based from the torso. It is not a lifting of the finger or of the wrist, but a transient pressure exerted through the arm.

We use pressure rather than movement to measure essentic form for several reasons. First, it affords a convenience of measurement. Second, in using pressure rather than movement, it is more readily possible to characterize passionate states—certain essentic forms in-

* "Degrees of freedom" of a movement refers to the ability to move in a number of independent dimensions and directions of rotation (degrees).

clude the experience of muscular tension that is provided by pressing against a finger rest. Pressing is more suitable than pulling. Even so because of the resilience of the finger tip, a small amount of movement necessarily ensues. (Small movements of one-eighth inch or so on the finger rest in a direction away from or toward the body are also acceptable.)

An important feature of these expressive pressure transients is that the *direction* of pressure is different for different sentic states. In expressing some states, the pressure tends to be away from the body; for other states, it has a neutral, close to vertical direction. For still others, it tends to be more toward the body. We have found that these distinctions have important significance.

It was necessary, therefore, to measure not only the amount of the momentary pressure but the angle of its direction. This is done with two pressure transducers, one measuring the vertical component of pressure and the other the horizontal component. By knowing each of these components at any one time, we know both the magnitude and direction of pressure at that moment. In practice, *the horizontal and vertical components of pressure are recorded as separate curves and the shape of these curves constitute the visual representation* of essentic form. (See Figure 4.)

Since producing a single E-acton may not adequately generate a clear sentic state in a subject, we request each subject to produce a series of E-actons for a particular sentic state. For instance, a subject is asked to express "anger." He then hears a sequence of soft, single clicks spaced at varying intervals a few seconds apart. He is requested to express anger as precisely as he can each time he hears a click with a single, expressive finger pressure action. The clicks are not spaced evenly in time but occur at quasi-random intervals so the subject cannot predict when the next click will occur. On hearing each click he expresses the quality of anger as precisely as he can with a single expressive pressure action and then waits for the next click, before he may express again. During the seconds of waiting for the next click the intensity of anger mounts. As he goes through this process, fantasy anger is generated in him. Thirty to fifty expressive acts are measured in this way and their forms in time are often averaged to obtain a more precise shape. The averaging may be done by a dig-

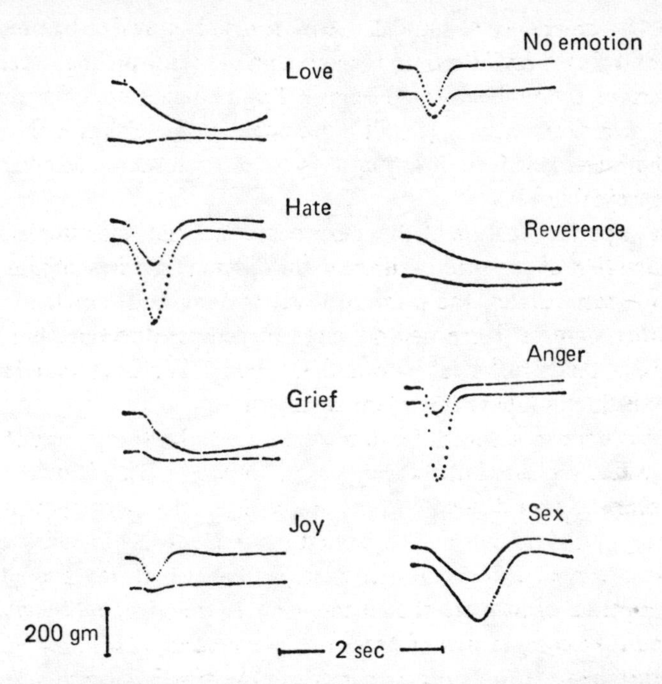

Figure 4. Sentograms of the essentic forms of emotions, as measured by the sentograph. The upper trace for each emotion marks the vertical component of transient finger pressure; the lower trace marks the horizontal component (at twice the scale). No emotion is the form of expression recorded when a subject is asked to express mechanically, as if depressing a typewriter key. Each form is measured as the average of fifty actons. The subtle differences in forms (e.g., between Love and Grief) are as significant as the more obvious ones.

ital computer such as the Computer of Average Transients (CAT) or other similar instrument available in most physiologic laboratories. Averaging the space-time shapes of many expressive acts minimizes the effects of minor fluctuations of the sentic state, and fluctuations of the precision of executing the E-acton. (Although averaging results in some loss of accuracy in regard to timing of each expressive form it is helpful in establishing systematic differences.)

We record the essentic forms as expressed through transient finger pressure, and also, in many experiments, the specific action of various muscles that are involved in the production of essentic form, includ-

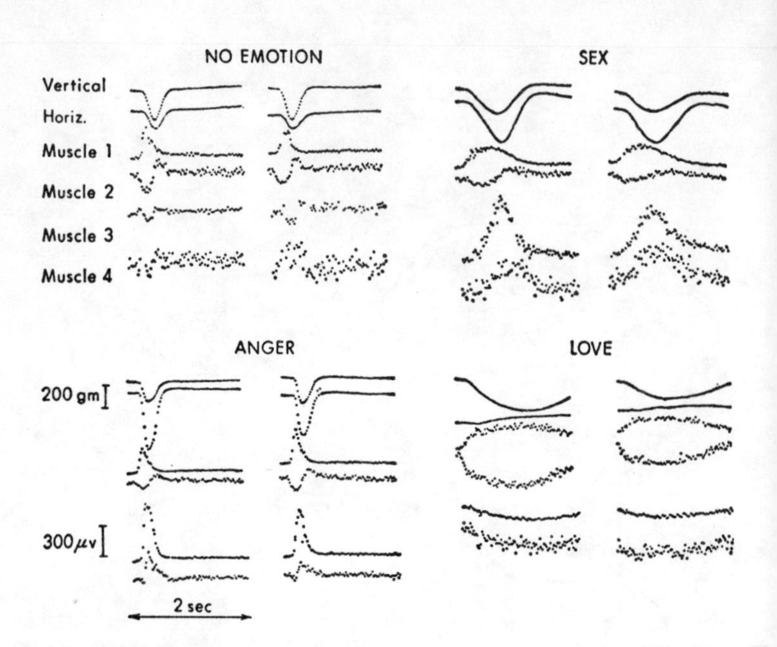

Figure 5. Recordings of essentic form as vertical and horizontal components of finger pressure, with four groups of muscle potentials recorded from the forearm, upper arm, front shoulder, and back, respectively (integrated and rectified with a time constant of 0.01 sec.). Each group is the average of fifty actons for each emotion, from the same subject. The comparison between groups, done on two different occasions, shows the stability of response. Note the marked accentuation of the horizontal component for Anger, indicating a tendency for the acton to be outward, away from the body. The characteristic shape for love (not sexual) shows a longer curved acton with often a slight reversed horizontal component, indicating a pulling inward or embracing tendency. The muscle actions reflect the differences of the essentic forms. The preprogrammed time of the acton for love is considerably longer. The characteristic for sex shows a strong secondary thrust with emphasized late muscle activity.

ing muscles of the forearm, upper arm, shoulder, and back. (See Figures 5–6.) The action of these muscles is measured through the electrical activity produced at the neuromuscular junctions. Recordings of such activity are called "electromyograms." (In order to observe the changes of activity in these more clearly, the elec-

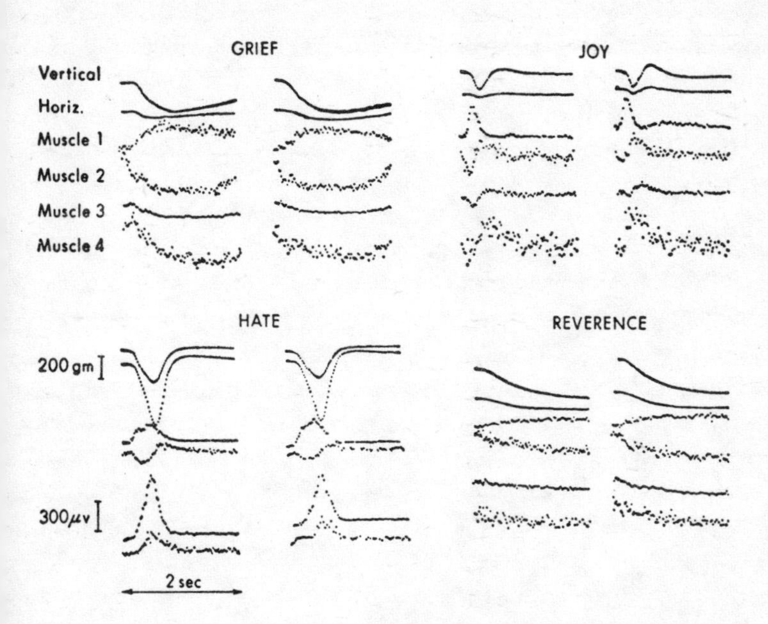

Figure 6. Typical response shapes illustrate the essentic form of grief, joy, hate, and reverence, respectively. Note the pronounced horizontal component for hate (indicating an orientation away from the body as seen with Anger in *Figure 5*), the late muscle acceleration in muscle 2 indicating a secondary thrust characteristic of passion. The response to grief is similar to that of love but is flatter and slightly outward. Muscular action for grief displays a lassitude which prevents the subject from actively lifting and releasing pressure—the opposite of that for joy, which exhibits a rebound overshoot after the initial downward deflection of the finger. Reverence shows some similarity to love but on a longer time scale—the programming of the acton is extended in time.

tromyogram is rectified and integrated with a time constant of less than .01 second.) In addition to such electromyograms, we may simultaneously measure the electric activity of the brain in a manner similar to that described in Chapter One for observing the brain's responses to visual stimuli. (See Figure 7.)

The patterns of change which we observe on various levels all tend to confirm the stability of the essentic form. The clearest measure of essentic form is provided by the recordings of transient finger pres-

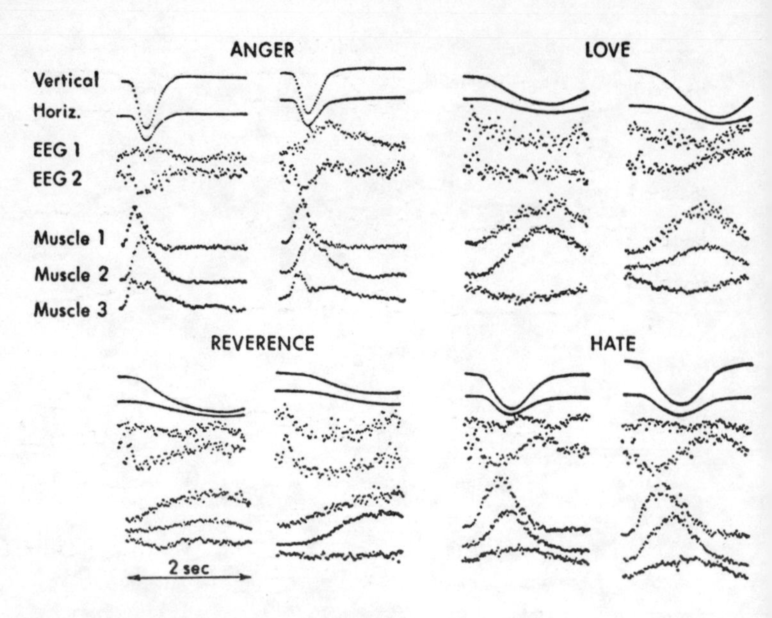

Figure 7. Comparison of various essentic forms including cortical potentials. Recordings show progressively less noise in the data as one compares the brain electrical activity, muscle activity, and the touch form, thus illustrating how the arm acts as a biologic filter. (The electrode position for leads 1 and 2 are frontal to occipital and parietal, respectively; EEG amplifier time constants of 5 sec. were used.)

sure. *The arm is in fact a biologic filter through which activity of the brain not connected with expression of a particular essentic form is eliminated.* The brain's electric activity, in addition to aspects related to essentic form, contains all other activity related to the innumerable conscious, unconscious, and autonomic functions. Thus the expression of essentic form can at present be revealed in the brain's electric activity measured from the scalp only through averaging.

We also measured processes that reflect changes related to particular sentic states, rather than to each separate expression. We observed and compared the changes in heart rate, cardiovascular function, respiration, oxygen consumption, and the electric activity of the brain for the duration of each state.

Procedures outlined above were conducted with a large number of

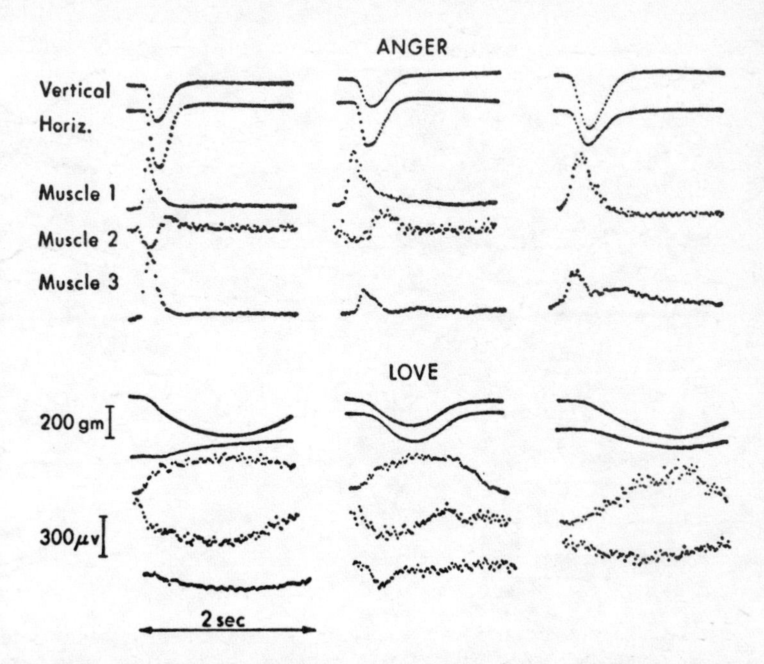

Figure 8A. Comparison of forms recorded from three different subjects expressing the sentic states of anger and love. Note the general similarities of corresponding essentic forms and also features of individual differences. Average of fifty actons.

subjects for seven sentic states: anger, hate, grief, love, sex, joy, and reverence. (See Figures 8A, 8B, and 9.)

In examining the results one would expect that the different shades of meaning ascribed to these words in various contexts by people of different age groups—and perhaps of different social strata —might tend to confuse the picture. Even more so subtle differences of the corresponding words in other languages also make it difficult to ascertain whether we are attempting to measure precisely the same sentic state when obtaining measurements in a different culture. Fortunately, however, we are aided here by the very nature of the existence we wish to demonstrate—since it turns out that *the qualities of the spectrum of emotions are more precise by far than the words used to describe them.* We find that, regardless of the imprecision of the language, sentic states tend to sort themselves out into character-

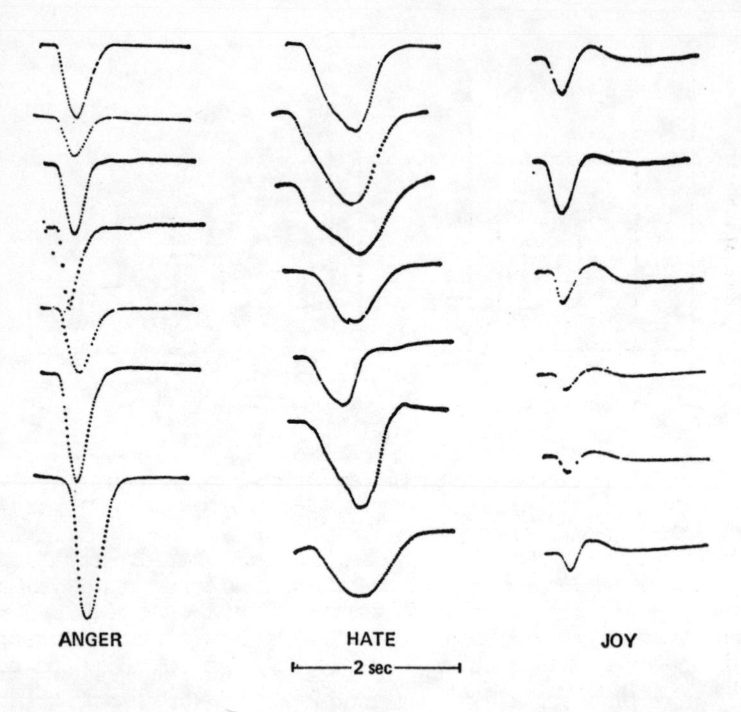

Figure 8B. Sentograms compared (vertical traces only) from different subjects expressing the states of anger, hate, and joy as illustrative examples.

istic ones of well-defined forms.† Let us now look at the sentograms of the specific essentic forms in some detail, in a sequence as given on pages 33–35.

† *By being in the right "ball park," the subject himself focuses in on the true existence, the form of which is inwardly given to him.* Being attentive to that inward form, he soon finds the expression that corresponds to it. The process is similar to finding a way to hit an object with a ball, once having a clear idea of what you want to hit. Because each expression completed is experienced as an entity by the subject, the subject knows the feeling of the correct expression. One can even say that the correct expression provides a minor satisfaction to the subject, in a way not dissimilar to having hit the target. The satisfaction is different, however, from that of hitting a target since it partakes of the quality of the sentic state concerned. An interesting point, however, is that this satisfaction is felt only to the degree that the correct form is actually produced. Because of the feedback that an E-acton has on the sentic state, the subject can be aware of the nature of his expressive act. The feeling of sincerity thus gains on operational definition.

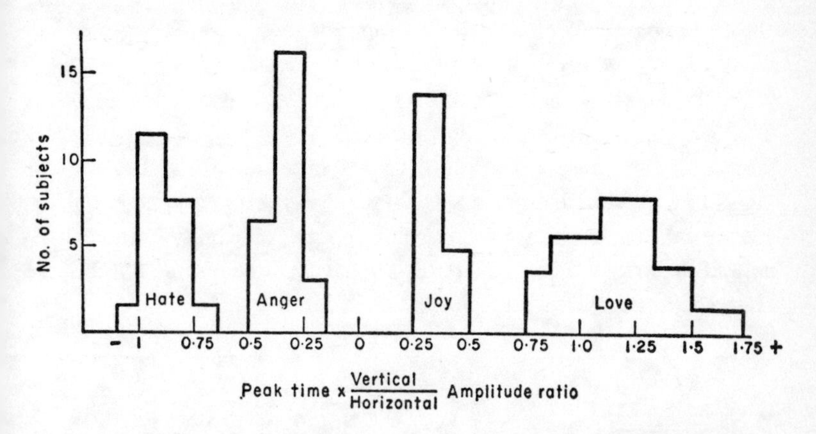

Figure 9. This bar graph illustrates how the observed sentograms for various sentic states (measured from a number of subjects) can be readily classified and identified according to parameters of the observed form. Measuring the interval of time from the beginning of the subject's expression to its peak pressure and multiplying it by a weighted tangent of the angle of pressure (calculated from the ratio of the size of the vertical and horizontal traces), one thus obtains an index which clearly separates the individual forms statistically into distinct categories. It is significant that each sentic state illustrated is clearly distinct for different individuals.

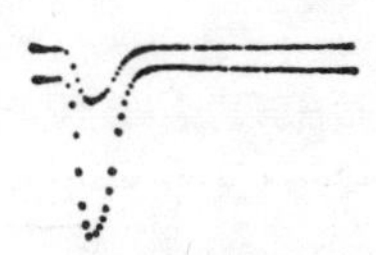

Anger

The essentic form of anger consists of a sharp movement in a direction markedly away from the body (a large outward horizontal component, downward on graph). The acton starts rapidly and ends after a relatively short time (less than one second). In terms of effort it is most intense at its beginning. It tends to occur together with a sharp, short expiration of breath and corresponding diaphragm contraction. (In generating these fantasy states, the subject is in the sitting position with the body quiet, as described.) The head tends to be in a slightly downward tilted position. The gaze is directed slightly downward. (Even the raising of the eyes or of the head is mostly felt as contrary to the natural expression of anger.) A firm jaw position with slight clenching of the teeth also tends to occur during anger, breathing tends to be rapid, and oxygen consumption and heart rate increased. (We shall not here describe indications of anger in the facial expression as they are well known. The facial expression during sentic states does not change transiently with each E-acton, in our method, but tends to have a steady and cumulative character for each state.)

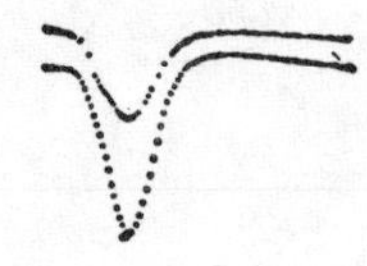

Hate

The essentic form of hate is markedly different from anger, but also shows similarities. At first, some subjects find it difficult to distinguish between expressions of these two. There is a passionate character in hate that finds its expression in a late-developing muscular activity within each acton. The late muscular tension is observed in specific muscle groups and is essential to its passionate nature.

The essentic form of hate starts more slowly than anger and is also strongly away from the body. The peak of intensity in terms of tension occurs considerably later than in anger. Through the specific secondary, late muscle activity (see Figure 6), the essentic form is also abruptly terminated with a rapid diminution of pressure.‡ This deceleration is far more rapid than the initial acceleration. The form ends abruptly with an exceedingly high rate of change of motion.

The experience of hate is also accompanied by expiration of the breath to some extent paralleling the dynamic course of the finger pressure. In addition to tension of the diaphragm, more extensive abdominal tension also accompanies the acton.

Respiration rate, heart rate, and oxygen consumption are increased

‡ In using the tone of voice to express hate, one may observe this late active muscle action in the rapid, tense termination of the voice, often associated with a tense, final closure of the mouth, and clenching of teeth.

during the sentic state of hate. Termination pressure of the acton generally does not coincide with the initial base level, so that a remnant of steady tension may continue to exist for some time.

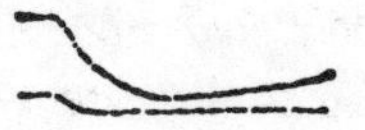

Grief

The essentic form of grief* is principally a letting go, an almost passive letting go or collapse. The acton is neither away from the body nor toward it. It appears to be governed by a special lassitude. The initial downward exertion is followed by a period of apparent weakness and relative immobility. The finger pressure remains relatively passive and constant. Respiration tends to stop at the bottom of the expiratory phase, like the end of a sigh. Before the next acton can be executed, one must "pick oneself up" and be poised for the next expression of grief which again is an almost passive dropping. The position of the head tends to be slightly inclined to the right, for right-handed people. The gaze is somewhat downward; the head may also be tilted slightly forward. The abdominal musculature is relaxed, as are muscle systems in general. There is no late muscular activity. Oxygen consumption, heart rate, and respiration all tend to be lower. Respiration particularly is slowed down considerably. The duration of the grief acton is greatly prolonged, perhaps three or four seconds, or longer.

Love

The subject is told that we are not dealing with sexual love in this phase but rather with "motherly" or "brotherly" love. Again, words

* Grief is distinguished from sadness in that it contains an irretrievable element; with regard to that aspect, no hope is possible. For example, the death of a loved one is often imagined by subjects; in music, the slow movement of Beethoven's Third Symphony provides an example.

are less precise than the sentic state and this state appears to be generally well understood by the subjects.

The essentic form of love is a prolonged, smooth curve. The direction of pressure tends to be slightly toward the body rather than away from it. The muscles participating display a smooth continuous action with greatest intensity near the beginning and toward the middle. The acton starts with a much lower acceleration than for anger or hate. Respiration rate and oxygen consumption are slower. During an acton there is slight tension in the diaphragm with abdominal relaxation. The breath does not rest at the end of expiration as it does during grief, but is smooth. Love actons are often begun near the end of inspiration and continue during the beginning of expiration. But they can be executed during various respiratory phases. Love actons are terminated gradually with a smooth diminution of pressure. There is a smooth return to the base level from which the next expressive acton can be begun. Position of the head tends to be neither raised nor lowered.

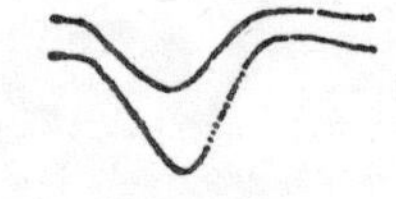

Sex

The essentic form of sex also displays a passionate element of "late" muscular activity (see Figure 5). The late active component arises from special muscle groups. There is a marked horizontal pressure component with some continuing steady state tension after completion of the acton. The dynamic form is highly characteristic of the manner in which the muscular activity develops, providing specific modes of pressure, acceleration, and deceleration with a marked horizontal component. The acton is somewhat prolonged but shorter than the love acton. There is some abdominal tension, but of a very different, more sustained character than for hate. Breathing tends to be rapid, and at times temporarily blocked during the expiration phase, so that the breathing contains abrupt panting-like short puffs that start and end abruptly. Similar abrupt phases of inspiration may also occur. Such a puffing nature of breathing is characteristic of sex corresponding to a particular degree of sexual excitement. This manner of breathing can be present in quite an unobtrusive manner without necessarily being accompanied by audible sounds. Heart rate and oxygen consumption are increased during the sex sentic state. Subjects experience degrees of physiologic involvement, such as erection of nipples, but the fantasy state does not normally result in orgasm. The position of the head tends to be slightly downward.

Joy

The essentic form of joy is expressed predominantly vertically. It tends to be neither away from nor toward the body and has a bounce-like character. A relatively small initial downward pressure is followed by the longer tail of a rebound ending in a floating kind of return to the base line. The common phrase "jumping for joy" appears to be reflected in this form. The floating sensation of the overshoot phase is an essential part of the acton experience. This sensation may well be related to aspects of the experience of weightlessness encountered by astronauts, or the frequently encountered dream phenomenon of floating in the air as if flying.† But the acton also includes an initial rapid though moderate push, with moderately high acceleration. The acton is characterized by a "free" manner of exertion, without late muscular activity or maintained tensions. The absence of a horizontal component also appears to contribute to the freeness of the implied motion. The duration of the joy acton is relatively short. The position of the head tends to be slightly raised, the gaze slightly upward, and the head inclined neither to the right nor to the left. Respiration rate tends to be slightly increased. The joy E-actons occur with inspiration and rarely with expiration. The inspiration tends to begin with a rapid phase, as if displaying an initial

† This aspect will be further discussed in Chapter Fourteen on sentics and space travel.

eagerness. Expiration is relaxed. Of all the sentic states considered, joy is most consistently associated with the inspiratory respiratory phase. Heart rate and oxygen consumption tend to be moderately raised during this state.‡

Reverence

The essentic form of reverence resembles that of love but is also different in a number of aspects. The horizontal component of pressure is not toward the body but slightly outward, or nearly vertical. Its course is even more prolonged than that of love and begins with very low acceleration. It is accompanied by a minimum of tension of any kind. There is no abdominal tension and very little tension of the diaphragm. Respiration is slowed down to a very slow rate, slower than in any of the other sentic forms considered. There tends to be a respiratory pause at the end of inspiration, the opposite condition as found in grief (an anti-sigh!). Heart rate and oxygen consumption tend to be lowered considerably. Head position and gaze are often slightly upward.

No significant differences between essentic forms produced by male and female subjects have been observed so far. Subjects are all able to experience at least some of the emotions on first trial. After three trial sessions the effectiveness, as reported by the subject in terms of which emotions they could feel, is well over 90 per cent.

Subjects who may have had difficulties with one or two of the states at first find that this difficulty diminishes with subsequent trials. Self-scoring indices, in which a subject scores himself one half hour after the completion of the test concerning the intensity of the separate emotions experienced on a scale from 0 to 5, give an average

‡ Sometimes, subjects do not imagine the idiolog of the E-acton described here: instead they imagine themselves joyfully hugging another person, and express the implied dynamics of the hugging which gives a very different form; such differences interestingly shed light on the idiolog processes involved.

intensity of emotions from four hundred subjects as 3.8. Subjects on the average tend to have least problems with anger, rarely with grief and sex, more with hate, love, and joy in that order. Difficulties are most often experienced with reverence, an emotion perhaps that half the subjects are "out of touch" with. It is usual in these subjects, however, to find scores for this rising from 0 to 1 to 3 or 4 after three trials. If instructions are misunderstood and subjects do not modulate their touch, they also report that they do not experience the states, but feel boredom instead. Near optimal mean time between initiating signals was 4.8 sec. for anger, 5.3 for hate, 8.2 for grief, 7.4 for love, 4.9 for sex, 5.2 for joy, 9.8 for reverence. Standard deviation of successive times of initiating ranges from 0.6 to 0.9 sec. and is proportionately somewhat less for the longer periods.

The sentic states we have described are those we have measured most.* There are of course other states which may be considered as basic, that is, states that are not mixtures of several sentic states. But an informed guess might be that there are not more than twenty such basic sentic states. As these studies proceed it should become possible to identify progressively the basic states, as has been done with colors and other systems of qualities.

Many states, on the other hand, are clearly mixtures (envy, for example). These too may have essentic forms. We are gradually finding out how the essentic forms of mixed states are synthesized from the essentic forms of the states making up the mixture. The study of this aspect is helped by analyzing sentographic personal relationship in profiles which we shall discuss in Chapter Eleven. Certainly, the essentic form of a compound state is not a simple sum of the essentic forms of the component states. One would not expect this to be so; as is known to every cook, the taste of a dish is not the sum of the taste of the ingredients. The elegant way in which the biologic design does seem to have solved this problem is also discussed in Chapter Eleven.

Thus, the essentic forms illustrated in this chapter can be regarded as a general frame for the emotional spectrum. We may hope to fill the gaps gradually as research progresses further.

* Others studied include hope, courage, guilt, and shame.

FIVE

Are Essentic Forms Culturally Conditioned?

Producing "Generalized" Emotion

In the experiments described in the previous chapter the subject at first finds it helpful to imagine specific scenes and persons in generating a sentic state. He soon discovers, however, that such imagined scenes are no longer necessary. It becomes possible to imagine the sentic state idiolog without any specific scenarios. This is of central theoretical and practical importance.

This process can be better understood through ridding oneself of a particular constraint of language imposed by the customary use of the word "imagine." Consider for a moment what we mean by the processes of "imagining." The word "imagine" is biased toward the visual sense. But not only a visual image (such as red) can be imagined; one can also "imagine" a sound, a smell, a touch, a taste, or as we find, a sentic state. If we use the word "imagine" for all these functions there results a tendency for subjects to evoke visual images that are actually extraneous to the brain processes involved. In this way we are the slaves of language's processes. For that reason it is useful to replace the word "imagine" with another word—"elogize." This word, derived from the Greek root *logos*, denotes a process corresponding to "imagining" a visual image, but applies to all the sensory modalities. The word may also be used, more generally, to denote the process of "imagining" idiologs. It is readily possible to elogize a sound, a tune, a particular taste, smell, touch, or a specific sentic state.* We observe that when we use the word "elogize," there is less tendency for subjects to imagine unessential visual scenes together with the qualities required.

As a subject is asked to elogize anger or grief or love, he can soon do so without reference to specific visual imagery. And, furthermore, he can also elogize sentic states without directing them at particular individuals. He can experience and express anger without having to be angry at a specific person, or he can experience and express love without necessarily imagining a specific individual. We may formally state this as the sixth sentic principle:

6. *Sentic states may be experienced and expressed as pure qualities or identities, without reference to specific auxiliary relationships to generate or receive these qualities.*

It is clearly important to realize that such experience is possible. In our daily lives we are prone to regard sentic states as arising mostly through specific reasons. When it is possible to realize that one can feel love without a specific or causative focus this tends to contradict many of our accepted social paradigms. A generalized love

* In a way, this is not really as surprising as it seems. This is the normal experience of sentic states in music, the natural functioning of musical experience and communication. Beethoven obviously composed this way during his last years when he was unable to hear. But this was not really difficult for him (his conversation notebooks bear this out) since any composer composes mostly by "hearing" first and sounding it after (although sometimes he may at times allow his fingers and mind to lead him on an instrument). In fact, any good musician "hears" first and then plays. The actual sound is used in part to check that his intentions were carried out. But everyone, whether a musician or not, can elogize specific sounds quite accurately. For example, you can think accurately of someone's voice, or the sound of a cuckoo.

ill-fits into society.† Many of the difficulties that artists encounter within society also are rooted, to a considerable extent, in their ability, not shared by others, to experience and consciously express generalized sentic states. This very ability, of course, underlies the processes by which artistic expressions find their power of communication.

Thus, the relation between "generalized" emotions or sentic states and of those experienced as directed at specific individuals or events is a central question. It concerns an examination of the nature of the relation linking fantasy and reality,‡ which shall be gradually developed in this book. A natural basis of that link is found in essentic form.

If essentic form can give rise to the experience of generalized emotions (that is, independent of specific content) and if, as we saw in our measurements of American subjects, essentic forms of different subjects within one culture are similar, we are led to ask further what reasons may lead us to regard these forms as biologically programmed or as culturally learned. The forms we have shown so far represent typical measurements from subjects in the United States. To what extent do these forms pertain to essential human nature and to what extent do they reflect the contemporary habits of individual cultures? To answer this question we looked at the essentic forms of people in other cultures, in particular in Japan, Bali, and Mexico.

Studying Essentic Forms of Different Cultures

Our research in the United States using the sentograph to measure emotional expression in a variety of subjects showed a similarity of forms among the participants tested, a similarity that could be due to cultural or biologic factors. We had to ask ourselves to what ex-

† Love that transcends the family has an element of danger in the context of our social framework. A political leader may *talk* about such sentic states, but were he actually to experience them, and be governed by them during his actual appearances, he would horrify and probably scare his electorate. Anger authentically expressed in public is much more socially acceptable.

‡ At this point in our discourse, it may impress the reader that fantasy and reality are not two entirely distinct, separate concepts.

tent these forms might have been the result of cultural learning among our American subjects, and to what extent they evidenced universal biologic brain programs.

To test whether essentic forms are free from cultural effects, we devised two methods of approach. One was to attempt to *retrain* a subject, so that the essentic form of anger, for example, would become the essentic form of love and vice versa. If the forms are arbitrarily learned, it should be possible to retrain or condition a subject to express sentic states with different or switched essentic forms. One can try to train subjects to do this, offering suitable inducements and rewards, that is to say, positive or negative reinforcements.

It is found, however, that even after prolonged periods of training, subjects are unable to express or to generate the specific sentic state through a different dynamic form. Such different forms will not act to *generate* the original state in accordance with the fifth sentic principle.* Nor can the subject, if he feels the sentic state of love, *express* that state through the form of anger or vice versa. A caress cannot replace a jabbing movement in expressing anger, and vice versa. Thus (and fortunately so) it does not appear possible to substitute artificial sentic forms for the natural ones. Moreover, the deliberate introduction and use of such artificial forms appears to cause continuing "blockage," an inability to experience the satisfaction of expression (a process equivalent to an aspect of repression).

The stubborn resistance of this natural process to be receptive to artifice is a further indication of the innate precision of the recognition process.†

Even though it proves not to be possible to retrain an individual to alter the function of essentic form, we needed to question further

* A schematic listing of the sentic principles discussed throughout this book can be found in the appendix.

† It is fortunate that this is so, otherwise our understanding of the qualities of love, anger, or grief would be as unstable as the changing tastes in fashions of the day. Instead, we find that the essentic forms of love, anger, and grief have as great a stability as the quality of red. Because of this we are able to communicate with and through the expressive achievements of the distant past, recognizing elements of humanity present in Greek sculpture, in the paintings of Rembrandt, in Bach or Beethoven as well as in Picasso or Stravinsky, and hearing cadences in the poetry of Homer and Shakespeare, whose mental time forms—idiologs—communicate unchanging qualities to us.

whether inheritance could result in different essentic forms among various human groups. To see whether the specific essentic forms we discovered were universal to human nature we carried out studies in several different cultures.

In a pilot study we sought to measure essentic form in a remote Mexican village, hoping to learn how to conduct a larger-scale study. We carried with us all the equipment including the averaging computer. This made the expedition perhaps more cumbersome than necessary. The Mexican people proved to be exceedingly friendly to us and everywhere we were gladly given all the help we needed. We found a young university student eager to help us as an interpreter, and after his simple explanations, Mexicans in even the smallest villages were readily willing to go through the procedures. Most of them seemed to enjoy the sessions.

Our attempts were futile, of course, in finding places of Mexican culture uninfluenced by North American life. Even the most remote villages prided themselves on their transistor radios and pin-up girls clipped from American magazines.

We did learn from that pilot project, though, the importance of adequately translating the key words denoting the sentic states. If these words are imperfectly translated, then observed differences are ambiguous; they might be ascribed to either different word connotation, or to a different essentic form. Perfect translations are, of course, never possible even with these so widely used words; each language has its own subtlety of meaning and connotation that prevents a completely accurate translation. Yet slight differences of word meaning should not really matter, since we had previously noted that a subject tends to discover the precise essentic form within himself and the commonality underlying the corresponding words should overshadow small differences in conventional meaning.

Sometimes, however, such differences are sufficiently marked to cause difficulties. For example, the word "joy" turns out to be difficult to translate into Spanish. Neither the word *alegría* nor *contento* is sufficiently equivalent to the Blakean or Mozartean concept of joy.‡ It proved to be an unsuspected confirmation of the theory

‡ On the other hand, there is a word in the Balinese language for the intense joy or delight experienced in a fraction of a second as one perceives unexpectedly

that significant "cultural" differences appeared in the production of that essentic form only when no really adequate word could be found in translation.

With the Mexican experience behind us we were able to be more efficient in our next expeditions to Japan and to Bali. The computer was left at home for these trips and we took the chance to record the data on tape. We waited with held breath until they could be processed at home. (This allowed me to make the trip by myself with only local assistance, an economically decisive advantage in view of our limited grant funds.) Leaving the computer at home was also taking a chance but it seemed better than running the risk of malfunctioning equipment in an inaccessible place such as Bali; what was more to the point, it saved much heavy lugging around of equipment.

The choice of the contrasting cultures of Japan and Bali was deliberate. The Balinese have a culture of rare artistic penetration; almost every Balinese individual is, in reality, some kind of artist. Dance, music, painting, sculpture are all cultivated to a high degree of proficiency and the sensibilities of the Balinese are almost universally high in spite of their material poverty by Western standards. In the beauty and fulfillment of their personal lives, the Balinese are anything but poor, and the objects with which they surround themselves are probably more beautiful than those found in the average Park Avenue apartment. The Balinese seemed an ideal group to study for the production of essentic form. (And Bali is certainly a great place to work!)

On the other hand the Japanese, with their highly cultivated, distinct cultural patterns, frequently advocate extreme restraint in emotional expression and the wearing of mask-like expressions. The prevalence of a stereotype expressive behavior so strongly at variance

---

an extraordinarily arresting, beautiful sight. Such an acutely intense, short wave of feeling (which is remembered for a long time) has found no word in English or any other language with which I am familiar. I was amazed to hear my Balinese friend, Dr. Denny Thong, explain to me the meaning of a concept which I had often experienced as a child but, unfortunately, had never heard named so that I could not communicate it readily. And here it was in current usage in Bali!

with that found in the United States seemed well suited for comparison. We wanted to concentrate on the old Japanese culture, so we studied mainly a group of Zen Buddhist monks and practitioners in Kyoto. We were fortunate to be able to have as one subject for sentic measurement the Head Abbot of the Temple Rianji, who occupies a position in Zen Buddhism somewhat analogous to the Pope of the Catholic Church.

A most striking aspect of these experimental studies was the readiness and ease with which subjects took to the specific expressive method. Although none had ever deliberately used just one finger for the concentrated expression of emotion, all except one subject readily seemed to feel comfortable with our method. (One Japanese subject, apparently misunderstanding the instructions, exclaimed, "I cannot possibly feel any love for that finger rest" and did not wish to do the measurements.) Most of the other Japanese subjects found the experience "enjoyable" and "revealing" and "a unique experience." They often expressed amazement at the ease with which emotions were generated and could be *experienced* by this method. Remarkably, none of the Japanese subjects had difficulty in clearly distinguishing between anger and hate—an interesting and perhaps significant cultural finding. In their daily lives it seems most Japanese subjects were constrained by a severely limited range of emotional expression, yet they seemed to be remarkably uninhibited in their ability to produce essentic form with our method. Some subjects enthusiastically expressed their sense of discovery of these forms in themselves, and found it a liberating experience. Others, with considerable experience of Zen, provided restrained yet highly characteristic collections of essentic forms. These subjects involved their bodies less in physiologic emotional reactions and appeared to concentrate more on the mental enjoyment of the sentic state idiologs. (Indeed, the Head Abbot of Rianji warned us that Zen training consisted in part of the suppression of emotionality, and that consequently we should not expect to obtain good results from him.) The less Zen-minded Japanese, on the other hand, appeared to find it easier, if anything, to generate sentic states spontaneously than the average American. For the expression of reverence, care was necessary to make it clear that reverence toward individuals was not the required state.

The result: essentic forms produced by the Japanese were basically and remarkably the same as those produced by a group of subjects in the United States! Differences between individuals of different cultures turned out to be no greater than those within a group from a single culture. It was found, in other words, that the Japanese, on the whole, appear to produce the same essentic forms as people in the United States.

Measurement of the Balinese also proved to be especially interesting. A difficulty was encountered immediately. It turned out that there was no word for hate in the Balinese language! The Balinese have retained their own language and their Hindu religious traditions although the island is part of Indonesia. The life of a Balinese man or woman is governed from birth until death by the lore of the Mahabharata, Ramayana, and other ancient Indian sagas and myths. Although Western influences are now felt in some parts, most Balinese villagers still believe implicitly these grand themes encompassing their lives. Their dance, music, sculpture, and other arts are almost exclusively based on these themes. Their daily lives are filled with serenity and enjoyment. (A frequent sight is one hundred or two hundred children playing on the beach joyfully without any signs of fights.) Yet their plays and dances exhibit an unrestrained vehemence of emotions that seems almost excessive to Western eyes, but are startling in their purity of expression. How would these subjects respond to our methods?

We found that they, too, produced essentic forms very similar to all others. (See Figure 10.) Their degree of sentic state generation and involvement was not noticeably higher or lower than elsewhere; as in other groups, about 20 per cent of the subjects cried during the phase of grief. The Balinese, too, were amazed at the readiness with which sentic states could be generated. An interesting, typical comment was "I was sitting and expressing with my hand, and anger *just came!*" As we have seen, the phenomenon of the sentic state "just coming"—as if by magic—that is to say without any specific situation or reason, is indeed a basic characteristic of the ability to gener-

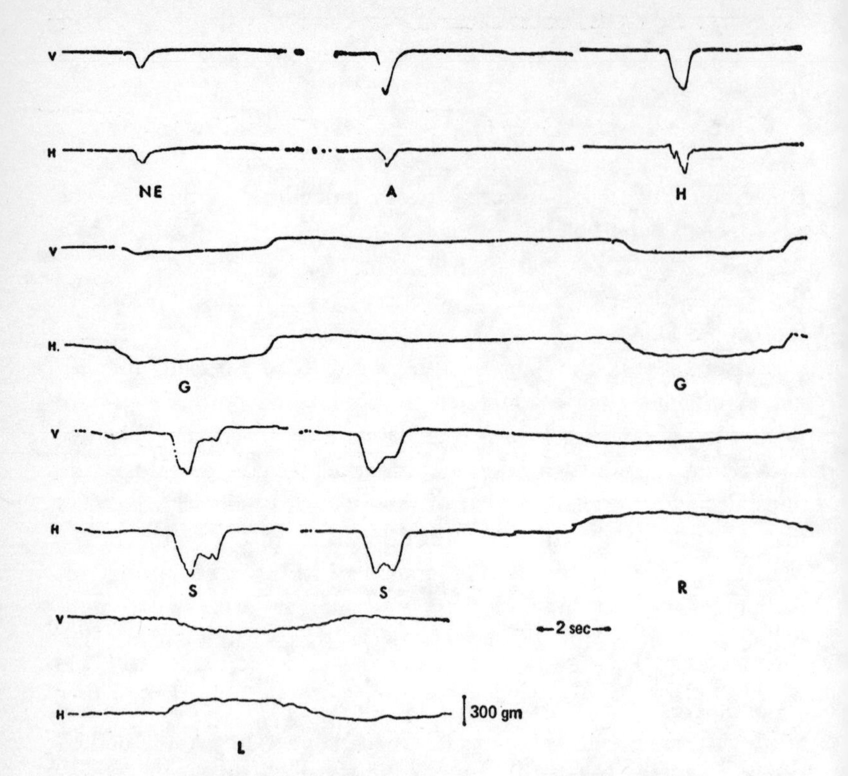

Figure 10. Examples of single E-actons expressing various emotions recorded by a female Balinese subject, age twenty-four. Tape-recorded data were replayed on a strip chart recorder. These examples show the character of the raw data before averaging. Initials below actons stand for emotions expressed: No Emotion, Anger, Hate, Grief, Sex, Reverence, and Love.

ate sentic states in this manner. For the Balinese, the quasi-magical aspect of this was prominent.*

Results of measurements of the Japanese and Balinese essentic forms confirmed the similarity of different cultural groups and sup-

* In our studies of the Balinese we were fortunate to have the assistance of Dr. Denny Thong, a remarkable young doctor who had pioneered medical services for the villages of Bali, where modern medical and surgical instruments are almost totally lacking. He also has pioneered in providing psychiatric services to these islanders, especially for those few cases of schizophrenia among the three million population that do occur. Through his enthusiastic help we were also able to obtain adequate translations of all the words denoting sentic states—except for hate.

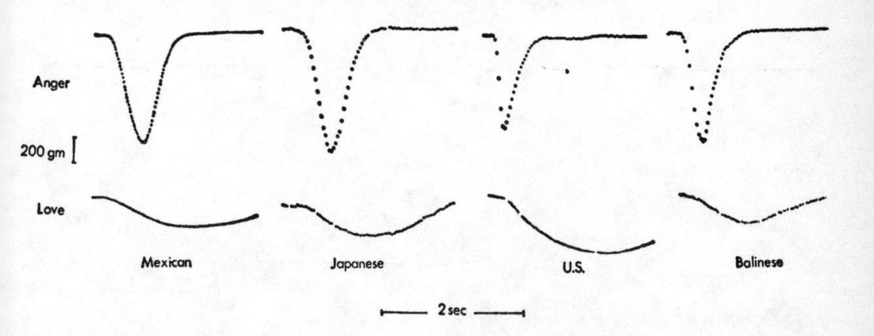

Figure 11. A comparison of the essentic forms of love and anger in four cultures: Mexican, Japanese, American, and Balinese (vertical component shown). Similarities of the sentograms are apparent. Differences between individuals are typically of about the same order as variation between cultures.

ported the view that specific essentic forms are characteristic of human nature, regardless of race and culture. (See Figure 11.) This is, of course, of inestimable value for the communication of emotions and qualities among all people of the earth. It is a documentation of our brotherhood, in terms of our common inheritance of unchanging, pure qualities of emotions and their expressive forms, which are potentially programmed, so it seems, into every man.

SIX

The Communicating Power and Mathematical Equation of Essentic Form

Perhaps the most remarkable biologic property of essentic form, next to being a bridge between the otherwise isolated inner worlds of individuals, is that its power of communication depends directly on the degree of faithfulness to which it represents the characteristic expressive form of the state to be communicated.

Unlike the recognition of the shape of a letter or numeral, for example, which fulfill their communication function regardless of imperfections in form, imperfections and errors in the production of essentic forms can directly interfere with the power of communication, *even if they are consciously recognized as imperfections. The essentic function places direct experience of form ahead of intellectual recognition.* It requires a person to be in a condition of connectedness so that the expressed form corresponds to the inner state for the communication to function fully. (Sometimes such a convincing communication may even exceed our own capacity to imagine precise essentic form and thus expand our capacities.)

We may state this property formally as the seventh sentic principle:

> 7. *The power of essentic form in communicating and generating a sentic state is greater the more closely the form approaches the pure or ideal essentic form for that state.*

We call such a pure essentic form *orthoessentic* form. The more nearly the expressed form approximates this true form the more powerfully does it appear to act in generating its specific quality. When we express an approximate essentic form we do not communicate as effectively (even though "intellectually" one may be able to guess the type of sentic state intended to be communicated). This principle can be demonstrated in our communication with other persons, with ourselves, and in music and the other arts. Perhaps the following short anecdote will illustrate this more clearly.

Some years ago, in the house of Pablo Casals in Puerto Rico, the Master was giving cello master classes. On this occasion, an outstanding participant played the theme from the third movement of the Haydn cello concerto, a graceful and joyful theme. Those of us there could not help admiring the grace with which the young master cellist played—probably as well as one would hear it anywhere.

Casals listened intently. "No," he said, and waved his hand with his familiar, definite gesture, "that must be graceful!" And then he played the same few bars—and it was graceful as though one had never heard grace before—a hundred times more graceful—so that the cynicism melted in the hearts of the people who sat there and listened. That single phrase penetrated all the defenses, the armor, the hardness of heart which we mostly carry with us, and with its power transformed us into people who were glad to be alive.

What was the power that did this? A slight difference in shape between the phrase as played by the young man and by Casals. A slight difference—but an enormous difference in power of communication, evocation, and transformation.

How did Casals derive his precise shape? What is the meaning of the function of such purity of expression in relation to the central nervous system?

Such purity used to be ascribed to "inspiration"—a concept where attempts at further understanding made a halt.* In the course of association with Casals one gradually came to some measure of understanding of the source of such purity, as one heard him reiterate over and over again to play "naturally." To understand the meaning of such a phrase invokes a highly precise process and an enlightening one, although one it may take years to discover. Playing "naturally" means two things: (1) to listen inwardly with utmost precision to the inner form of every musical sound, and (2) then to produce that form precisely. It means to have a precise idea, as well as a precise execution of it. And the crucial and amazing fact is that if one really believes this and listens with great care, then it also turns out to be beautiful.

This operational principle, simple as it is, can be of revolutionary import in musical performance. All too often the faithfulness required by teachers is not to the inner sound but merely to so-called tradition, or the totally inadequate notation of the score. The musical score is not able to define the real subtleties that are essential to give a truly living character to the music. It is no exaggeration to say that in the hands of a master such as Casals the sound is defined to a precision of hundredths of a tone, (that is to say, a single tone is shaped with such meaningful detail that if represented by a curve such a tone would have to be divided into one hundred ordinates to denote its course adequately). This estimate is not far removed from the ability of the ear to distinguish changes in essentic form amounting to less than 100th of a second.

Thus the power of essentic form to generate sentic states in the perceiver is greatly dependent upon its purity (the degree to which it approximates or is faithful to the inner essentic form), and that in turn is a function of how clearly the idiolog of the sentic state is experienced.

There are many different experimental ways to demonstrate the

* In conversation with Casals, his answer to this question about the source of such quality of imagination was a devout gesture. Holding his arms out toward the heavens, palms facing each other, he said, "I always used to say it comes from above." From the point of view of sentics this is not absurd. By being open to being "used" by the source of purity, we may be enabled to communicate it, becoming its vessels. And the shape of such gestures is not to be considered primarily "symbolic"—it has a biologic basis in the essentic forms of qualities.

dependence of communicating power of essentic form on its purity. One such method is to present a subject with a deliberately distorted dynamic essentic form, and, through adjustment of the control knobs, allow him to adjust the form to be maximally expressive of that particular quality. For example, joyous or angry exclamations can be distorted by passing them through a process that alters one or more chosen aspects or parameters, such as dynamic contour, pitch contour, timbre contour, or timing. The subject can then take one or more of these and by turning the appropriate control knobs try to optimize the expression by restoring the contour to be an optimally joyous or angry expression according to his own interpretation or feeling.†

The important point is that *for the recognition process to act it is not sufficient merely to judge and classify the phenomenon from a rough indication of its nature*. The nature of the recognition process is such that an approximate essentic form acts very differently from a pure, faithful one. The "error accumulation" interferes with the effective data processing of the quality in our nervous system. This is the essence of the purity concept in the action of the essentic form upon the nervous system.

This aspect of precision, as stated in the seventh sentic principle, makes it possible to proceed to a mathematical representation of essentic form. In such a representation, an objective would be to find an equation that would describe the ideal essentic forms. And secondly, having found such an equation, we might try to search for mathematical relationships that determine the specific nature of each essentic form. At that point we could ask the question how it comes about that a specific essentic form is what it is. Or, to put it in analogous terms more familiar to the reader in exploring the world of physics one can observe the orbit of a planet to be an ellipse and find its exact equation as Kepler did, and then one may further ask how it comes about that the planet moves in an ellipse, to which

† A different, but related confirmation of the essentic form that we observed has also come from the work of Bruce Brown at Brigham Young University, who constructed his own sentograph and found similar essentic forms in the sentographic responses of fifty-four subjects to a set of emotional speech sample stimuli. (He in fact found a clearer differentiation of affect through sentographic responses than through verbal responses, given by the Osgood semantic differential measures.)

Newton found an answer. Similar questions may be asked concerning essentic form.

The Mathematical Equation of Essentic Form‡

To answer the first question would allow us objectively to characterize essentic form and obtain some predictions concerning new relationships of essentic forms and their effects. We have, in fact, been able to find such a differential equation that represents the specific essentic forms we have discovered. The equation was found with the help of computer simulation, using analog computer models to set up physiologically plausible models until we found the simplest, adequate, meaningful representation in terms of a differential equation capable of representing all the essentic forms. Each essentic form represents a particular solution or eigenvalue of the equation. These solutions have time constants as parameters; their specific values determine the specific essentic form. The equation is presented below.

The differential equation whose solutions for impulse function inputs are the various essentic forms is given in Laplace Transform notation as:

$$\frac{U(s)}{I} = b\left(\frac{\tau_1\tau_2\tau_3 s}{(1+\tau_1 s)(1+\tau_2 s)(1+\tau_3 s)}\right)\left(\frac{\tau_4 s}{1+\tau_4 s} + \Omega k_p \frac{\tau_5}{(1+\tau_5 s)}\right)$$

where s is the Laplace Transform

$U(s)$ = the Laplace Transform of $u(t)$, the essentic form

I is the input impulse

τ_1, τ_2, etc. are time constants, parameters that have characteristic or eigenvalues for each specific emotion

k_p is a "passion coefficient (positive for hate, sex; zero for love, joy, reverence)

Ω is an operator*

which has the value 1 for $\frac{du}{dt} \geqslant 0$

0 for $\frac{du}{dt} < 0$

(upward being taken as positive)

b = a scale factor

‡ This section is included for readers of mathematical inclination (see elaboration in Appendix III). Other readers may pass on to Chapter Seven.

* The unidirectionally rate sensitive operator as defined in Clynes 1961, 1969b.

The differential equation was derived from a control system approach. Utilizing Laplace Transform terminology allows a much simpler notation than if it were written as a conventional fifth order non-linear differential equation.

The input to the equation is fixed as an impulse function. The equation is partially non-linear due to the necessity of introducing the "passion coefficient" and its associated function, which is required by the introduction of the late muscular activity found in actons of passionate states, as described earlier.

The parameters of the equation also allow us to construct a vector space of the emotions. The construction has a butterfly shape, which circumscribes the manner of gradually proceeding from one sentic state to another. It describes how we can go from certain states to others only through passing through the areas within the butterfly shape and not directly across.

Mathematical representation may also clearly separate the measured essentic forms according to their horizontal vector direction away from or toward the body. Those strongly away include those usually classed as "negative" emotions (anger, hate) whereas those more toward the body (or vertical) are often termed "positive" (love). We thus have an objective characterization of this aspect of psychologic significance.

The correspondence of the essentic forms calculated according to the equation with those experimentally observed may be seen in Figure 12. We may thus say that we have found an equation which describes essentic form in the sense that it describes the "orbit of the planet," according to our previously cited comparison. We may say that these phenomena of expression which combine experience and behavior (mind and body) have yielded their mathematical form.

As for finding an answer to the second question, to discover what determines each essentic form to be as it is, in its coherence with a specific emotion—this would involve to begin with a far greater understanding of the language of the genetic code than we have today. At this point we have no answer, but it is a perhaps not negligible merit of the theory that it can be posed at all. And we have at least a few clues on how to proceed in our search toward that goal. If there

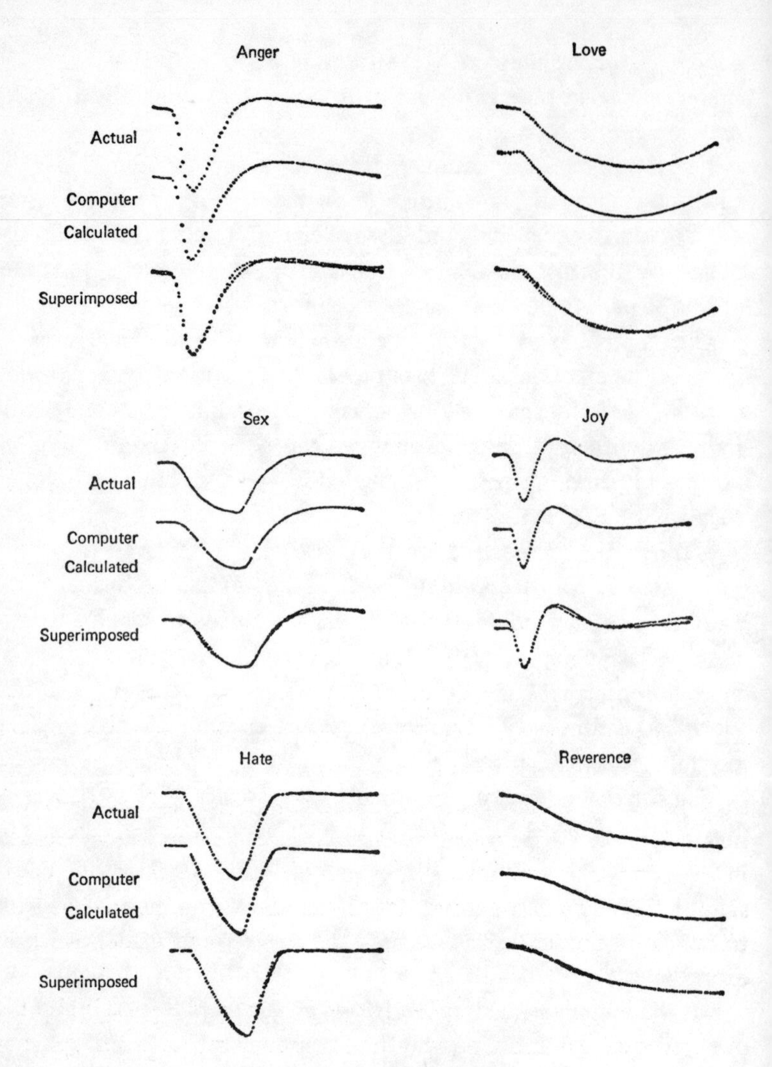

Figure 12. Measured and computed essentic forms.

is an answer to this question (and there could be reasons why an answer could not be formulated), it may be that within some decades it could be within our grasp.

SEVEN

Producing and Recognizing Essentic Form, Empathy, and Sympathy

Consider again the anecdote related in the previous chapter which illustrated how a great artist like Casals communicates qualities and sentic states with a potency that can be marred by even small departures from specific, natural essentic form. This phenomenon, the power of precision, is indeed true not only in music but also in the personal communication of qualities and sentic states. Precision of tone of voice, gesture, touch—all can communicate and act to transform the sentic state of both the receiver and sender of sentic expressions.

But the human sender, unlike his electronic counterpart, is also his own receiver. An artist constantly communicates with his growing work of art. As the work grows, its communicative power imbues the artist as much as the artist gives to the work. Goethe, for example, speaks of having lived "under the thrall of the 'West Östlichen Divan'" during the months he was writing this extended series of poems that was to constitute one of his masterworks. Similarly, Beethoven attested in his notebooks how specifically transformed he was by the music he wrote—each symphony creating a special world within him even as he was creating the symphony!

But the effect of expression on its producer is not limited to art. Precision of expression has a remarkable function in daily life and in interpersonal relations. The authentic expression of essentic form is experienced as "sincerity." More than that, it has a force of inducing empathy. (We not only enjoy the productions of a great artist, we also tend to feel love for *him*.) This empathy arises when, in the manifest openness of the person expressing, we sense that the expression arises from the center of his being. We see no "artifice" in it and nothing intrudes into the pattern of communication to act as a warning sign of another level of communication, hiding behind conventional, learned clichés or other "superficial" influences. We intuitively distinguish a genuine, deeply felt communication from superficial expressions.

Superficial expressions may have sentic significance in revealing a person's psychological condition, particularly in the way he may be blocking deeper, more meaningful communication. But we recognize the sharp differences between such expressions and authentic ones precisely through the perception of essentic form. In order to do this, only one's natural sensibilities are required; to pay attention to these, however, is an attitude we may have thoroughly forgotten. It involves an intense quietness, a true listening. One of the most encouraging applications of sentics is that it provides a means to sharpen the sensibilities and reawaken forgotten capacities in this regard.

Production of Essentic Form

The production and recognition of essentic forms are coordinated through design of the biologic data processing systems, involving different processes. In producing an expressive form, such as a gesture, several modes of sentic connectedness may significantly affect the process. We may list three types of such modes in the production of expressive form: (1) mimicry, (2) full sentic involvement, and (3) empathic viewing. The sentic drive is connected differently in each mode and the involvement of the body is different.

In mimicry,* the sentic drive is not connected to the motor expression. The production of the expression is entirely "intellectual," without experience of the sentic state that corresponds to the expressed form. Nor does mimicry entrain the processes of empathy. It is an "unfeeling" production of expression. (Its humorous aspect, where encountered, arises precisely from this disconnectedness.)

The second mode, which may be called "Dionysian," entails the full involvement of the person in the sentic state, with corresponding involvement of the physiological systems.†

In a third stage of expressive function, the sentic state is relieved from the urgent requirements of inner drives. A different mode of experience becomes more accessible, which we may call the empathic viewing mode. In this mode of connectedness one experiences and expresses the sentic state from a different point of view: a view corresponding to meditative, or the "Apollonian"; the sentic state is viewed and savored and body functions are involved in a different way. This mode allows the particular sentic states to be enjoyed in their purity, while retaining control of mental freedom. The exercise of this freedom also allows us to switch sentic states voluntarily, and to proceed easily from the empathic viewing of one sentic state to another.

The faculty that allows one to switch sentic states in the manner described we call "pre-sentic control." Free exercise of pre-sentic control implies sentic fluidity; one is not stuck rigidly in any one sentic state, but can experience the spectrum of sentic states, freely and readily. The condition of sentic fluidity, it becomes apparent, is an important aspect of mental health. Many individuals are caught in a "rut," unable to get out of their rigid sentic condition. Sentics can alleviate such a condition, as will be shown in our subsequent discussion of sentic cycles.

The three modes of connected function are distinguished by their "point of view," and are to a degree open to choice. The choice an

* Not to be confused with the superb art of a mime, such as that of Marcel Marceau; he does not "mimic" in the above sense, but portrays.

† The second mode, full sentic involvement, may at times be preceded by the mimicry mode in the experimental production of essentic form. After a few E-actons, however, the sentic drive becomes more fully connected and the second mode tends to become established.

individual makes affects the nature of his relationships with other individuals, with himself, and with his environment. Through sentic studies and practice one can become more clearly aware of the nature of these choices of "point of view." Interestingly, these choices have effects upon the *perception* as well as on the *production* of essentic form.

Perception of Essentic Form

Perception of essentic form occurs in two ways: (1) perception of one's own essentic form expression as it is being produced, and (2) the perception of essentic form separate from its production.

Perceiving our own essentic form as we produce it is different from perceiving essentic form when produced by others or perceiving our own forms at a later time. The nature of this difference varies with the degree of awareness of the individual. For example, we are generally less receptive to the quality of our own tone of voice than to the same quality in another voice.‡ Similarly in touching we are generally less aware of the quality of our own touch than is the person whom we are touching. This is because the simultaneous production and perception of the same essentic form cannot be carried out by the nervous system without a degree of interference.*

We are capable, however, of a great degree of latitude (or, in a sense to be defined, "improvement") in the way we recognize the qualities of our own tone of voice, even while speaking, and in the manner in which we experience our own touch while touching another. Even though the full sentic impact of perceiving our own essentic form production cannot be experienced simultaneously, awareness of the faithfulness of the form to the inner sentic demand *is* possible. We can increase that awareness of the quality of our expressive actions without fully experiencing the impact of the expression itself. Understanding the quality of the expressive act

‡ We are often surprised when we perceive the essentic forms contained in our speech as we listen to a tape recording of ourselves.

* This of course does not apply if the produced essentic form is perceived later. For instance, an artist who draws a line or form can then look at it, or a composer having produced an essentic form in sound can then listen to it. In doing so, he will not have to be limited by the simultaneous production and perception as happens in hearing one's own tone of voice.

derives from a *continuous experience of the coherence* between the sentic state and its experienced expression. This sensation of coherence is not easily explained in words. In part, it is associated with an aspect of satisfaction felt when the essentic form expressed truly corresponds to the sentic state. We experience a sense of being true to ourselves at that moment. But another aspect of the experience of coherence lies in the savoring of the quality itself, both as it is expressed and as the experience of the state.

Thus, one can have various degrees of awareness of the effect of the essentic form one is expressing. But how necessary is such awareness? Can essentic forms be expressed with complete unawareness of what they are or of the state they are expressing? And if so, what would result from such unawareness?

Consider, for example, that in writing a poem one may be in a state where the lines come to awareness one after the other, with a wholeness that could be impaired by any degree of self-consciousness or a disturbance of the state from which they spring. In the creative act it is important to allow the essentic form to be born as the issue of that state—to allow the state to be intensified and focused through the act of expression—but to avoid contamination of the state through perception of incongruous forms. In short, we have a paradigm very similar to that of the generation of sentic states by the method of repeated E-acton expression.

But in personal interactions awareness of the quality and point of view of expression can be not only helpful; it can transform the relationship. In creative interpersonal relationships the self-steering interplay of perception and production of essentic form is central. And the processes of dream formation also partake of these functions in ways we shall discuss in later chapters. Indeed, production and perception of essentic form are biologic bridges for the dynamic interchange between fantasy and reality, and in a different sense, between art and life.

Precision of Essentic Form Perception

Let us now turn to the second, more general process of perceiving essentic form, that of the person who perceives the form while not simultaneously producing it. What about the precision of these processes? If the essentic form produced is not precise, there will be room for possible ambiguity. But ambiguity could well exist even with a precisely expressed essentic form.

In order to clarify this important question, we need to look in more detail at the modes of connectedness between the sentic domain and the perceptual function. In Chapter One we discussed the identity of qualities. We noted that in addition to the identity of each quality there appeared to be a genetically programmed loose coupling of qualities, but we did not pursue that significant topic further.

Let us consider the quality of red once more. There is a physiological characteristic of red which we have not yet considered. It is that in addition to being "red," the quality of red is also *exciting* (just as in a similar way blue is calming). It is readily seen that this characteristic of colors is not culturally conditioned.† Indeed, evidence of specific brain function shows electrical responses to red measured in the brain to be more marked than to other colors of equal intensity (Clynes 1968b).‡ This "exciting" aspect of red is also a quality of red that we experience. Thus we are faced with an apparent paradox —the unique quality of red, which we said could not be composed of other qualities, does in fact contain, or at least is inherently associated with, a second quality. To understand the meaning of this paradox, consider the example of a person taking a tranquilizer: the drug does not change the redness of red for him, but it does suppress its "exciting" aspect. Neurophysiologically, the two properties must arise through different portions of the brain and through disparate brain processes. Their coupling,* though inherent, is subject to changing influences. This is an example of a loosely coupled, genetically programmed interrelation of qualities. This aspect of programmed human nature is highly important and has bearing on the interrelationship of sentic states and on other qualities and unconscious functions as well.

† In fact, one can readily think of phylogenetic reasons why red might have become exciting in the course of evolution.

‡ Or even than a white light containing the same red stimulus as a component.

* Synaesthesia, the coupling of different sensory modes so that, for example, specific sounds appear to evoke or be associated with specific colors, is another manifestation of a loose coupling of qualities.

The nature of the relationship of sentic states to one another, as well as the possibilities of programming ordered functional relationships among them, may be considered and explored in these terms. Aspects of "loose coupling" apply especially to the connection of perceptual functions with the sentic domain. In the example quoted, we have a flexible choice to allow ourselves to be aware of red as exciting or to ignore this function. We do not enjoy the redness of a stop signal light as we might the redness of a rose. Red becomes a mere sign—not an experienced quality. Thus the disconnectedness forced upon us by the artifacts of civilization may often become habitual (and also forgotten) and may to various degrees atrophy our ability to reconnect the sentic domain at will, and so to experience the perceived qualities freely.

The action of essentic form was characterized earlier as somewhat like a key in the data processing lock of our nervous system. (Ethologists† also refer to "innate release mechanisms" in animal behavior, though without any specific ways of measuring their precise dynamic forms.) Such actions can take place only if there is appropriate connection between the perceptual and sentic domains. Habitual disconnection corresponds to a process of alienation. Such alienation results in part from and is reinforced by an inability to communicate and experience freely in terms of pure essentic form.

Another source, thus, of possible uncertain perception of essentic form, in addition to ambiguity of improper production, lies in the readiness of the perceiver to be open. A sentically closed condition leads to uncertainty of perceived quality. The lack of intensity of the generated state educes its nondescript character.

A number of factors may contribute to achieving openness. A high school student looking at a Rembrandt painting may not perceive its qualities because he has not discovered how to "focus" on them. Yet a few suitable remarks may well serve as guideposts to orient him to the qualities to look for. Such a guide is helpful also in the sentic orientation toward music. By looking for the wrong qualities and not finding them, many people are disappointed and turn away from works of art. They miss out on discovering the qualities they did not look to find.

† E.g., Eibl-Eibesfeldt, Lorenz.

To distinguish between the essential and non-essential but contributing qualities in the complex sensory experience of a particular work of art requires an appropriate sensory orientation. If a person listens to the Ninth Symphony of Beethoven for the sound of the piccolo he will not experience the communication inherent in the work, to take an extreme example. Such an example is by no means as absurd as it may seem. The enjoyment of specific qualities such as of the sound of a violin, or of a particular shade of color, of even form, can obscure the perception of other qualities, and even essentic form. In a well-integrated work of art all these sensory aspects will reinforce each other in the right context, but exaggerated attention to any one of them interferes with the experience of essentic forms.

Precedence of Essentic Form over Other Sensory Perception

This leads us to consider how the power of the essentic form acutely perceived transcends the power of other sensory perceptions. A genuine, "captivating" smile will tend to make us forget other competing sensory stimuli. A powerful, purely expressed essentic form in a particular sensory mode gives primacy to that mode over the others, whatever it may be. A pure expression of anger too has a particular "arresting" beauty. Essentic form, purely—arrestingly—produced in the tone of voice, in a musical phrase, in a touch, can make that particular sense by far the most important to us (during the time of expression).‡ If love is expressed purely, it does not matter through which sensory modality it is conveyed—but more than that, if the expression is recognized, it will have priority over all other sensory impressions—it can make us forget cold, warmth, rain, even burnt food—for a while.

The sense of touch has some special communicational aspects that will be considered later. Perhaps it is odd that as yet we have no symphonies of touch; essentic form touch communication is almost

‡ This experience of essentic form through a particular sense modality is thus not considered as acting by being perceived as *symbolic* as in the philosophy of Susanne Langer, but as a direct biologic experience, a common neurophysiologic factor extracted by the central nervous system from the sense modalities, which, to an extent, animals too are capable of sharing.

all interpersonal.* However, certain forms of massage such as those developed at Esalen Institute, when well performed, can be like a symphony performed upon the body and constitute aware essentic form communication both to the performer and to the receiver. This type of massage coordinates breathing and felt emotion with the quality of touch, as an art, in such a way that the communication of essentic form supplants the merely sensual.

Distinction between the sensual and the expression of essentic form is very important. It is especially important in the communication of sexual excitement. There is an enormous difference between mere "mechanical" stimulation and the communication of passion through the sexual essentic form.

Communication through essentic form always presupposes a person as the sender. This is so even in a work of art. We sense that it is a *person* who created this work. Through a great work of art, we may even become aware of intimate aspects of the creator's personality. (This aspect will be considered in more detail in the following chapter dealing with music.) A mechanical sensory stimulation is sensed as "mechanical," precisely because no originating personality is inherently sensed simultaneously with the stimulation. Only through the expression of essentic form is sensory stimulation given a personal image. Although mechanical vibrators can perhaps provide a greater, more intense sensation at times than a human touch, in sexual communication essentic form sets a completely different stage which in its own way can increase the intensity of sensation as the sexual communication progresses. (The stimulus enters at a different point of the chain of nervous system processes involved.) The difference is similar to experiencing a work of art through essentic form as compared with its mere sensation-perception—the difference between sensory titillation and the contagious communication of human essentic form.

Similar comments apply to music, in which the experience of essentic form takes precedence over the sensory sound experience (and even dictates the type of "tone quality" required) in the works of most major classical composers, who are (in this sense) "expres-

* We do not touch ourselves to communicate and express, as we sing and play music for ourselves.

sionists" with the notable exception of Debussy (whose music is "impressionistic").† Thus it happens that a phrase played by Artur Schnabel on an old 78 record continues to be more meaningful and satisfying than the latest "hi-fi-est" version which preserves all the overtones—but misses the undertones of essentic form.

In an open, receptive condition the experience of essentic form supersedes other impressions and fills the sentic domain with a degree of intensity that is directly related to the purity of the essentic form. In this state, it appears, there is no ambiguity at all. Mendelssohn said that music cannot be expressed in words—not because it is vague, but because it is *more precise* than words. This dictum applies also to pure essentic form as experienced through touch, tone of voice, and through the other modes of communication.

For example, there are many phrases in music whose expression might be either loving or sad. In the printed score the essentic form is not unambiguously defined. As the reader may have noted in Chapter Four, the essentic forms of Grief and of Love bear a certain resemblance. This creates a possible ambiguity and range of interpretation; yet it depends on the manner in which the phrase is heard inwardly; there is an inner choice we may make between "loving" or "sad." Having made that choice, for reasons which are beside our present considerations, the expression may then be made as faithful as possible to that inner essentic form. In this way the ambiguity of the score is resolved to one or the other solution for the re-creator of the score. An imperfect execution of the form will however leave the ambiguity up to the listener.

This is not to say that combined essentic forms may not also function where this is the desired communication—for example, in the state of melancholy. The point is, however, that we may have complete confidence and trust that a purely expressed essentic form will

† Debussy's contribution to the language of Western music was in fact to reverse this priority: his eloquence is not achieved directly through essentic form; in his work, it is merely "quoted" and alluded to. Communication is not achieved through production and recognition of essentic form but rather through sounds that directly suggest sensory environments. It is thus both more direct and more indirect, in different ways, than expressionist music. This tradition has continued to much electronic music of today.

be received as such by the open receiving individual.‡ The touch of essentic form may have a myriad shades of meaning which, in the proper circumstances, are inherently communicated. Many of these qualities are sentically perceived even by animals.

Distortion through exaggeration, too, is rather easily detectable and detracts from the transforming power. Certain diseased states, however, appear to be connected with an exaggerated interpretation of essentic form as communicated through tone of voice. For example, certain cases of mania, and paranoia, as well as drug-induced psychoses, appear to involve exaggerated or distorted essentic form perception. In other words, "essentic form hallucination" may occur apart from other hallucinatory processes. Such aberrations may be regarded in a way as confirming further the natural function and perception of essentic form.

Empathy and Sympathy

To what extent do the implications of a personal origin of essentic form affect the nature of the experience? To what extent do essentic forms generated by specific individuals create expectations, personal images in us? How does the origin of essentic form create personal relationships, and how are these a function of such communications?

In *producing* essentic form, we did distinguish between three possible modes of interconnectedness: mimicry, full bodily involvement (Dionysian), and spectator-like viewing (Apollonian). These different modes of interconnectedness apply also to *perceiving* essentic form, and they result in different viewing of the producing element or entity.

Corresponding to the function of mimicry in essentic form production, there is the "cold," sentically disconnected perception—a form of alienation previously discussed.

Second, there is the full sentic generation afforded by the experience of essentic form with awareness of the human (or living) origination of the form but without the experience of the person as

‡ These may not always be easy to find! And, in a new language of art, it may take years for a substantial number of individuals to receive it.

such. In this mode of perception we resonate "*sympathetically*,"* and are subject to the contagion of sentic communication for both positive and negative sentic states (a function widely used by seducers and political demagogues, and persuaders of Madison Avenue).

The third mode is the mode of *empathy*, in which essentic forms are all viewed as related to the person as a single entity. Essentic form is experienced not only as the expression of a single sentic state but also as related, through pre-sentic control, to the unitary form of existence of the person (sometimes referred to as "inner self" or, poetically, as a "point").

The distinction between the second and third mode of perceiving essentic form thus involves a distinction between *sympathy* and *empathy*.† By "sympathy" we mean the experience of a similar sentic state in two individuals, as that state is produced in one individual by communication of the specific essentic forms from the other individual. The process includes sympathetic resonance for both positive and negative sentic states, and there is no need to experience the other individual as an entity, to understand the other individual in terms of sentic states other than the one that is communicated at that time. The process of sympathy allows sentic states to spread by contagion, like waves. Love, anger, hate, grief, joy, and others thus may spread through the contagion of essentic form. This process may be desirable for positive states (we do not even really know many of the consequences of this, and hence distrust and fear the

* We should emphasize that we are using the word "sympathy" in a somewhat more specialized sense than it is generally used. Thus, in events of misfortune or bereavement we say we express our "sympathy" when we might really like to convey "empathy." We have no ready phrase for communicating our "empathy," which could well be more appreciated by the individuals concerned. Here again we are facing the prison of our language! Empathy is a more subtle attitude to communicate than the co-resonance of sympathy. In empathy, pre-sentic control is involved—sentic fluidity and a "touching" at a different level of the experiential process, which has to be communicated. How this may happen is discussed in the chapter concerning sentic cycles and their effects.

† In considering our specific distinction between the words "empathy" and "sympathy," we are struck by the difficulty in finding appropriately corresponding words in other languages. Thus, in French, there is *sympathie* and *sympathique*, but no word at all for "empathy." The German word *Einfühlung* seems to have given rise through translation to the English usage of "empathy" (according to Webster's Dictionary), while *Sympathie* is also used in German.

contagion of positive states) but it is distinctly dangerous and often degrading and disruptive in the contagion of negative states. In the process of sympathy (as the term is used here) the seductive element of essentic form has full reign.

When we are projected into an "emotional atmosphere" it is quite difficult or even impossible not to be influenced to some degree. A person placed in a group environment will be influenced by the sentic states that surround him. The influence of such group states is far greater than one may often realize. Although a person can to some extent isolate himself from his sentic environment, he is essentially defenseless; for even by the act of defending or isolating himself, he is constrained to make an effort of repression, and this associated with some anger (as it nearly always is) is bound to affect his creative, free impulses—his fantasy processes.

Yet in daily life we need to strike a balance between sympathy and empathy. We cannot avoid being influenced sympathetically by the multitude of seductive influences or often, by political demagoguery. Deliberately to close ourselves off from their sentic perception imposes a strain that in the long run tends to close us to empathy as well.‡

Let us consider further how we distinguish empathy from sympathy: how the experience and communication of sentic states relate to empathy, and how they influence interaction between people. If we look in the Oxford dictionary, we find empathy described as "the power of projecting one's personality into and so fully understanding the object of contemplation." Webster's dictionary calls it the "imaginative projection of a subjective state." In our use of the term here, we mean just the opposite—namely, the imaginative projection of another subject's state and personality into our own awareness, so that in imagination we *become* that subject. Empathy is a creation in

‡ This is the sentic dilemma of man in our civilization. He can avoid watching television, or neon signs, or ugly highways, but when he has succeeded in avoiding all of these, he is also alone and apart from society. The strain of maintaining his sentic integrity is a heavy price to pay, and not many are willing or able to pay this price, even if they are aware of the bargain. We need to develop society so that man is not sentically assaulted from all sides, so that he is free from the barrage of sentic insults hurled at him from his own creations and re-creations, and so that essentic forms can be enjoyed in relation to the specific human entity from whom they arise: the individual.

our own awareness of the idiolog of another's being. It is the process of elogizing another individual.

If this seems too difficult a task, as it may if we look at it naïvely, we can point to the creation of consistent "living" personalities in our dreams. The brain processes that allow us to create living dream personalities are related to the process of empathy. We do have the potential capacity to create idiologs of other individuals. Through the processes of empathy as in our dream another individual in a real sense may "live" in us.

As is perhaps true of all brain functions, the aware portion of the empathic process appears to be only a small part of the total function. In a dream the dreamed person may unfold through a varied stream of actions, yet remains consistently the same person. There is a brain program that comprises and directs the totality of that person's personality as conceived in the dream. That we can do this in dreams is proof of our ability to conceive personality. Such a conception is often more real in a dream, indeed, than we can achieve in the awake state.

In the awake state, however, empathy involves a specific experiential quality. This quality of experience is very different from that of sympathy. Empathy is not determined primarily by the specific quality of the sentic states experienced. An additional integrating function gives perspective to the experience—a perspective of the sentic domain from which each sentic state is "savored," so to speak.

Empathy is inherently constructive; insofar as we willingly permit another being to live within us, we also apply our own forces of self-preservation to that individual who now lives within us—in short, we have good will.

The point of view of empathy may allow us to feel good will even toward someone whom we might otherwise hate. It benefits both individuals involved in the relationship. Seeing an individual as he is, even if that individual were to be a criminal; it is largely irrelevant, in fact, what the specific configuration is: the sense of wonder and awe at touching the entity of a unique individual supplants all other sentic implications. Empathy is not judgmental; its nature is not to offer advice.

The idiolog of a person, the basis of empathy, is not only momentarily present. Like idiologs of qualities, such as the tone of voice by which we recognize an individual, the idiolog of a person may be stored in the memory, and can partake of unconscious processes. Also, like idiologs of other qualities, personal idiologs have great stability. We may dream of individuals many years after not having had contact with them, with a clear and undiminished dream generation of their personalities.

Empathy and love are related. The essentic form of love, as we have seen, involves a tendency to move toward the body, to include, incorporate, to merge into us. With respect to the principle of inclusion, empathy and love are similar. But with respect to action they are different.

Empathy is achieved from an attitude of quiet. There is an inner stillness on which the sentic impressions are projected, yet with full recognition of the quality of each sentic state. This mode of perceiving essentic form parallels the third mode of producing essentic form that we have called the meditative, Apollonian, or spectator-viewing mode. (It might seem strange to name an *expressive* mode "the spectator-viewing" mode. This derives from the aspect of quietness essential both to the production and to the perception of essentic form in this mode. That quietness may correspond to the concept of the Zen masters requiring one to "walk two inches off the ground" and yet to experience fully.)

There are thus two systems of data processing of our nervous system involved in empathy: one system which provides rock-like stability; the other which is sensitive to every slightest nuance of essentic form.

To elucidate this function better, we may look at other, similar aspects of double data processing which occur with some sensory systems. For example, we possess an extremely stable spatial orientation provided by the visual and kinesthetic systems, in spite of the impingement of changing experience. Perhaps the earliest development of such double data processing is our capacity to sense a quality of touch together with the sense of where in the body it is occurring. For example, a sensation of warmth on a finger is felt as warm and simultaneously is experienced to occur at the finger. In the highly advanced visual system, we can see a retinal image as stable in space as we move our eyes. When we turn our head, we do not see the room rotate—*it* stays oriented in space because of compensation by the system.*

The sense of hearing also exhibits such double data processing. The sensation of pitch corresponds to the kinesthetic sense: different portions of the basilar membrane are stimulated by different frequencies. The double data processing here becomes the sensing of both pitch and intensity.

It is possible to consider that such double data processing methods may extend to processes relating to emotional qualities. A prevalent tendency of evolving organisms is to use already developed design principles in further stages of development—we find this on many different levels. (Cellular construction, unidirectional rate sensitivity, inhibition-excitation are some applicable design principles.) A design principle once adopted is not easily rejected in subsequent evolutionary development. And so the complementary function of empathy and sympathy may be similarly involved in our biologic design for orientation in emotional space.

* A simple but revealing experiment is to produce an afterimage on the retina by looking at a bright image, and then observe how the afterimage moves as the eyes are rotated with lids closed. Although the afterimage represents a particular fixed spot on the retina, it will be seen to move as the eyes are turned. This is because the retinal image is projected onto a second, oval, dark "screen" and thus is experienced as stable in space with respect to the head. We can see this oval dark "screen" in front of us, with eyes closed. It, in turn, will appear to move as we move the head (Clynes 1968).

EIGHT

Music and Sentics: Music as a Sentic Mirror

The Sentic Foundations of Music

Essentic form is a form in time. How may one capture such a form so that it can be experienced again? The artist in a primitive culture can *draw* a form, a spatial form that may suggest specific movement to us. But how could primitive man capture the evanescent forms in time of the tone of voice or an expressive sound? How can one indicate the course of the sound? Music is the invention that answers this question. Music differs from other sounds in using stable, defined pitch—sounds that have a beginning, middle, and end. It partakes of the precision of essentic form.

That music is largely an expression of inner gesture and song is widely understood. Thus, for example, Roger Sessions says in his book *Questions About Music:*

> It is the *quality and character of the musical gesture that* constitutes the essence of the music, the essential goal of the performer's endeavors . . .

> . . . We experience music as movement and gesture, and that movement and gesture, if they are to retain their power for us, have to be constantly reinvested with fresh energy . . .
>
> One must emphasize that a real gesture is in its very nature organic. It takes precise and characteristic shape by virtue of its own energy, its own inherent laws, its goals, its own curve and direction. There is nothing whatever fortuitous about it.

Meaning in expressive music arises from the essentic forms of its idiolog elements. Gestures, dance steps, vocalizations—all having idiolog representations in the brain—are the elements of music. How do musical tones precisely express those idiologs of E-actons? A cat or dog can perceive essentic form in the tone of voice or gesture, but to perceive essentic form in musical sounds one needs the psychologic key to understand musical language.

Because this key is often missing, many individuals fail to hear essentic form in music. Such persons often describe themselves as "tone deaf." Yet in modulation of their own voices they can be as expressive as anyone else, and they perceive others' voice inflections quite normally. These individuals can gain entrance into the world of music, in fact, once they regard music as a language of essentic forms.

A *Biological Basic of Musical Talent*

Musical talent is to a considerable extent the natural ability to recognize essentic form in music and communicate through it. This is independently discovered by the "talented" child. A child who has discovered this "key" independently will gain familiarity with this form of communication that appears to give him a great lead over his peers, and so we say "this child has musical talent!" It is capable of being taught, however. If a child did not have to wait for chance to discover essentic form as musical communication, musical talent would be a much more general phenomenon.*

* Sentic training, including the practice of sentic cycles, provides a new method for musical training and makes it possible for music students and musicians to discover individually how to be naturally expressive in music, while eschewing exaggeration. Developing musical talent and ability through sentic training is the subject of a book presently in preparation by the author. If one

Only rarely are individuals not capable of modulating their voice according to their sentic condition. Although individuals inhibit such modulation in various degrees, even everyday communication requires a continuous modulation of the voice. Lack of such voice modulation, encountered rarely, is perceived as clearly pathological. The ability to think in musical sounds is in essence no different from the ability to modulate one's tone of voice. Music uses discrete frequencies, forming separate tones, but in the relationship of tones essentic form may always be discovered.†

Traditionally, the question of how music communicates—how it changes our states and gives us insights—has mainly been the concern of aesthetics or of music criticism. But we may regard the language of music also scientifically, in the perspective of the existence of essentic forms. A good composer who intends a particular portion of music to communicate joy can do just that. The performer who understands the composer's intention can transduce joy, and a listener can be sensitive to the performance and perceive joy, a reflection of the vision of joy the composer created perhaps hundreds of years before—all this is possible through the function and stability of essentic form.

Essentic Form and the Dynamics of Musical Expression

Pitch, intensity, tone color, duration, and harmonic progression are some of the variables that may be used either singly or in cooperation to create sound images of essentic form.

Most music has another characteristic: a repetitive rhythmicity. We need to examine the sentic significance of both these mental processes: the organization of the sequence of sounds according to motifs or phrases, and the recurrent generation of the beat.

---

considers how much time musicians spent practicing technical aspects and how little, if at all, emotional qualities are generally practiced (or are even known how to be practiced), it is apparent that a method that permits systematic emotional practice is long overdue!

† In the present discussion, all references are to "expressionist" rather than "impressionist" types of music.

In great music of the classical period in Western culture, a special aspect of the beat developed, *the inner pulse*, which became a vehicle for a most intimate revelation of the composer's personality; the inner pulse became sentically charged.

In such music, the inner pulse provides an unvarying framework or context, from which the sentic meaning of individual phrases derives perspective. The inner pulse represents a certain "point of view": an empathic identification with the composer. Like a conductor's beat, a rhythmic alternation modified in various dynamic ways, the phenomenon of the inner pulse consists of a sequence of imaginary actons: it is in effect an internally conducted beat. We can *think* music without sound—the inner pulse consists of repeated acton idiologs.

As we pointed out earlier in Chapter Three a sustained rhythmic repetition requires only a single action pattern idiolog; there is only one decision. The pattern is then automatically retriggered and the rhythmic activity continues as long as a decision to stop is *not* made. Likewise, the inner pulse, once set, will tend to continue without special separate decisions for reiteration.‡

The inner pulse is an alternation of two phases, which we may call active and resting phases (a repetitive programming of impulse response movements, in control theory terminology). The important point is that when the inner pulse is sentically charged (this inner alternation is not a mechanical clock, but contains characteristic dynamic forms) the result is a specific inner pulse form. The shape of this pulse form becomes a personal signature of the composer. But it is not only a signature; it is also a sentic matrix representing his own specific point of view or identity. We feel it as "presence." Without it, music may be "correct" but it does not communicate the immediate, intimate experience of the presence of the composer. The inner pulse is a key to the empathy we experience with a composer. Through it we can also come to love the composer as a person.

The process generating the repeated inner pulse in music as personal presence seems to be related to the dream process through

‡ The inner pulse may be measured with the methods already described of measuring essentic form—expressive finger pressure—with only slight modification, as we shall discuss in the second half of this chapter.

which the personality of a dreamed individual remains the same from moment to moment in a dream—our creation of the personality of a dreamed person. A similar continuity of personal presence occurs in great music through the phenomenon of the inner pulse.*

The specific pulse form of the inner pulse is characteristic of the composer's individuality. But together with the underpinning of the inner pulse, every good composer uses a wide range of essentic forms in his musical expression; they are portrayed in the phrases, harmonies, rhythms and motifs, tone color, dynamics, and silences of the music. The two processes—the generation of the inner pulse, and of various essentic forms—go on *simultaneously*. The basic form of the inner pulse is unaffected by the specific expressive forms and continues unchanged even during rests. It will continue for a certain number of pulses after the last sound of the piece.†

The specific phrases are in a subtle way affected by the inner musical pulse. The inner pulse works as a matrix, permitting certain types of essentic forms, excluding others. Thus the purity of the specific mixture of essentic form used in each phrase is to some extent governed by the inner pulse, which serves, as mentioned before, as a "point of view."

Apart from the influence of the inner pulse, each phrase or motif communicated needs to be as faithful as possible to the particular essentic form it is chosen to express. This affects not only the dynamics and rhythm but every aspect of the sound produced down to the smallest detail. Expression becomes a process of purification, of avoiding all aspects not contributing to its quality. Only when the sound produced is perfectly faithful to the inwardly heard essentic form is the communication process really effective: then it can be "beautiful." These aspects of the produced sound may be refined down to fractions of tones, fractions of note values.

This does not mean that there is only one way to perform a given piece, but rather that all ways should be *living* ways, i.e., faithful to some essentic form. There are many possible living forms based on

* This idea of the correspondence of these processes in fact presented itself to the author first in a dream!

† It may however stop briefly during the course of the piece at the end of a large section, thereby clearly demarcating large subdivisions.

sentic states and orthoessentic forms, but the class of dead forms is infinitely greater. The interpretative choice of a musical phrase or section consists of choosing what essentic form to express—which sentic state and its orthoessentic form—and following that form with greatest faithfulness or inner precision. In addition, the inner pulse must be there to provide the personal presence.

Musical Notation and Inner Fidelity

How does this inner precision relate to written music? The true essentic form rhythms are not capable of precise musical rhythmic notation. A dance rhythm cannot be accurately notated, since the rhythm idiolog is based on essentic form, the precision of which does not divide neatly into half-, quarter-, or eighth-note values. The stopping and starting of the successive actons and the precise acceleration and deceleration govern the inner faithfulness to the expressive character of the dance. That may be only approximated by musical notation. A good musician, however, feels and experiences the expressiveness of the rhythm and will—unless constrained by faulty academic teaching—be faithful to that inner form. A musician may indeed rely on that form with greater trust than on his ability to reproduce mechanical subdivisions of time. (By "mechanical" we mean here arbitrary subdivisions that have no biological counterpart in terms of essentic form programming.)

It is not only with respect to rhythmic notation that conventional musical notation is inadequate. In hearing or thinking a melody we mentally shape each tone. The manner of growth and decay of the tone is implied precisely in our mental thought of the tone. But not often do we in fact hear performances where the tones are shaped according to our inner hearing. Mostly, a conflict occurs between the actual and mentally heard sound. Such conflict is inevitable part of the time. In a great performance, however, this conflict largely disappears: the tones which we are led to anticipate confirm our anticipation, and this contributes to the special ecstatic experience that the performance gives. The wholeness of such an experience derives from the coincidence between our inner expectation and the actual heard realization.‡ At rare times the actual heard sound may exceed and transcend our expectations. Such performances are truly mind-expanding. They enlarge our own capacities and our sense of discrimination and of values. That this should be possible through music we shall be discussing in the following sections.

Expectation, Satisfaction, and Style

The functions and effects just discussed depend to a degree upon "expectation." Since essentic form is a form in time, we do not experience the meaning and the satisfaction of the form until it is completed. Accordingly, we have an expectation that extends to the end of the particular essentic form being experienced. This means that the duration of expectancy varies, depending on the phase of the essentic form one is experiencing at that moment. This expectancy may cover a period of anywhere from 0 to 4 seconds.

What happens at the end of an essentic form? Is there any further expectancy? At this point a different kind of expectancy phenomenon occurs. We may be led to expect a repetition of a similar essentic form, beginning at that time or shortly thereafter. The nature of this expectancy, however, is different from the expectancy of an unfinished essentic form. If, through the sentic state generated, we are led to expect another similar essentic form, we may experience several possibilities. Either this expectation is fulfilled, and another similar essentic form does in fact occur; or the form may be somewhat modified, to a slight departure from the previous form with a modified experience—perhaps of a more intense or less intense aspect with a subtly different shade of emphasis. However, we may also be presented with a strongly contrasted essentic form which deliberately runs counter to our expectation of continuity. In the first case we shall be led, step by step, into a gradually altered, intensified, or

‡ G. Kanizsa has demonstrated recently that the visual system can automatically supply precise curved as well as straight contours and even angles to missing portions of incomplete figures. This visual process appears to be analogous to the auditory phenomena we are discussing. Moreover, essentic forms, regardless of the particular sense modality, appear to have this property: if their forms are constituted through a number of fragments that are precise and of sufficient extent, the nervous system will interpolate the rest. The error must be one of omission, not commission. How much may be omitted remains to be determined.

shaded experience arising from the original state; in the second case, we shall experience surprise and be jolted from the previous state into a confrontation arising from the contrast between the two states, a confrontation which we are accustomed to call "dramatic." In the second case, instead of the security of continuing expectations, we may experience humor, awe, perspective, or perhaps wonder.

After the newly established essentic form is repeated a few times, we are again led to expectations as before. Accordingly there is the possibility of an alternation of the satisfaction of expectations that are fulfilled, with the special sensations of sentic contrast. Each phase by its nature may last only for a specific duration. Therefore, one method of building a significant piece of music consists of using the appropriate alternation of the satisfaction of *continuity* of essentic form in turn with the deliberate juxtaposition of *different* sentic states. (For an obvious example of this, consider the slow movement of Mozart's "Jupiter" Symphony.) The proportion in which different composers employ the expectancy of continuous essentic form versus the contrasted juxtaposition is a function of both the style and personality of the composer. Certain composers and styles favor continuity (for example, the baroque style), others favor juxtaposition (for example, the classical style.)

Another difference concerns the nature of the juxtaposition itself. If the transition from one essentic form to another is in the nature of opposites, the surprise experience will be mitigated by the new integration of the two states as opposites. If, however, the juxtaposed states are presented without this implied unifying relationship, the surprise will have elements of "magic." In this meaning, *magic* is the opposite of *inevitability*. The experience pulls away from the past or anticipation of the future, and we lose control. The dictionary meaning of "magic" is "supernatural," the suspension of some aspects of natural law and of continuity. The use of magic in this sense in the composition of music characterizes the primarily "romantic" approach to music.

In a different sense of the word, all music partakes of magic. But the "magical" effect of much of the music of Bach, Beethoven, and Mozart, say, lies in its ability to expand our comprehension of essentic forms through continuity, expectation, and meaningful contrast, as well as in the specific experience of qualities of essentic form that particularly involves love and reverence. On the other hand, in romantic music, expectations tend to center around situations of longings, or of unaccountably tragic events, or magical reprieves, of fairy-tale-like transportations into imaginary worlds. The first type of music gives us an impression of increasing our empathy, our ability to be in touch with natural sentic order. It provides us with immediate knowledge of essentic forms in relation to their place in the larger order. Romantic music, on the other hand, is more seductive in nature, and will give us ecstasies of the moment—forgetfulness—but will not generally provide as lasting a sense of security.

The Composer's Point of View

These considerations imply that a relationship between various sentic states can be brought into play. Thus, for example, the sense of bliss and terror in Mozart are diametrically related. But in Chopin's Fantasy in F, longing, turmoil, and grief do not in themselves constitute such opposable states, but form part of a dramatic continuum where each sentic state is felt as a result of a situation or action rather than as an existential quality in its own right.

More generally, we can distinguish various attitudes of communication in the way essentic forms are used by composers. We may classify these "points of view" first according to whether they represent: (1) action in the present, (2) reminiscence of the past, or (3) anticipation of the future. Secondly, we can also classify them as representing either a "spectator" or "actor" point of view. This distinction is similar to the ways in which we may actively participate or be a spectator in our own dreams.

There are six such points of view. If P stands for point of view, then we may have:

P_p, P_n, P_f where p stands for past
n stands for now
f stands for future

And further we may have:

$$P_p^a, P_n^a, P_f^a \text{ where a stands for actor}$$

$$P_p^s, P_n^s, P_f^s \text{ where s stands for spectator}$$

The inner pulse consists of acton idiologs modulated by the point of view of the composer. For example, Mahler's point of view is frequently that of "spectator reminiscing"; his pulse form corresponds to this. Beethoven is predominantly "actor in the present"; Mozart is "spectator in the present"; Schubert is mostly "actor with expectations of the future," and so on.

Within each category of point of view, there is a range of possible sentic implications. Thus, the quality of expectations of the future may vary according to various forms of longing. The object of longing may be of a sexual nature, or "romantic" in the colloquial sense, or may be a longing for deliverance or salvation. We can observe that quite different essentic forms are involved. Does the difference in shape imply that these longings relate to basically different drives? We shall explore aspects of this later on.

Looking thus at the relationship of the inner pulse and the point of view, we may ask cryptically concerning *how* the character of the inner pulse and the corresponding acton idiologs is experienced: *who is doing what?*—in terms of the actor versus spectator point of view and of the temporal function of living in the present, reminiscing, or hoping for or dreading the future. We need to ask ourselves further about the nature of the "who." Some form of image of self, of identification, is sensed in the inner pulse. This is of particular importance. Let us consider how it applies to the last works of Beethoven and their particular psychedelic power.

Quantum Leap in Identification Achieved by Beethoven's Last Works

The psychological function of the "who" may be reframed in terms of a personal image, or an image of the universal implied. If we are considering music as a dance, who is dancing? Is it "I" or "You" or the whole living world? In the language of psychology, with whom does the "who" identify? In middle-period Beethoven, a

Promethean attitude dominates—the contrast between universal forces or spirit, and the striving of the individual. This contrast sets up a tension, which we feel as reflecting enormous power—the inner pulse of Beethoven has a massiveness that appears essentially unshakable. This rock-like strength conveyed in every dynamic form forms the basis of the ethical character of Beethoven's pulse in this period. There is, as it were, a continuing relationship, the striving of the individual related to universal forces—a dualism revealed in an interlocking pulse form, within which yet a sense of separateness is maintained.

In his last works Beethoven surmounted this sense of dualism and achieved a fusion of being that eliminates struggle and its tension from the inner pulse. This is replaced by a projection of a "peace that passeth all understanding" whose own strength far surpasses the tensile strength of his earlier pulse. Although the outward shape of the pulse is not substantially changed, it is now no longer accompanied by the steady muscular tensions that resulted in the pulse's effectively very high inertia. The implied strength of this pulse derives from its universality. Even the liveliest dances of Beethoven's last quartets no longer incite the feet to dance. Instead, the "heart inside dances." Beethoven found a new way of uncoupling the motoric output from the expression of essentic form by allowing inner forms to dance without corresponding motor outputs. He embodied in his music a way to live fully and be at perfect peace at the same time. In this music the meaning of essentic form appears no longer as a communication directed at motoric outward expression. When the universe dances within who needs to be told?

In terms of sentic communication, when several individuals together experience this, they "know" that they are brothers. Beethoven once said about his music, "Anyone who understands my music is saved." Let us try to understand what he may have meant by this. Anyone who has *heard* Beethoven's last quartets tends to become stronger. The sentic images of this music act as a powerful shield providing refuge from attack, from personal sorrow, from cynical disbelief. Transfused in this way with love and universal energy, we become purged from vicissitudes, destructive thoughts, doubts, and hostilities of our own making. In his music he succeeded in expanding our minds to boundaries and intelligence far exceeding our ordinary abilities.

Today we begin to realize the scientific basis of the "mind expansion" produced by the magic of musical forms. The magic is not supernatural, although it is universal. It touches the sentic ground of our existence, and follows its laws. The point of view of Beethoven's last music incorporates the precise transfer function* relating the universal essentic forms to domains of awareness, in experience that needs no further expression. This transfer function can be seen to be in theory precisely analyzable—to be the mathematical relationship of what has also been called *satori.* In that relationship we experience that we exist and are "at home," secure beyond possibility of doubt.

How did Beethoven produce this identification with the universal in the expression of each single essentic form? How was he able to program us in such a way that the dancing and love within is not felt as dancing of our individual egos, the "I," but of universal forces? In order to experience the great calm that is programmed, a disconnection as well as a connection is made in our internal programming. Our own individual drives are disconnected from their usual outputs. (Again, we are reminded of the Zen dictum of walking two inches above the ground.) More than detachment is implied, however. We are also connected in an immediate, direct way to what appears as a "source" of universal energy and love.

An aspect of this special state is that it can be remembered: we remember here not only a specific sentic state, but the quality of the point of view, of feeling a different sense of connectedness—a state that allows the simultaneous experience of energy and peace. Such a quality is not to be found, for instance, in the music of Chopin, where energy is generally coupled to passion, and peace to situational realization and satisfaction. The peace of the last quartets of Beethoven is not the peace of a lullaby.†

* A mathematical statement in differential equations relating input and output variables.

† The identification of the "who" with the universal in the inner musical pulse, which so pronouncedly occurs in the last works of Beethoven, is not necessarily unique to this music alone. Bach, and Mozart at times allow us to partake of this in their own way. However, it is present concentratedly in the last quartets of Beethoven, largely freed from unessentials of style and epoch.

It is an apparent paradox that this sense of utmost peace is at the same time combined with a state of energy. If we examine this paradoxical combination closely we note that it is also combined with absence of anxiety. The strength it gives is not that of the armed aggressor, but that of the man who is home in the wonder of existence. Yet, all that brought this experience forth are only sounds, vibrations of the air, tones. How can these relationships transform us to such an extent? Sentic analysis of music and the meta-music of sentic cycles in the following chapters, together with observation of brain behavior, may help us further to elucidate this question.‡

Precision of Execution in Musical Performance

In the first chapter of this book, we showed how the stability of the quality of red and of similar idiologs that are one-to-one translations of the physiologic code demonstrate the high degree of precision of our nervous system. Idiologs of qualities and emotions as portrayed by music may show a perhaps even more astonishing precision.

An example of this precision is made clear by data drawn from a study we made of performances by Arturo Toscanini separated by many years. Recorded music makes it feasible to compare performances of the same composition by the same individual separated by a long period of time. The stability of the performance is primarily a function of four influences: (1) stability of the idea and concept (i.e., idiologs and their organization), (2) stability of execution, (3) influence of environmental factors (i.e., acoustics, humidity) and their effect on both the idiologs and execution, and (4) the presence

‡ The concept of "assimilation" was recently introduced by Segal to denote the process whereby real stimuli may be incorporated into imagined images so that the image itself contains some aspects of the stimulus, without the awareness of the individual that this relates to an external stimulus. In creating an image we also create certain expectancies and tend to assimilate those features of the environment which meet these expectations.

Such assimilation phenomena are even more widespread in the experience of sentic states. When we are in love, we see spring all around us. Our sensibilities are selectively changed by our moods and what may move us to ecstasy in one sentic state will hardly move us at all in another. So also in music, the intensity and specific effects of separate essentic forms depend on the context from which they spring. The context of the sentic state needs to be established. In that established state, specific musical phrases gain added significance.

of "noise" elements with respect to idea and execution (e.g., inattention, anxiety, fatigue, lack of concentration, etc.). Appreciating the many sources of possible variability in the performance of a complex musical composition, one would expect a relatively limited possibility of stability.

To estimate what stability is humanly possible in this regard we carefully examined many years of recordings of Arturo Toscanini—a musician whose precision was legendary. The published timings of these in some instances varied so little over many years that they aroused both our interest and doubt. With the kind help of the conductor's son, Walter, we secured access to the original master tapes of the performances to eliminate errors in timing on the commercial recordings due to the transfer from the master, variability of pauses introduced, and confusion due to splicing of different takes. Comparisons were confined to entire continuous "live" performances, recorded in the same NBC studio with the same orchestra (although the personnel of the orchestra varied slightly).

Among the works available, we chose to analyze three performances of the Brahms Haydn Variations Op. 56B (performed in 1935, 1938, and 1948) because of the number of variations that permit convenient comparison of both the total performance time of the work and of the times of the individual sections, the variations, within it. We were amazed to discover that the total timing of two of these performances differed only by 0.3 second in 16 minutes 50 seconds (about 1 part in 2,000) although recorded ten years apart! (See Figure 13.) Comparisons of individual variations show most of them to be within one second of each other, illustrating that the similarity in over-all timing was not just a coincidence. Major portions of the 1935 performance also coincide with the 1938 performance, further confirming the stability. Where deviations appear, they are relatively substantial. The timing data illustrate that if the idea and concept remained the same there was a great stability, but if the musician changed his mind about a variation, the change would amount to at least an order of magnitude greater than the variability. Other performances show similar results.*

* Toscanini indicated his own metronome marks in his score: however, he was in practice an order of magnitude more accurate than the increments of the metronome steps!

	1935	Cumulative Time	1938 Feb. 26	C.T.	1948 Feb. 21	C.T.
Theme	1.56		1.52		1.53	
Var. 1	1.08½	3.04½	1.11	3.03	1.10	3.03
2	.51½	3.56	.53½	3.56½	.54	3.57
3	1.33	5.29	1.35½	5.32	1.37	5.34
4	1.57	7.26	2.01	7.33	1.59½	7.33½
5	.48	8.14	.48	8.21	.48½	8.22
6	1.07	9.21	1.07	9.28	1.07	9.29
7	2.01 1.01	12.23	2.03 .59	12.30	1.58 .58	12.25
8	.55	13.18	.55	13.25	.52	13.17
9	3.26		3.25½		3.33½	
Total	16.44		16.50.6		16.50.3	

Figure 13. Timings of three performances of the Brahms Haydn Variations Opus 56B by Arturo Toscanini and the NBC Symphony Orchestra in 1935, 1938, and 1948, respectively. A great similarity exists in the last two performances in the sections from the theme to variation 6, while the sections from variations 5 to 9 are very similar in the first two performances. The differences in the timings in the other variations are considerably greater and indicate a change in concept. Variation 7 has two time markings, the second one is for the repetition. The changes in variations 7, 8, and 9 of the last two performances are mutually compensating so that the total time of the performance differed by less than 0.5 sec. (Accuracy of the timing system was about two times greater than this deviation.)

That the idea and concept could remain the same over so many years—during which time there occurred a major world upheaval and thirteen years of aging of the conductor, as well as members of the orchestra—is astonishing. The stability of the idea/concept that Toscanini's execution demonstrated here is a remarkable proof of the precision of feelings and idiologs. Such precision is probably present in all great art, whether it is a line in a Raphael painting or an eloquent phrase from the cello of Pablo Casals. (See Plates 4–8 in photo insert.) The source of this precision is the human qualities and corresponding idiologs and not a stability of repetitiousness due to rote learning. There can be no question of Toscanini trying to remember how he did it ten years previously: a good artist always feels the work anew—besides, memory alone would hardly allow such accuracy!

We have considered aspects of the stability, identity, and dynamics of idiologs, and we may now see how generalized emotions have been used through idiolog representation in music. A composer may (and frequently does) think of idiolog forms in music without actual sound, as Beethoven did. Even after he became deaf, in some instances he could judge from the facial expression of the performer whether he was interpreting the music in the right spirit.† One senses muscular tensions and relaxations in the expressive shapes of sound, in particular those of the throat and chest muscles. These sensed idiologs of muscle tensions and relaxations reconstruct the essentic form in the hearer—thus producing sentic communication. If there were no idiologs of muscle tension and relaxation, most music would cease to communicate.

Such an approach in terms of muscle tension and relaxation patterns makes it easier to analyze the actual sound in terms of sentic communication than frequency and power spectrum analysis of the sound alone, which has been stymied in its efforts.‡ (K. N. Stevens has reported expressive forms of anger and grief in voice production that compare well with the essentic forms we have found.)

† In fact, what Beethoven sensed is in accordance with measurements of how the dynamics of the tone of voice in expressive exclamations such as "ah" or "oh" are produced. These measurements suggest that the expressive character of the sensed qualities follows the essentic forms when observations are taken of the dynamic muscular changes that produce them rather than by analyzing the sound alone.

‡ Since the information and significance lie in the transient form itself, frequency analysis is at a disadvantage, since it must take separate, finite time segments for analysis.

Measuring the Inner Pulse Shapes of Music

As we have seen, thinking in music largely combines a succession of expressive actons which have beginnings and ends and precise shapes with a simultaneous, repetitive motor idiolog pattern. The recurrent initiation of action, the inner pulse, is not, however, the same as meter, rhythm, or beating time. Two pieces of music with the same meter or notated rhythm may have entirely different essentic pulse forms.

In fact, we can measure the inner musical pulse without producing any sound at all. (See Figures 14–21.) As in the measurement of essentic form, a subject sits in a chair and presses the middle finger of his right hand (if he is right-handed) on the pressure transducer expressing his experience of the inner pulse as he thinks the specific piece of music, without producing any sound. In a way, this is a kind of conducting in which the movement of the arm is replaced by transient pressure of the finger. As the musical piece is thought through (one thinks the music, not about the music) in real time, the inner pulse is expressed repeatedly. To standardize the measurement of the form of the pulse we normalize the tempo to sixty per minute, or one second per pulse (in order to have comparable pulse forms—the active and resting phases of the inner pulse "telescope" differently at different speeds). This in fact is not far removed from the real tempo of the pieces we are investigating. (It turns out that the deviations in the tempo from that otherwise desired by the subject do not affect the specific nature of the inner pulse.)

A counter is used as a visual synchronizing agent, but no auditory synchronization is used.* Fifty pulse shapes (of fifty seconds total duration) are averaged with a CAT computer for each music piece.

The shapes generated seemed to be related to the personality of the composer in a highly intimate manner. It was found that with some care we could reliably observe pulse shapes characteristic of individual composers, regardless of the particular piece chosen. But

* An auditory synchronizing signal (as opposed to a visual one) causes one to tend to synchronize not with the initiation of the downbeat, but with its lowest point, thus phase-shifting the observed pulse form.

only musicians capable of an intimate understanding of the composers could produce their characteristic pulse shape in this way.†

The shape of the inner musical pulse as measured, from an average of say fifty pulses in a given piece, is an image of the composer's personality, as seen by the interpreter. As noted before the process is similar to the dream process in which one dreams of a person and that person continues to retain her or his personality during the dream; it is the dreamer who creates this consistent continuity. Just as in a dream, the personality of the composer is retained in the character of the continuing musical pulse. In fact, the absence of the characteristic musical pulse is immediately recognized as an absence of the "living presence" of the composer.

As Becking (1927) already recognized so clearly, one cannot take a musical phrase from Mozart and put it into Beethoven—even if it is identical note for note—without stumbling over the beat when one arrives at the phrase; there are different underlying musical pulses involved. The change from one pulse to another involves a major change of program in the brain—e.g., switching from a Beethoven pulse to a Chopin pulse.

The stability of the pulse form as produced by different musicians does not mean that the subjects are equally good at performing but merely that they share certain ideas about the nature of the composer. These ideas would in the past have been described as "intuitive"—but we can now relate them to the performer's discovery of the type of idiologs and essentic forms that "fit" (somewhat in the manner of a sentic jigsaw puzzle) the point of view of the composer.‡

† In his book *Theme and Variations,* Yehudi Menuhin speaks of meeting Béla Bartók for the first time. "I shall never forget my first meeting with him: it was in November 1943. . . . I was anxious to play for Bartók—to receive his criticism before performing his music in public. . . .

"Though I had had no preconceived idea of his manner or appearance, his music had already revealed to me his innermost secrets. A composer is unable to hide anything—by his music you shall know him.

"Immediately, with the first notes, there burst forth between us, like an electric current, an intimate bond, which was to remain fast and firm. It was as if we had known each other for years. I believe that between a composer and his interpreter there can exist a stronger, more intimate bond, even with the exchange of words, than between the composer and a friend he may have known all his life. For the composer reserves the core of his personality, the essence of his self for his works."

‡ A few examples are given in Appendix IV, where certain phrases by Beethoven, Mozart, and Chopin are compared to show how essentic form provides meaning and expression.

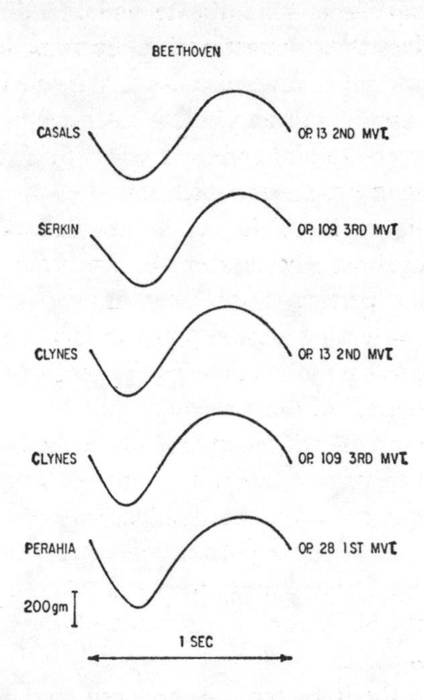

Figure 14. Essentic form of the inner pulse of slow movements of Beethoven (vertical component). Different movements are compared, as well as the same movement for different interpreters. The lowest trace is of a first movement in triple meter whose pulse is considered comparable in an appropriate time scale (one pulse per bar in this case). The inner pulse shape continues into periods of rest. Considered as a second-order dynamic system, it has a damping factor equivalent to approximately 0.2, indicating about three afterbeats before cessation, and comparatively high inertia. The high inertia tends to give both an inherent propulsion and a comparatively late down (negative) peak. There is a prolonged initial acton preprogramming as compared with the low-inertia pulse of Mozart (see *Figure 15*). The relative symmetry of the pulse precludes introduction of late sexual elements of longing as observed in the second phases of the inner pulses associated with romantic composers, and gives rise to an impression of "ethical constraint." (Average of fifty pulses.)

Such discoveries are readily made even by talented children—and even often better by them, before sentic fluidity is blocked as they grow up. The music itself implies them. The manner of implication has not yet been analyzed, so that one still depends on individuals at this time to have the "sensitivity" to perceive these implications.

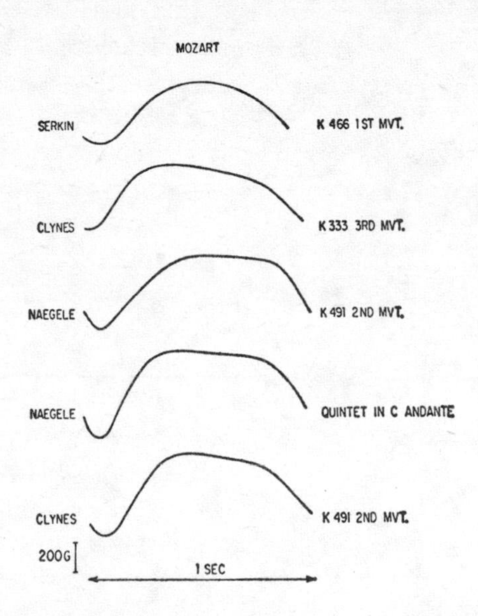

Figure 15. The essentic form of the inner pulse of Mozart shows considerably lower inertia than that of Beethoven. The down peak occurs much earlier, and there is a small overshoot with damping of about 0.7. The Mozart pulse has no more than one afterbeat compared with several for Beethoven. Its relatively light and buoyant character is related to the low-inertia term coupled with slight underdamping and a response time corresponding to a normally preprogrammed free acton. In that sense the Mozart pulse is freer than the Beethoven pulse and we may see how it could well be associated with such descriptive terms as a "cosmic pulse" as compared with a "Promethean pulse" of Beethoven.

The stability, however, shows that, like red, the personality Beethoven revealed in his music has a precise existence that continues.

This stability is not a result of "tradition" or of "style." Mozart and Haydn have very different inner musical pulse shapes! So have Debussy and Ravel. However, the study of changes in pulse shape with the history of music is interesting as an indication of the change in the sentic matrix (the inclusion of sexual longing, of disdain, of anger, of despair or hope, of enthusiasm, etc. as important elements of the pulse point of view at various times and with various composers).

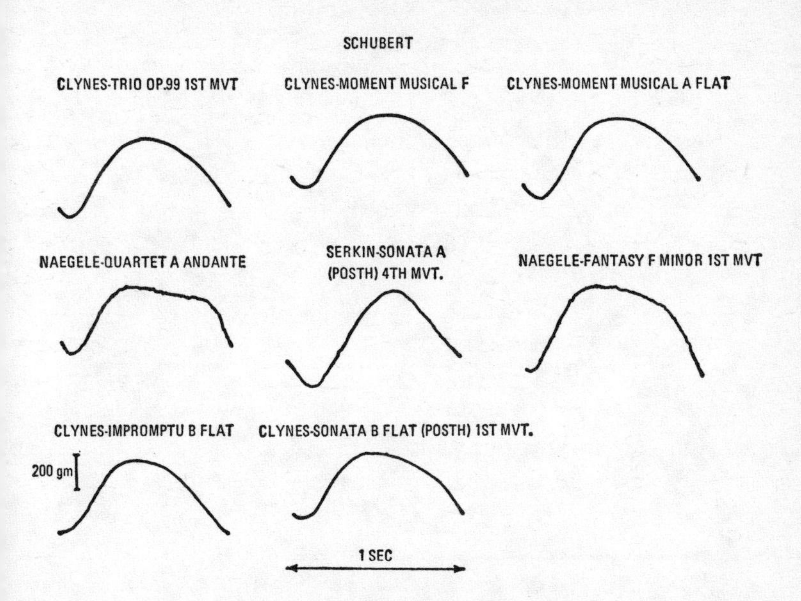

Figure 16. Essentic form of the Schubert pulse illustrated shows a generally very early down peak, and low inertia, but also a fast rise leading to overshoot. There is a characteristic upward deflection related to elements of hope and longing. But this characteristic Schubert rise is very different from the romantic sexual rise, accompanied by higher inertia and tension. The Schubert pulse is relatively highly damped. (Lyric Brahms has a high inertia and low damping.)

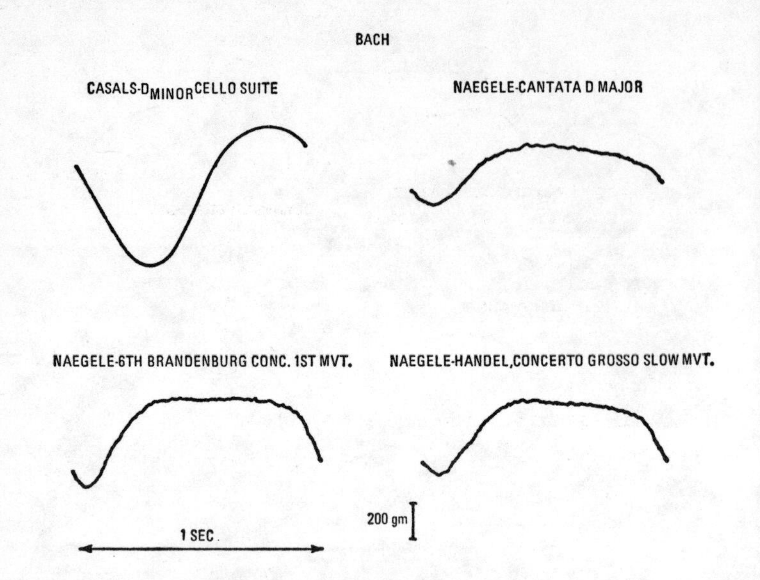

Figure 17. Baroque music as conceived in the customary baroque style has a pulse which is primarily time beating and not charged with essentic form. (Though this is not so for Casals, whose interpretation of Bach rather has aspects of a super-Beethoven pulse.) It is interesting that differences in interpretive approach are so clearly brought out by the measure of essentic form of the inner pulse.

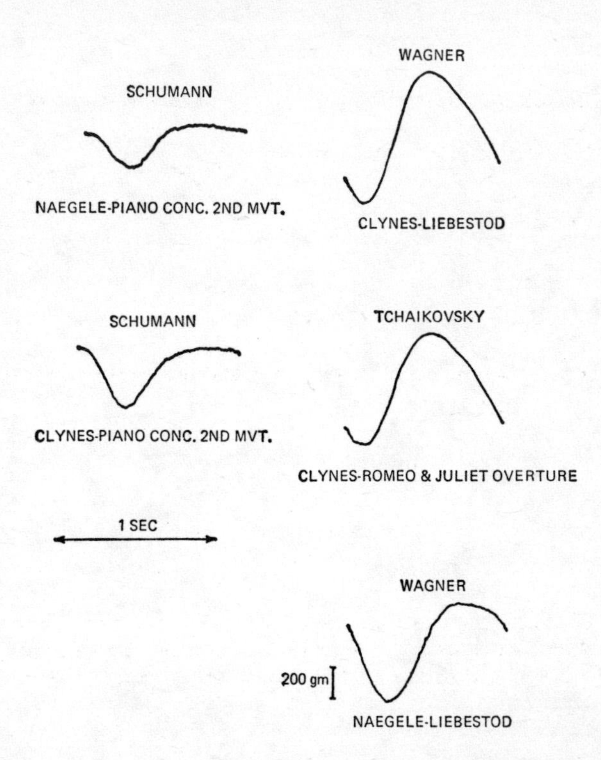

Figure 18. Essentic form of the inner pulses of romantic composers. Schumann in his slow movements has a pulse form of medium inertia, no overshoot, and high damping. This essentic form has a character of special intimacy, a gentle touch to the inner core of a person. The second portion of the pulse is in a state of suspension and tension mounts as one awaits the next pulse. Each pulse becomes a special act, a gift or miracle almost—wonders appear every second as if created out of nothing.

The longing and passionate romantic themes of Tchaikovsky and Wagner show a very marked second phase with a strong overshoot of high inertia. It seems that the effective inertia and tension is not as constant as in Beethoven but fluctuates periodically with an increase in the second half of the pulse. This appears to be related to the increased tension of opposing sets of muscles in the second half of the pulse. The horizontal components of this music (not shown) are far more outward as compared with that of Mozart and Beethoven (vertical). The preponderant second phase is associated with the secondary muscle activity seen in passionate actons, as illustrated in the Sex responses (see *Figure 4* in Chapter Four).

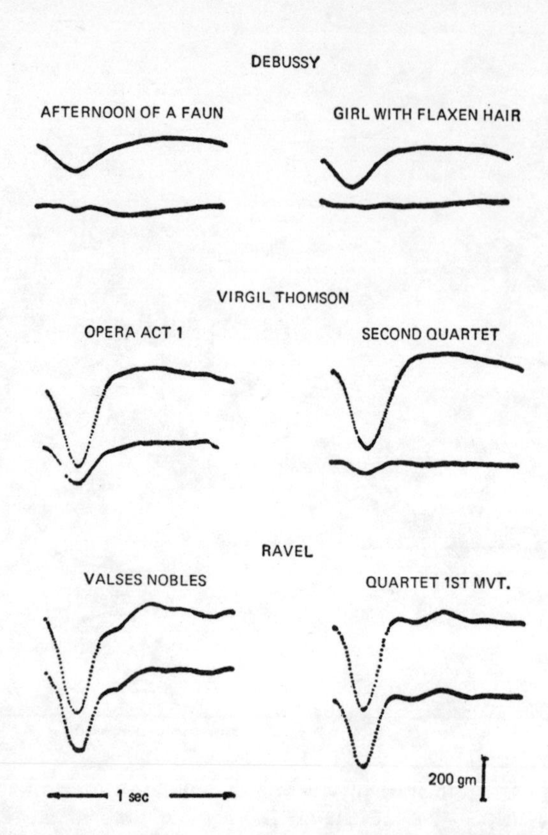

Figure 19. Inner pulse of compositions of Virgil Thomson as produced by the composer himself and compared with his interpretations of Debussy and Ravel. Both vertical and horizontal components are given. Note the similarity of the two different pieces of each composer to one another and how the essentic form of Virgil Thomson falls between those characteristic of Debussy and Ravel. Virgil Thomson's music has frequently been characterized, in fact, as having kinship to both Ravel and Debussy. It is desirable to measure essentic forms of living composers, as they think their own music, giving us their authentic form.

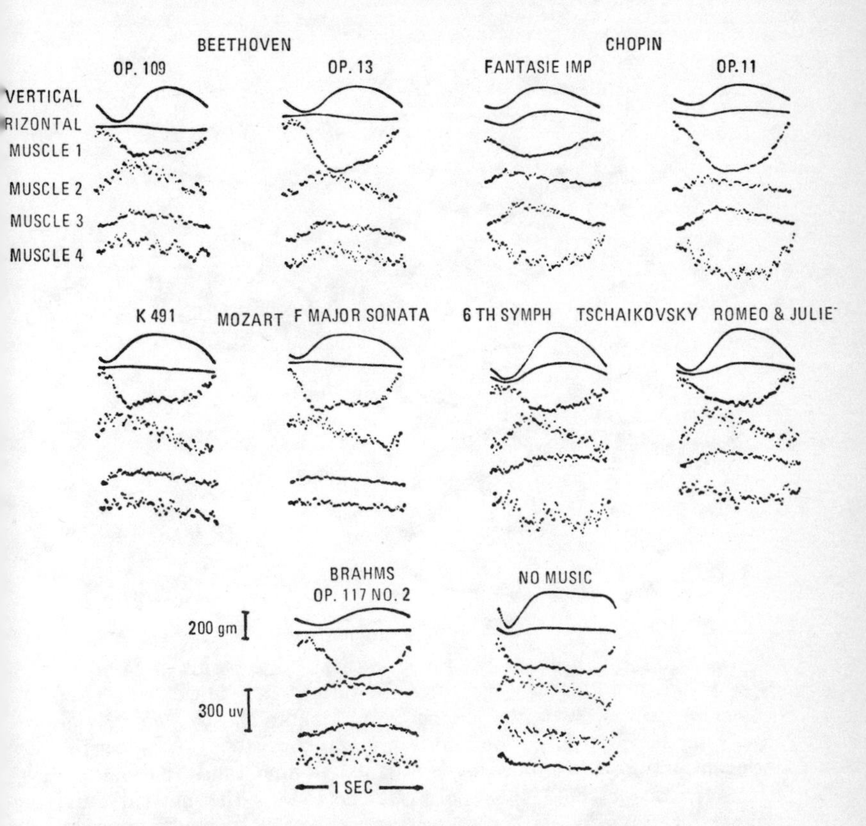

Figure 20. Comparison of essentic forms of "romantic" and "classic" composers together with associated muscle activity (recorded as in *Figures* 5–6 in Chapter Four). The marked outward horizontal components of romantic composers are in concordance with elements ascribed to sexual longing. Note the reversal of phase for muscle 4 for Chopin as compared with Beethoven.

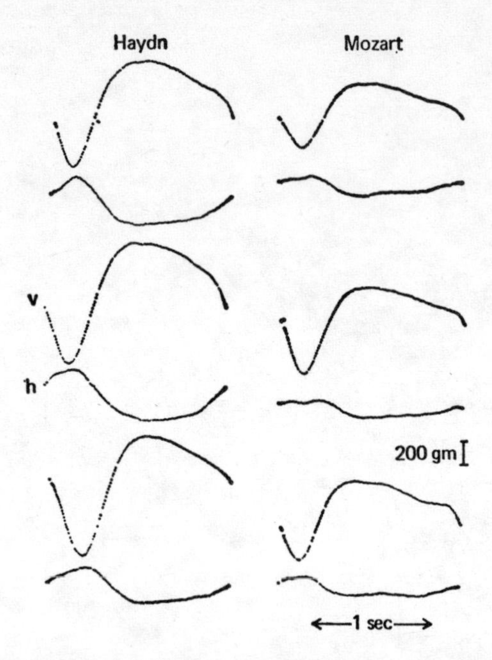

Figure 21. Comparison of the inner musical pulse forms of Haydn and Mozart. These forms were measured for various slow movements (K.491, 467, and 570 for Mozart; Sonatas in C Major, E Flat Major, and D Major for Haydn). Note the interesting and consistent differences in the horizontal trace also. The sense of awe, wonder, and "natural piety" characteristic of the Haydn pulse is reflected by the upward striving, rounded top portion of the pulse compared with the more sober pulse shape of Mozart. Note particularly that, though the composers share a style, the context of their individual personal character results in different pulse forms.

PART TWO

Sentic Cycles, Personal Applications and Extensions of Sentic Theory

Cell Cluster
that names itself brain:

I am, says the order of cells
And moves some matter
In a living space.
I feel, says the multitude
Of atoms, and moving
Weaves a trace
In an empty One.

And presently essentic form becomes
A trace to touch—
One and One, now
Is transformed to
    Thou.

NINE

Sentic Cycles and Their Capacity to Transform

How remarkable it would be if one could experience and express the spectrum of emotions embodied in music originating from oneself—without the crutch of a composer's intercession, without being driven by the composer; and to do so moreover whenever we wish, not when circumstance may call them forth. This, indeed, has become possible through the development of sentic cycles.

In the previous chapters, we observed various temporal properties of essentic forms. We have seen how the biologic time forms that communicate emotion are stored in music, keeping them timelessly fresh across centuries. In each vital experience of music, these forms are regenerated anew.

In music, essentic forms are enjoyed through ordered relationships between tones; but the tone of voice and touch are not so schematized. Can we make the source of essentic forms permanently available to the individual, using only his own fantasy, not a composer's, independently of musical instruments and of sound itself? Can the touch that lies behind music be tapped?

That is, can we generate and newly experience sequences of sentic states, using the biologic temporal "deep structures"—the time lattice of *meta-music* that lies behind musical communication?

The discovery of the universality of essentic forms *has* in fact led to the development of a simple, direct method by which they can be repeatedly produced and experienced—creatively, meditatively, and freed from their customary sensory coding of sound or of visual form. This work has yielded a program making it feasible to experience sentic states at will—a programmed sequence which we call "sentic cycles."

It was found that tapping this source directly could indeed help a person be more in touch with the vital sources of life. This process largely eliminates a distinction analogous to that between composer and performer: the subject becomes both (without learning to perform on a musical instrument).* The power of sentic cycles and music to generate emotions shares a common source. However, doing sentic cycles requires no production of sound, no laboriously acquired skills divorced from sentic discrimination. Everyone can readily do them.

Sentic cycles is a simple means by which a person, in his own home, can generate in himself substantially the entire spectrum of emotions in a period of approximately thirty minutes. This method allows one to experience emotions from different points of view, meditatively and with active expression, and has led to a variety of therapeutic effects.

What Are Sentic Cycles?

The method of expressing and generating sentic states (as described in Chapter Four) can be employed to engender creative ex-

* In the study of music, the practice and development of sentic discrimination is clearly different from the development of skills in mastering instrumental technique. The monolithic drive to develop technical skills frequently leads—except in those exceptionally "gifted"—to the neglect of practice of sentic discrimination and development. Finger exercises have been foisted on music students for generations, but no one until now has devised systematic "feeling exercises"—although it is certainly obvious how much they are needed. As we shall see, sentic training afforded by sentic cycles accomplished this also.

periences of organized sequences of sentic states—somewhat like a new art form of touch.

To do sentic cycles, all that is necessary is to have a sentic cycle cassette tape, a finger rest, and a means of playing the tape. (*No measuring instruments are required.*) A person sits on a simple chair without armrests, preferably with a cushion behind his back and one on the seat, with his feet firmly placed on the floor (shoes may be removed); legs should not be crossed. The finger rest is positioned on a coffee table, or on a second, hard-seat chair. The person starts the tape, puts the third finger on the finger rest, and closes his eyes.

Whenever he hears a click, he expresses with a single expressive action of pressure the quality of the state called for, as precisely as he can. States to be generated are announced by the tape: no emotion, anger, hate, grief, love, sex, joy, and reverence. Each state lasts several minutes and contains a sequence of timing clicks initiating expressive actions. The participant cannot predict when the next click will occur. The person is ready to express the quality called for and awaits the next click to carry out the expression. One expression for each click is to be done.

At the end of the cycle (or several such cycles) he sits quietly for a minute or two before getting up and resuming his activities. He may not want to talk for some minutes afterward.

The Discovery of Sentic Cycles

One day in 1968, having worked long hours in the laboratory, I made a strange discovery: I noticed myself feeling unduly well! I had often spent many hours expressing essentic forms to obtain precise measurements. But after seven or eight hours of being constrained and hooked up to several instruments, instead of feeling tired, I found myself fresh and exhilarated. At first I thought this to be just the result of having accomplished a good day's work. But the phenomenon kept recurring, and it soon became clear that something else was involved.† Results with other subjects confirmed this. So we

† I even started to look forward to coming to work—to spend hours doing this—and to get paid for it as well!

decided to try to make the experience more compact, to concentrate the beneficial effects and study them systematically.

The order and selection of sentic states, and the duration of each, were refined step by step, and the biologically optimum durations for the mean intervals between acton initiation and for the degree of randomness between actons were gradually discovered for each sentic state. These turned out to be quite different for different states.

As the design of the sequences of intervals was undertaken, every interval was sculptured in relationship to those before and after. Every change produced a change in the effect of the experience on the subject. To try to perfect the sequences was at times like training a dog to choose between an ellipse and a circle: as the differences are made smaller and smaller, the dog tends to go insane! It was necessary to sense the differences of each change, but also to compare the new effect with how it was before the change was made. In spite of the benefits of sentics, this seemed sometimes enough to drive one crazy! But, persevering over several years, programs and tapes were developed for initiating each acton and for the sequence of sentic states that seemed close to optimal. The real payoff, remarkably, was that the subtleties of timing being nearly optimal for one individual were also nearly optimal for others. Considering sentic theory, this is perhaps really not so surprising. In fact if it were not so, music would not function either. Still, it was gratifying to observe this result.

The Therapeutic Effects of Sentic Cycles

It is found that sentic cycles have many possible therapeutic and preventive uses. The effects of their regular practice are far-ranging. Well-adjusted persons can use them to generate a "high," and like forms of meditation and physical exercise, they can be used on a regular basis to maintain a general sense of well-being and of being in "touch" with the self. Doing sentic cycles can increase self-assurance and expand one's sensitivity to a range of emotional experience, affording insight into the nature of feeling, interpersonal relationships, and, in general, the nature of being. It is a form of emotional training.

Those suffering from unusual anxieties, phobias, severe stress, and a wide range of psychosomatic symptoms can use them (with supervision) to alleviate their symptoms and facilitate normal functioning. And sentic cycles used regularly over longer periods of time can gradually modify attitudes, patterns of behavior, emotional reactions, and improve relationships with other people. Couples, especially, can use them jointly to enlarge and improve their relationship. The insights that their continued experience provides can implement positive changes in character structure.

Sentic cycles have distinct effects on the mental state and on a number of physiologic processes. The experience of sentic cycles is unique and cannot be completely adequately described in words, but it is not at all difficult to experience for most subjects.

In over four years, 72 per cent of about three thousand subjects (ages twelve to eighty) were able to perform sentic cycles successfully at their *first* session, and to experience their effects. Of those subjects who completed three trials of sentic cycles, 83 per cent of the fantasy emotions called for were readily experienced (only 17 per cent causing any difficulty), according to subjects' reports. And 68 per cent of the subjects had no difficulty in expressing and fantasizing all the seven sentic states: anger, hate, grief, love, sex, joy, reverence. Reverence proved to cause difficulty most frequently, less frequently hate, and more rarely joy. After two additional trials, three quarters of those subjects reported no further difficulty with the particular emotion that they had previously been unable to express.

The experience of other investigators who have used sentic cycles extensively has been similar. For example, Drs. Alfred French and J. Tupin report that there is no question that sentic cycles are indeed effective in generating fantasy emotions. The two scientists reported "clyning‡ is clearly a process wherein affect is experienced, expressed, and made accessible to the psyche." The effects on the mental state are a sense of calmness, relatedness, and, at times, insights into the nature of the emotions themselves, and of the subject's relationships with them. To be able to summon up various sentic states at will and express them without fear or embarrassment is a satisfaction in itself. In addition, the subject has confidence that he can

‡ "Clyning" is the term introduced by Dr. A. French to describe carrying out sentic states.

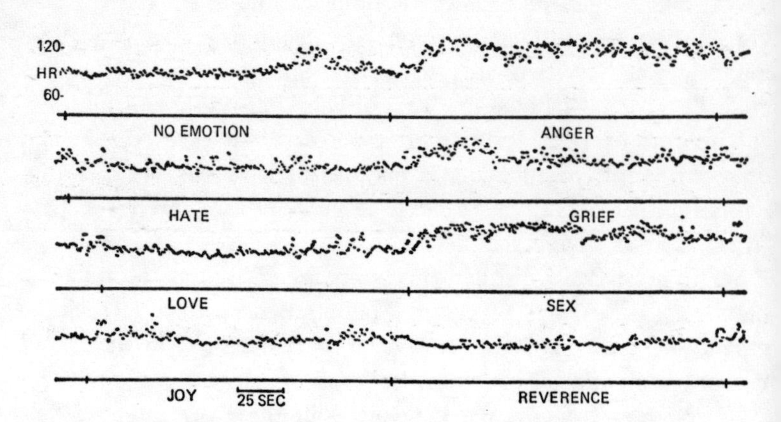

Figure 22. Variations of heart rate during a sentic cycle. Many subjects show marked increases in heart rate especially during anger and sex.

and may act freely, spontaneously, without worry that it will have a punitive effect. Subjects are often afraid to express emotions in real life for various reasons, but they are willing—and even glad—to experience similar emotions while doing sentic cycles. The fear of losing control which they experience in a real situation does not seem to play an inhibiting effect during sentic cycles.*

The state produced by sentic cycles is very different from hypnosis. One is very alert and in full control at all times. Physiologic responses include changes in heart rate and respiration. These vary systematically with each sentic state, as does oxygen consumption. (See Figures 22–25.) Huenergardt reported that heart rate increased on the average from 75 to 115 beats per minute during the experience of anger and joy, generated through the repeated expression of essentic form in response to images presented on a screen showing scenes suggestive of these states. Some 20 per cent of the subjects tested cry during the state of grief during the first time they do sentic cycles.

* Even a musical performance does not have such freedom; an audience is more or less critical, and there also is self-criticism. But when one plays to oneself, perhaps a fantasy, without thought of success or failure, listening and "speaking" at the same time, one comes closest to some aspect of the experience that sentic cycles, without the need for hours and years of dulling practice, can give.

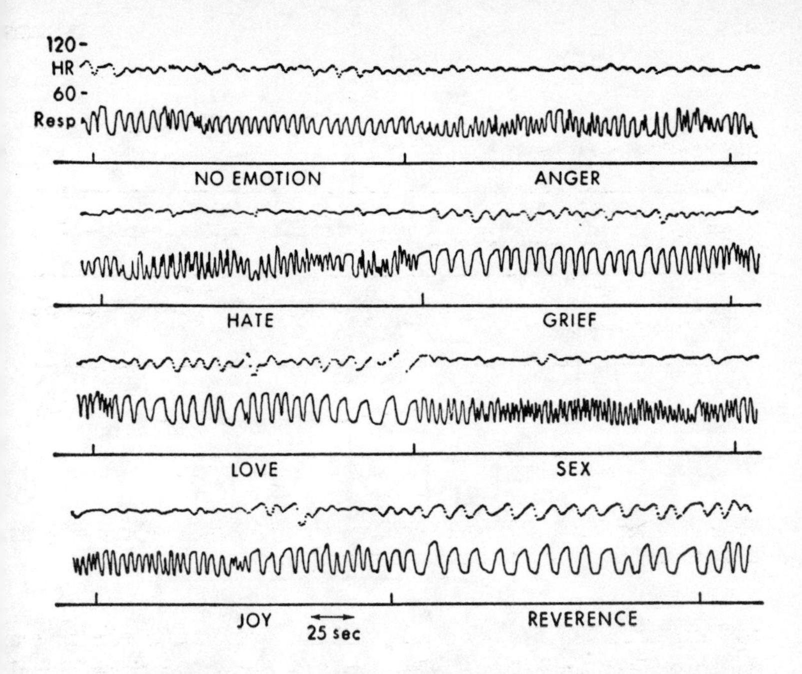

Figure 23. Changes in respiration and heart rate during a sentic cycle. Respiration accelerates during anger and hate. During grief the respiration has a gasping character with rest periods at the expiratory end of the cycle. Respiration slows during love, and speeds up markedly for sex. (Inspiration is downward in the figure.) During reverence there is a marked slowing down of respiration with resting phases at the inspiratory phases of the cycle (paralleling those at the expiration phases for grief). Heart-rate cycles in the subjects are related to respiration. (This subject shows otherwise fewer deviations in heart rate than the subject in *Figure* 22.)

There is a marked difference in respiration during different phases of sentic cycles, as would be expected. Respiration slows during grief, love, and reverence and increases during anger, hate, and sex. Different phases of respiration tend to coincide with expressions of specific sentic states—for example, anger with expiration and joy with inspiration. Also, though both grief and love induce slowed respiration, they differ in that there is a marked pause after the expiratory phase for grief before the next inspiration.

After sentic cycles, subjects' faces are slightly flushed, their eyes sparkle, and they comment often on "having had an experience" or

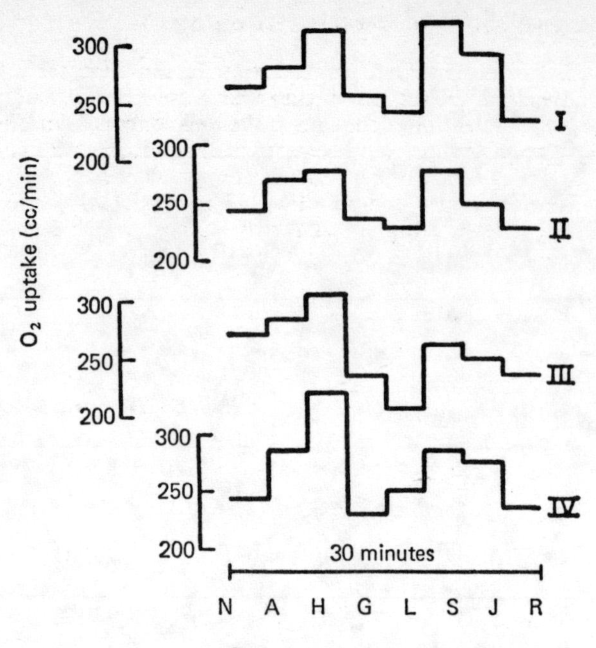

O_2 uptake during a sentic cycle

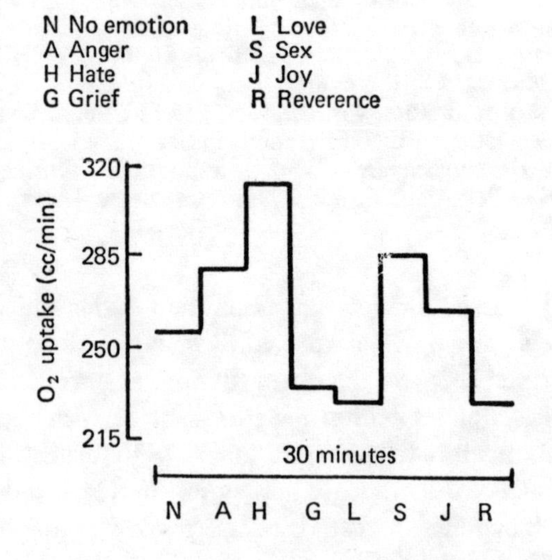

Average of 4 cycles

Oxygen uptake during a sentic cycle

Figure 24. In the upper left graph oxygen consumption for four sentic cycles of the same subject shows consistent change for the various sentic states. Changes in all four cycles are in the same direction for corresponding states, except for one step between grief and love in the fourth cycle. Passionate states tend to show greater oxygen consumption. Note the relation between oxygen consumption and respiration rates indicated in *Figure 23.* The lower left graph shows the average oxygen uptake for the four cycles.

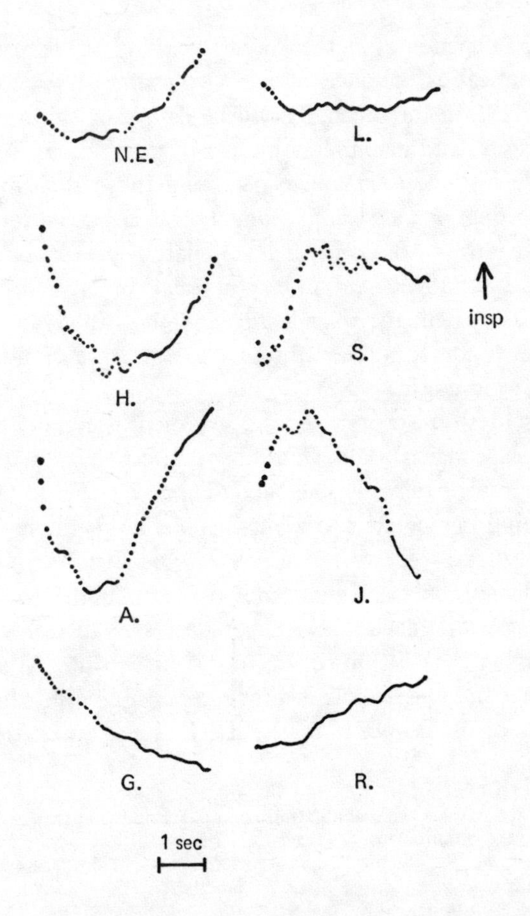

Figure 25. Typical transient respiration forms during E-actons for no emotion, love, hate, sex, anger, joy, grief, and reverence, respectively, based on an average of twenty actons. (Averaging began 0.5 sec. after click.)

having been "turned on." Even agitated patients are generally able to express their feelings with this method and at these times their over-all bodily agitation ceases.

Practice of sentic cycles teaches one discrimination in the expressive language of touch. As this language becomes known more precisely, communication with others through touch becomes more effective and powerful. It becomes easier to know what one is communicating through touch—as well as in voice inflection and other modes.

However, depending on the "point of view" as discussed earlier, the communication of touch forms may occur without a deeply felt origin or cause for the touch. The social danger of lightheaded touch communication and manipulation must be pointed out. As discussed earlier, in a form of touch there may be a full commitment of the entire individual or merely the production of a known form—one of human relationship, the other a manipulation or a quasi-artistic expression. On the other hand, in playful use of essentic form, pleasant feelings may be enhanced and the communication of unpleasant feelings can become modified through the pleasure of the purity of expression, as in music.

For persons who are in a sentic "rut," sentic cycles improve the fluidity of their mental state, abolishing sentic rigidity, a symptom of depression and anxiety. French and Tupin have reported, "Some subjects found immediate and dramatic relief of symptoms of depression, anxiety, and sleep disturbance after the first forty-five minute session following only a few minutes of instruction." However, one does not necessarily have to have been depressed to feel increasingly alive through the ability to control one's sentic state. We may perhaps say that the sentic cycle is a form of discipline in which a man is a disciple of his true or natural self.† It is also interesting that in

† Sentic cycles share with meditation the remarkable property of self-refining. The forms of the emotions as practiced in sentic cycles lead to an increasing degree of refinement in their production and perception. This occurs as a natural process. A similar process takes place in meditation, as a mantra is inwardly refined and takes on more subtle qualities.

Sentic cycles also share with meditation the filling of the sentic domain—which normally partakes of random-like perturbations—with an entity, a focus of unchanging quality about which the world of change and permanence is viewed.

practicing sentic cycles one often comes to enjoy most, and look forward to, the state of love as a favored state.

Sentic Cycles and the Satisfaction of Inner Drives

Perhaps the most important application and effect of sentic cycles lies in their ability to influence the urges and driving forces of the personality. The sense of calmness and satisfaction of being, as such, or the sensation of being emotionally drained, which occasionally replaces this, noticeably alters the dynamics of drives. One may observe the replacement of the neurotic anxious drive—the rigid drive toward self-imposed goals—by a creative drive coupled with joy in its exercise. *This displacement of a drive whose satisfaction lies in a distant goal (which cannot be achieved in the present) by a creative drive whose exercise provides a continuous flow satisfaction coupled with joy) is a remarkable aspect of sentic cycles.* It appears that needs for smoking and perhaps even drugs may be seriously altered through the use of sentic cycles.‡

In practice, the length and frequency of the sentic cycle dosage should be adjusted to individual need. Generally, the longer the total length of sentic cycles, the greater the attenuation of drives. Too prolonged or intense sentic cycle sessions can attenuate drives excessively and produce a "psyched-out" state of being overtranquilized. Events that probably should cause one displeasure and anxiety may be shrugged off under these conditions as insignificant. An appropriate degree of moderation is called for; not more than one hour per day, say, should be devoted to sentic cycles, except for special therapeutic reasons to relieve specific psychosomatic problems. For the person in daily business activity, twenty to thirty minutes of sentic cycles a day may well be best, or one hour every other day.

‡ No one has ever asked to smoke during sentic cycles. Heavy smokers do not desire to smoke then. This is significant, since a heavy smoker frequently asks for a cigarette particularly during periods of mental concentration.

Modifying Aggression

One characteristic effect of sentic cycles is frequently observed—a special form of contentment. After completion of sentic cycles, one's face may portray a characteristic "contented smile" that persists for some time. Immediately afterward one often wishes not to talk but to allow the experience to "sink in." Yet at those times one does not feel isolated; on the contrary, there is a sense of sharing an inner existence one feels is common to men. This feeling communicates itself, even in the absence of verbal expression.*

Removal of anxiety or anger is not invariably desirable, in fact. A subject may feel that the experience can, so to speak, cheat him out of his maintained rightful anger. A person may not wish to give up the emotional set deriving from a specific individual situation. In preventing this, a person can always exercise his choice to use sentic cycles judiciously. The absence of anxiety and anger may require some reorganization of one's life habits, which is sometimes an uncomfortable phase.

Another effect of sentic cycles is often to lower the threshold of emotional experience, and to enable subjects to produce short-lasting outbursts in daily life. Again, this is generally a favorable effect, although one should avoid excess. What constitutes excess in this respect is difficult to know, however, at this stage of our knowledge.

Taken all together, the evidence of the remarkable power of sentic cycles to modify levels of aggression clearly has social significance—in the life of the family, in the prevention of crime and suicide, and in releasing the creativity of the individual.

* The teacher or therapist, too, is often moved to a spontaneous flow of love toward the subject at these times. (This kind of experience has also been reported by Dr. French.) Frequently, the condition of the subject immediately after sentic cycle is so free from hostility and aggression, and yet full of such a special vitality, that it seems as if a natural flow of love, which is present in the teacher or therapist but has been previously inhibited by the sentic messages of the people around him, is allowed to flow toward the subject without hindrance.

Such an empathic experience is furthered by the knowledge that the subject has just experienced all the emotions of the cycles. Like a shared musical experience of the late works of Beethoven, a bond appears between therapist and subject, even if the therapist or teacher has not participated in the cycle himself. The two individuals are no longer strangers, but have "shared" a particular, rather beautiful intimacy, like a sunset witnessed together.

Personal Experiences of Sentic Cycles

These various points may be made clearer by the following examples of individual sentic cycle experiences. These are a typical cross section of sentic cycle experience describing in the subjects' own words the effects of several sessions on some subjects, and first sessions only on others.

I should like to let these comments speak for themselves. As the subjects describe the experience in their own words, we also gradually get a fuller and more comprehensive view of the nature of the effects of sentic cycles. The newness of the experience (and perhaps the effect of sentic cycles to some extent) seems to spur some subjects at times to description of almost literary quality and authenticity, and to reveal unsuspected powers of self-expression.

T.C. (Female) Age 26†

First Session (2/22/72) Two Cycles

Upon completion of first session I found deep sense of calmness or "peace." Condition before starting was depressed, bitchy, irritable. Anger and hate sequences seemed very long. Senses very aware of changes in heat, sounds in house, etc. During sex sequence very aware of dimple in button which was not noticeable in other emotions. Joy and love called forth spontaneous humming, also aware of pleasant smell. These sequences seemed very short. Anger seemed to call forth red image. Reverence seemed to be more difficult to express. Sense of greenness accompanied sex.

Later (five hours) held lover in different way (according to him), noticed increase in lubrication for intercourse, length of climax extended.

Second Session (2/27/72)

Repetition of impression of red during anger. Hate like a black curtain rising, falling, flowing, flickering. Angle of finger on finger rest changed with different emotion. (This was noticed in first ses-

† Initials and names have been altered here to preserve the privacy of the subjects.

sion also, along with changes in position of other fingers.) Not as much of a feeling of extra length of hate and anger this time. First cycle of reverence interminable—second cycle had vision of holy person and eyes of person which seemed to communicate the feeling; the cycle seemed very brief. Feel it best to have time alone after a session before discussing experience. Marked feeling of lightness accompanied joy. The pressure exerted during anger and hate even between "clicks" much heavier than other emotions. Physical side effects: Headache disappeared. Increase of lubricatory discharge, lessening of menstrual cramps. Hunger disappeared. The first tape seemed more even in emotion generation. Three hours after session noticed faster calming down of upset condition. Hands more sensitive.

Third Session (3/28/72) Two Cycles

After a month of heavy smoking (one or two packs a day) and some drinking I was able to undergo a complete session with a new tape. The reaction was extremely positive. There was a marked sense of calmness which included a feeling of unity of self. In the modern vernacular I "got it all together." There was no desire for cigarettes (which I quit smoking the day before) and a release of tension. I also had a slight headache and heavy menstrual cramps at the beginning of the session which were relieved. The calm feeling extended to enable me to endure very heavy emotional harassment that evening.

Fourth Session (3/29/72) One Cycle

Calming effect still in evidence. Went through one cycle. Felt restless during cycle but got benefit after. Very aware of increased tactile awareness. Experienced many of same reactions related to color and music as noted before—more confidence in self and awareness of others.

The next morning, following two restless nights, felt very exuberant and energetic. (This is an unusual reaction for me. I think I need a lot of sleep and am usually tired and depressed from lack of it . . . this seems to be common among many women of my acquaintance.) Perhaps clyning reduces need for sleep.

My increased tactile awareness exemplified by impression of taste and texture of blackberries. The fruit felt smooth, hairy, plump, bittersweet in an almost excruciatingly sensual way.

During the day felt "stretched" time sense as though I was able to complete tasks in a very deliberate, complete manner which I would normally rush through, but this deliberateness did not extend the time of the task at hand. I felt able to accomplish more, better, in the same amount of time.

In a very real way I believe the continued clyning experience seems to give a feeling of having that insulating layer which we defensively construct against ourselves, the natural world, our awareness of and relationships with others, and our senses stripped away, enabling a more clear, beautiful, and true view of life as a man.

Fifth Session (3/31/72) *One Cycle*

Had difficulty concentrating today. I felt frustrated at the lack of a comfortable place, but afterward experienced sense of calmness and heightened awareness usually associated with the process . . . can feel air, ground, self, smells, etc. much more keenly. During sex sequence felt nipple tissue become erect. After clyning feel desire to be "quiet," i.e., not to communicate orally (if I do talk notice marked change in rate of speech [slower] and pitch of voice [lower]). Feel that mind is very active, though. It's not a desire to be uncommunicative; quite the contrary, one would like to share the feeling. Perhaps it's a need to absorb the experience.

J.C. (Female) Age 42

First Experience (12/15/72)

Upon hearing "no emotion," I was not yet relaxed or comfortable with what was happening. It was helpful to have the suggestion of imagining my finger on a typewriter key and feeling the relative detachment of that. The pressure of my finger was light and did not last long. After a while images began to form of what I was typing, though. One was a letter to my mother. I felt ambivalent emotions rising in me and reminded myself that I was to feel no emotion. The ambivalence ebbed and flowed on its own nonetheless. But the pressure of my finger did not seem to change a great deal. I think I was consciously trying to express no emotion.

Upon hearing "anger," I immediately plunged into another milieu. I could hardly wait for that first click to sound. My finger responded autonomously and angrily pushed at the button, a thrusting, away-from-me motion. As the clicks continued, I had the impression of shoving someone I was angry with. A number of people appeared to me whom I had been irritated with recently—Barry and his narcissism, Charles and his pomposities, my mother and her paranoia, but most of all myself and my own confusion. I had several distinct impressions of shoving myself off balance. Gradually, more peripheral people began to appear—students who make inconsiderate demands, acquaintances who seem insensitive. I took some pleasure in flicking them away, but they'd circle and come back, and my irritation would increase. Finally, though, my anger seemed to definitely dissipate. I couldn't even summon up much anger toward myself any more. I felt a little bored toward the end and wondered what was next.

Upon hearing "hate," my finger began to feel very warm, as if mobilizing itself to hate. My heart began to pound fast again. I tried to express hate as an emotion and could not find anything to direct it to. I conjured up people I thought I really felt negative about but could not find an appropriate feeling. All the time I was pressing the button very hard as the click sounded. There was warmth going to it, but not feeling. Perhaps I should say heat, not warmth. After a while, as I realized that feelings were not going to accompany, I concentrated on the effort. I pressed down passionately, and abstract thoughts began to form. Revulsion of the Vietnam conflict, friends who had been severely injured, injustices in general. Whatever hatred I could summon was injury to my beliefs. By now my finger was pressing very hard, so hard that I found a severe cramp was forming in the first knuckle, and I wondered if the finger was breaking or broken. I kept on pressing as the clicks sounded, but my feeling wasn't with it, really, and I thought it would never end.

On "grief," an entirely new world happened. Sadness enveloped me quickly. Perhaps because of my overwhelming feeling for injured friends. I sank down into that. My finger motion must have been gentler, more caressing, more toward myself but at the same time reaching out toward the other person first. For a while I had been hearing faint voices calling and hadn't thought much about it: it must have been down the street. Voices began calling my name. I was not sure it was Peter calling my name from some hospital. But at the same time I saw the vision I'd had of him since then, standing in a corner of our kitchen, looking as he did before he went away, smiling, coming forward, calling my name. Seemingly simultaneously, I had been hearing my father's voice, calling my name in a very familiar way; it made me laugh, or at least smile. Then I felt the grief at his death. Then a hallucination I'd had of him at home, lying in his coffin in the fireplace as he was at the mortuary, but he turned to me and said, "Death is O.K.," just turning his head a little. I then projected myself into my mother's death and felt enormous pain and guilt. Then visited the funerals of both Charles's parents and felt similar emotions, but more concerned with what Charles was feeling. As the clicks continued, I tried to enter myself into grief, it was not difficult for me to do. I can feel sad. Each situation was fairly easy to get into.

Upon hearing "love," a whole myriad of voices started coming. My finger became gentle. The voice of a friend of mine came first; David said, "The reason you're feeling angry with Barry and Charles is because they have been so kind to you lately and you don't feel deserving of such extreme kindness, and you react by releasing anger." I sit stiller and try to express love with the button. It goes out warm and clear, with a steady pressure. I also feel it coming in, like when Charles touches the back of my neck as he passes me, and when Barry consciously sends loving feelings to me in a warm glow. My reaction to that is a back-and-forth motion of my finger on the finger rest as I am sending and receiving, but not always on equal frequency. The loving feeling begins to expand to a more general feeling toward mankind and then compresses back to the personal. (I feel this must have been expressed in the pressing, but maybe not significantly.) Then I begin to see a whole bunch of people, some of whom surprise me to come up in the context of love, as I don't feel that close to them. Laura I barely know, yet feel warmly toward; still, she has "come up" earlier as an angry woman, and now as trying to be loving. A young man I've felt estranged with comes riding up the street from the West End on a bicycle and turns into the driveway; I am standing in the shadows of the garage, but he sees me and pedals in an oval around me; hands me a gift and leans down and kisses me; I feel dazzled by this light kiss. The scene begins to fade, as there is a steady presence of Charles in the form of my feelings about love.

Upon hearing "sex," Charles leaps right into the limelight. My finger begins to have back-and-forth caressing motions on the button. I begin to feel mild orgasms. I sort of glide with that for quite a few clicks. I feel Charles turning toward me, touching me, sometimes in the night, sometimes as we are around each other anywhere. Warmth coming up in me, my finger motion seems to warm and intensify. I experience sexual feelings coming from and going toward other people, but they are more undifferentiated; sometimes faces fade by, but they seem unrelated to the body. It is more my own feelings I am feeling, and everyone is contributing to that. Again many of my sexual experiences with Charles are primary; they seem to represent what is important. A significant part of it is the pleasure I can give him, not just what I am receiving. The orgasms become quite intense, and this segment seems quite short.

Joy was a funny feeling. My finger was hesitant for a while, then began tentative, leaping motions away from me, very light; yet aware. Dancing motions, visions of lovers and forests. Myself in a filmy nightgown running through the forest, dancing very gracefully, feeling sunlight filter onto me, yet coolness envelop me refreshingly. I see someone at the end of a meadow and cry out with pleasure, begin to dance toward him, and when I get closer, he is running to meet me; air is rushing around; it is all so intense and happy; we collide in a burst of laughter and stimulation, and fall to the earth in a tumbling, chuckling embrace. Of course, it is Charles.

Upon hearing "reverence," I feel more solemn. My whole body relaxes, my finger slows to a more quiet caress. I feel a misty, pale sunlight start to come. Maybe it is moonlight. Tears form in my eyes. I close my eyes as my finger continues its gentle motion, mostly toward myself. A force gathers in the atmosphere around me and reassures me, lifts me. I know I can fly if I want to. I know I can also sink. I feel I should stay here and somehow cope. I feel myself lifting and permit myself the ecstasy of letting myself go upward. I feel cradled by some great but gentle force, then placed gently back down where I belong for now.

I.K. (Female) Age 35

First Session (1/9/73)

I found that I had to make up scenes to experience anger. I had to be angry at a specific person. Then, I got involved with whether the anger was justified. It was hard to sustain any one scene or the feeling. I had to keep working at it. Hate was even more difficult. Hate, to me, is a very big emotion, bigger than people, and so I had to think of impersonal forces, e.g., Nazism, injustice, the bomb at Hiroshima—and then I felt impotent, because what could I do about these bigger-than-life evils?

For grief I needed to conjure up pictures too—being in the funeral parlor, after my father or my brother had died—being in the hospital room, when my brother was dying. Also, I remembered taking my little dog to the hospital, and the doctor calling soon after, to tell me he had died. Then, in the midst of true situations, I saw myself standing alone as a very small child, in the middle of nowhere, and totally bereft. I recognized myself as the child, but I have no real memory of such an incident.

During love, I saw the faces of my husband and children, individually, and I had the feeling of love being a circular force that flowed around through me and whoever I was seeing. How their eyes looked was very important. I saw my dog that way too.

Joy was nice, I had to imagine skiing in a fresh snowfall, and then I got involved with WHO was skiing with me, and I realized that in each joyful fantasy, my happiness was contingent upon someone else.

Sex was very easy. We had just seen the movie *Deep Throat.* I recalled scenes from that. They were very vivid, and I really felt sexy —but then to my surprise, I found that I was thinking about clothes or what to have for dinner; in none of the other categories had my attention left the emotion so entirely, although it was the one I had initially been the most engrossed in.

When I came to reverence, I experienced great relief. It was the only category in which I didn't have to fantasize—I really felt reverence. I saw blue sky and just felt great. I thought, that's why being stoned is referred to as "high." I felt way up, as if I were above all problems in some heady atmosphere. It was certainly the emotion that I enjoyed the most. As I thought about it later, it seemed to me like being in Alpha or meditating, in a way it seemed like a cop-out. That is, in experiencing all the other emotions I had "to get involved" with other people, or deal with my feelings of impotence to change the world, or myself. The feeling of being outside these involvements, and at the same time one with some larger benign force, was wonderfully inviting. But upon realizing this, I was later depressed, because I saw it as a sign of my shortcomings—because isn't it precisely in those "involvements" that we find "where it is at"?

Later in the day I went about my business as usual, although I did feel as though I had had some sort of revelation. I planned to review it and work on it later.

Today I felt quite energetic early in the day, but now it is mid-afternoon and I have run downhill. I feel the sentics revealed an aspect of myself that I was not aware of, but I am puzzled as to where to go from here.

Second Session (1/11/73)

In the anger phase, the fantasizing episodes were briefer than the last time. I was not really frowning or scowling, but separate muscles all over my face seemed to be contracting and relaxing at different rates. Towards the end of the anger, I began to feel there was no real justification for my anger in the imagined situations, and it all felt contrived. I had even more trouble than the first time stirring up hate. I just could not really feel it since I could not conjure up any situation that would really warrant hate. But as in the anger, my facial muscles seemed to be very busy. It also suddenly occurred to me that as a result of the first sentic session where I found I was hating the feeling of impotence about "doing something" about our downstairs playroom—I had in the interim actually refinished the floor and straightened up the room!

My feelings in the other three emotion sections were not notably different from the first sentic session, except possibly less intense.

I do feel, however, that the two sentic sessions have in some inexplicable way helped me to "unhook myself" from some emotional hang-ups that have been bothering me for a long time. I couldn't say just how, because I did NOT think about the problems while doing the sentics, but I feel able to flow along more freely now. I look forward to doing sentics some more.

P.V. (Male) Age 25

First Session (7/2/72)

A mind-boggling experience. Feel very calm; a peaceful state of mind—not depressed although not really happy. Feel exhausted but tenseness in stomach is gone. Feel more alert. The following night slept very well and felt I didn't need as much sleep. Awoke feeling very alert. Still feel the reaction from yesterday's experience. After the sentic cycles was a little disoriented in speech two or three hours later. At the same time I appreciated Balboa Park more—noticed more details like flowers, grass, etc. Also didn't feel much like talking —wanted to be alone.

In the first part of the cycle had some difficulty with expressing hate and anger. Grief came through very well—started to sob toward the end of the grief phase. Joy came through very well. I felt myself smiling. Reverence was probably the most difficult—my head was slightly bowed.

During the second cycle everything was more intense, especially anger and hate. With anger I was almost jumping up and down in the chair, breathing heavily. Joy was all "tingly." Joy lingered more than any other emotion. During the second cycle I didn't have to think of specific scenes or examples generally, as opposed to the first time. Just a general thought would bring on the emotions. Emotions were exaggerated, more exaggerated than in real life—all emotions more intense: for example, anger. Afterward felt a comfortable tiredness and wanted to lie down for ten to fifteen minutes.

Second Session (7/3/72)

Thinking emotions came without any problem. Strongest was love and joy. Reverence became stronger. I felt awe. For hate I was thinking of Hitler and the Nazis. I was not tired today as I was yesterday.‡ Not that I was bored the previous day, but today's seemed shorter. I cried slightly during grief. Sex was enjoyable but had been stronger the previous day. I had no difficulty at all in switching from one emotion to another nor did I yesterday either.

D.E., Ph.D. (Psychoanalyst, Female) Age 29

First Session (1/9/73) *Two Cycles*

NO EMOTION—Some tension, feeling expectant, impatient, then awareness of tension and relaxation, awareness of breathing.

ANGER—Every time start to feel the anger also experience a gleeful feeling of the liberation involved in feeling the anger—makes me want to laugh or smile, then get into the anger itself, lips tighten up, feeling increased tension and almost strain, and then feel very tired and drained, too tiring to sustain the feeling.

HATE—Find myself sneering with each click, involuntarily. Seems diabolical and almost amusing to sit there and voluntarily feel hate —get into it though and tension builds up, finger hurts from the amount of pressure, whole thing becomes too tiring to sustain. Remember some wild aggressive fantasies I have had and the weird relief they offered at times I felt in an impotent rage though I never acted on them; just the satisfaction involved in conjuring them up in all their gory detail.

GRIEF—Limpness, heaviness, head down, no energy, depression, image of myself at the funeral of someone I cared very deeply about, wondering if one ever fully recovers from such a loss, image of myself talking about these feelings in analysis and crying as I talked about them then—not crying now.

‡ The subject estimated that he spent about fifteen to twenty minutes in the sentic session whereas actually the tape was an hour long.

LOVE—Warm glow in chest, smile, feeling tender, thinking of those I love, feeling much warmth but also it is intense, feeling emotionally "turned on" rather than relaxed, feels warm and nice, and sort of full.

SEX—Feeling vaginal contractions every time I respond to click. Feels good, makes me smile. Also feels a little funny in room full of people like this. Very localized. Then think of feeling love and sex together, it's much more complete—now feeling contractions plus the warm glow and it's really nice. Makes me think of the difference between a simply sexual experience and one where you are feeling much love too and how different orgasms are under the two conditions. Combination produced a total body shudder, like having the chills, that was surprising and pleasant.

JOY—Light feeling, headiness, smile; image of a new baby. Feeling of things floating up—almost expansion of inner space in head. Think of feeling close after sex; and of people I love. Main feeling though that strikes me is the actual physical sensations of lightness and how particular they are and how they are different from love, and sex. The uniqueness of each emotion.

REVERENCE—Think of my grandfather, of a teacher I revere, image of the temple at Miyajima in Japan, built on the water. Very serious quality to this feeling and somehow more intellectual than the others, not quite as kinesthetic. Not as expansive—almost constraining.

Aware of posture and breathing throughout. By second cycle, tired and resenting having to do it over. Throughout seemed arbitrary to start a feeling and have to hold it back between clicks.

Second Session (1/15/73)

Finger wanting to persist once an emotion started—seems unnatural to stop and start, finger getting tired and stiff, much tension, mouth very expressive.

Started exhausted and with severe headache, after felt very relaxed and pleasantly tired. No desire to do second cycle though. Enjoyed getting into the awareness of posture and breathing and the quietness of sitting in dark room and getting into self in this way. Kind of feeling I often get from writing. Feeling of getting into self and exploring inner space.

D.M. (Male) Age 22

First Session (2/25/72) Two Cycles

Found clyning to be very relaxing both physically and mentally. Surprised that it relaxes my mind as well as my body so much. Conscious of physically tensing-relaxing, tensing-relaxing. Changed mood, more mellow after. Had feeling that brain had been working.

During second cycle felt flow of emotion from one to next, on first cycle some overlap of emotions. Anger seemed longer than others, and hate and reverence were also long. Felt grief most because of recent personal experience. Felt mental picture of each emotion, and felt apprehension and tenseness drain from body. Voice appeared softer and speech slower than before session. Found experience totally absorbing. Every businessman should clyne every day to prevent ulcers. Felt build-up of body heat through face and chest.

K.L. (Female) Age 28

First Session (3/26/72) Two Cycles

Definitely experienced all of the emotions called for. Feel drained, it was fascinating, an experience. Even a piece of music does not always have all those emotions. During reverence, I was in Chartres Cathedral or listening to music. Felt reverence for creativity. Enjoyed love, sex, joy, and reverence most. Feel like I have gone through a complete experience, unique and intriguing. On another level, I feel absolutely exhausted emotionally. Next morning still felt rather exhausted.

D.G. (Polio Paralysis Victim, Male) Age 38

First Session (12/28/72) Two Cycles

I was impressed by the phenomenon of triggering emotional programming in the absence of events external to one's conscious awareness. The love phase and the sex phase evoked very strong images of past relationships. Except for the no emotion cycle, all of the cycles were pleasant—even the negative emotions.

The over-all effect experienced afterward was a mild high with

Plate 1. Recording dynamic forms of emotional expression with the earliest model of the sentograph.

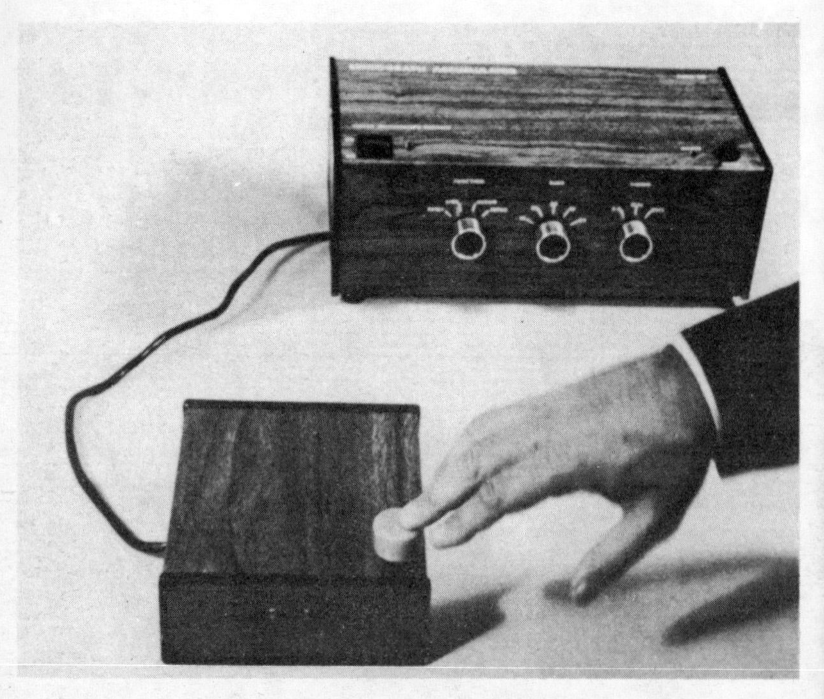

Plate 2. Detail of hand position during expressive measurement on the sentographic transducer. The accumulator in the background stores and adds individual response curves to obtain an average form.

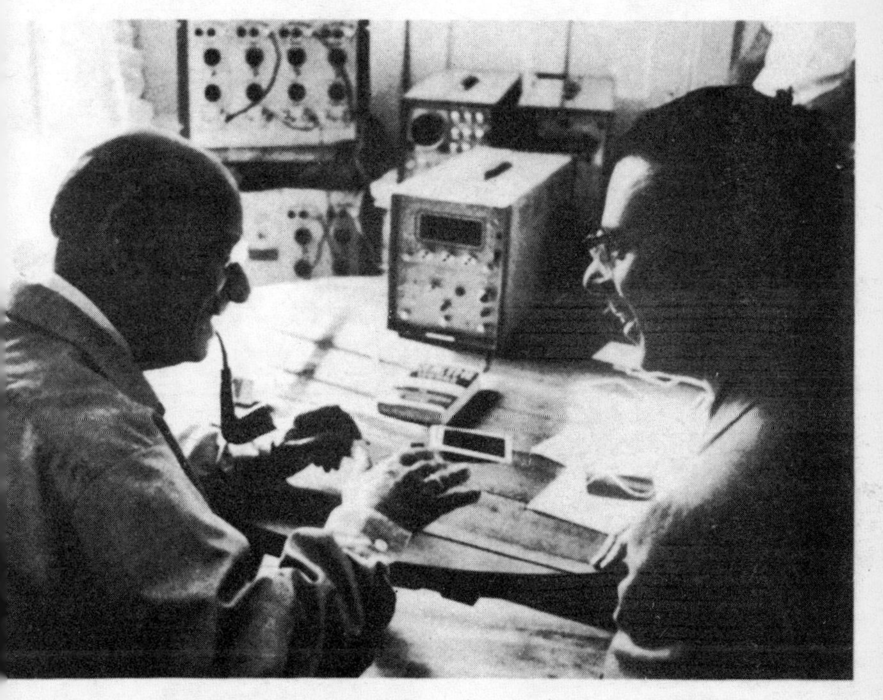

Plate 3. A photograph of Pablo Casals and the author, as Casals prepares to produce inner pulse forms of various composers using the sentograph, at the Marlboro Music Festival, Vermont.

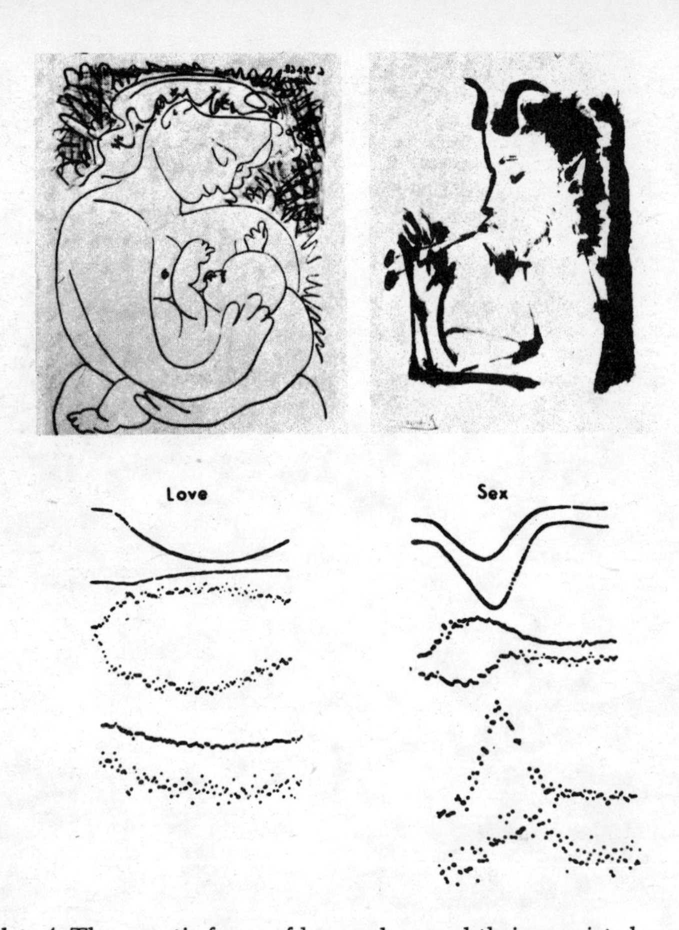

Plate 4. The essentic forms of love and sex and their associated muscle activity are here compared with drawings by Picasso of Mother and Child, and Pan, respectively. There appears to be an analogy that may well not be altogether accidental between the uniquely rounded forms of the Mother and Child drawing (the enfolding arms) and the measured essentic form of love. An embrace illustrated visually and its dynamic tactile representation in essentic form show a resemblance. On the right, the accentuation and particular angularity of the horns, arms, and shoulder with strong dark accents and implied thrusts compare well with the measured essentic form of the sexual quality with its secondary accents of muscle activity. It would seem as if the dynamic visual impressions, communicated by a great artist, correspond to the biologic shapes of expression as measured in essentic form. In attempting to obtain pure essentic forms in emotional expression, one is not too far removed from the aspirations of the artist.

The examples given here show one way (through the use of curved forms) that dynamic essentic forms may be represented in art. Other visually expressive techniques, using color and light for example, are not directly graphically comparable to dynamic forms we have measured.

Plate 5. Pietà of Michelangelo (1499). In this unique masterpiece, archetypically powerful in its expression of grief and compassion, the form of the collapsed body (torso and thighs) is a pure representation of the observed form of grief, the expression of which is also experienced as a collapse (see example of the form in Chapter Four). Auxiliary lines of the folds in the draped body sheet (lower left) suggest the essentic form of love; also the extended line of the right arm (left center). Angular forms of draped sheet and legs on right lower center suggest harsh negative forces; the fold proceeding out and upward from the extended arm (lower center) may be experienced as an aspect of hope. The angle of Mary's head is also similar to that observed frequently during states of grief in sentic cycles as part of the body image of grief and of compassion. (Photo from *Michelangelo Pietà* Copyright © 1975 by Robert Hupka. Used by permission of Robert Hupka.)

Plate 6. Goya's painting *Saturn Devouring His Child* (c. 1820) portrays essential raw, destructive violence. The dynamic angular forms of the arms and legs correspond to measured essentic forms for hate (see Chapter Four). (Photo, from Museo del Prado, Madrid, by Lee Boltin from Time-Life Library of Art: *The World of Goya,* © Time, Inc.)

Plate 7. This work of Giotto, *The Epiphany* (c. 1320)—perhaps one of the most beautiful paintings ever painted—has a harmony related to its extraordinarily purely expressed essentic forms. The dominant central figure reflects the essentic form of reverence (see Chapter Four); other essentic forms are orchestrated around it. The curve of the arm (left center) corresponds to the essentic form of love; the forms of the horns of the goat correspond to joy; hope, exaltation, awe, wonder, apreeneness, and transparent wisdom are all variously represented. But most of all, the picture succeeds in representing what it does not depict: the unseen force above that draws and captures the rapt attention of the two angels at the top—the ineffable source of essentic form. (Photo courtesy of The Metropolitan Museum of Art Kennedy Fund, 1911.)

Plate 8. This is the work of an Australian aborigine artist. It represents the Mimi spirits, a guardian heritage of the aborigine people. Art representations of Mimi spirits are kept and renewed by successive generations. The implied movements largely suggest joy, implied by their relationship to the essentic form of joy (see Chapter Four). Experiencing the painting in this way seems to be also in accordance with its significance to the aborigine people. (Photo courtesy of the Art Gallery of New South Wales.)

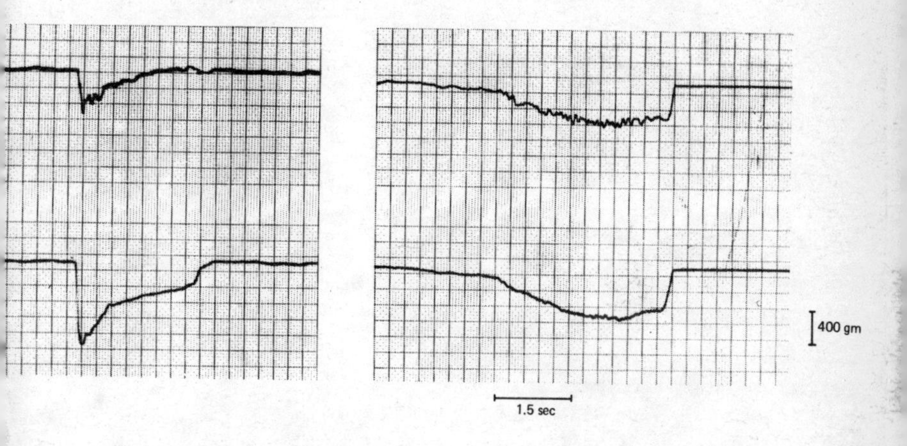

Plate 9. An example of the essentic form of hope (right) and courage (left) (single responses, not averages). The essentic form of hope takes a minimum of 3.2 seconds to complete—it is thus one of the longest essentic forms we have observed. There is a steady prolonged rise in pressure, followed by a secondary, reinforcing phase. It is accompanied by inspiration. Unlike most emotions, hope can also be well expressed by an upward pressure with an inverted sentographic transducer. (This process is described in Chapter Fifteen.) The essentic form of courage, by contrast, is clearly downward, and has the character of a step response with overshoot (in control engineering terms) of a certain definite duration. The horizontal trace shows the presence of a subliminal tremor, characteristic of the state, evidence of which is averaged out in the averaging process we usually employ.

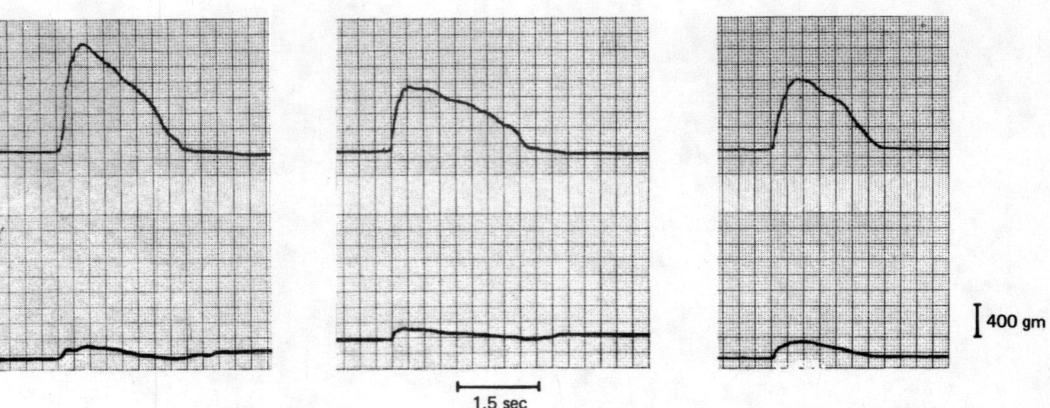

Plate 10. The essentic form of being apreene. The expression of this state cannot be adequately carried out with a downward pressure. Thus, the sentograph transducer had to be turned upside down to permit a vertically upward pressure to be applied, which the correct expression of this state requires. (Interestingly, in this sentic state, the pressure is also directed slightly to the right, the upward angle being about 80°. The 10° deviation to the right of vertical is not registered, however, by the sentograph.) Hope is another emotion which may be measured with the inverted transducer.

The apreene acton is an expressive form that resembles the expression of a particular kind of question; the tone of voice in the phrase, "Now *let* me see," spoken with a degree of ardor, comes close to its spirit.

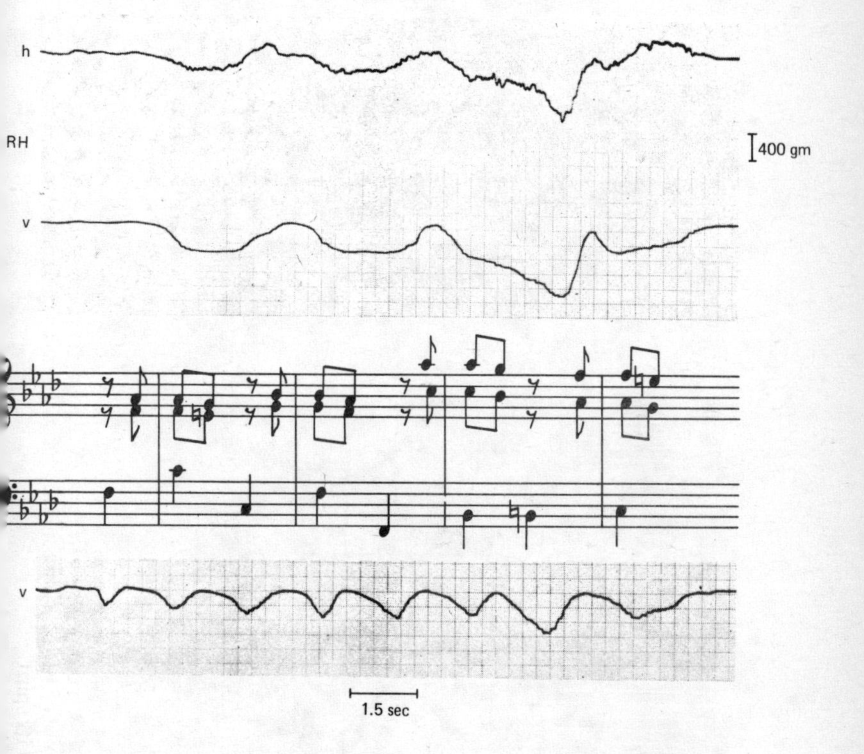

Plate 11. Bach, Prelude from Bk. II, *Wohltemperierte Klavier*. The bottom trace (right hand) is recorded from Sentograph I. The upper two traces are the horizontal and vertical traces recorded from Sentograph II (left hand) representing essentic forms. The horizontal trace contains a slight muscular tremor, invisible in the actual expression. (For the description of the forms, see text.) Although this example and those that follow are piano pieces, the sentic phrasing principles discussed equally apply to singing or other instrumental sound production.

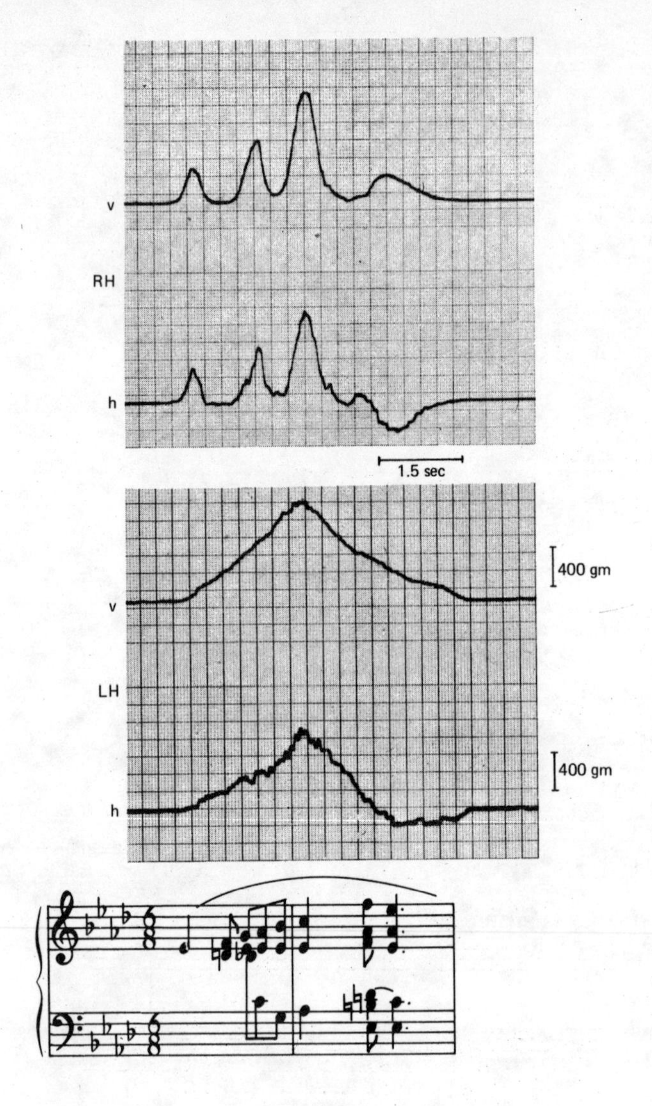

Plate 12. Example II

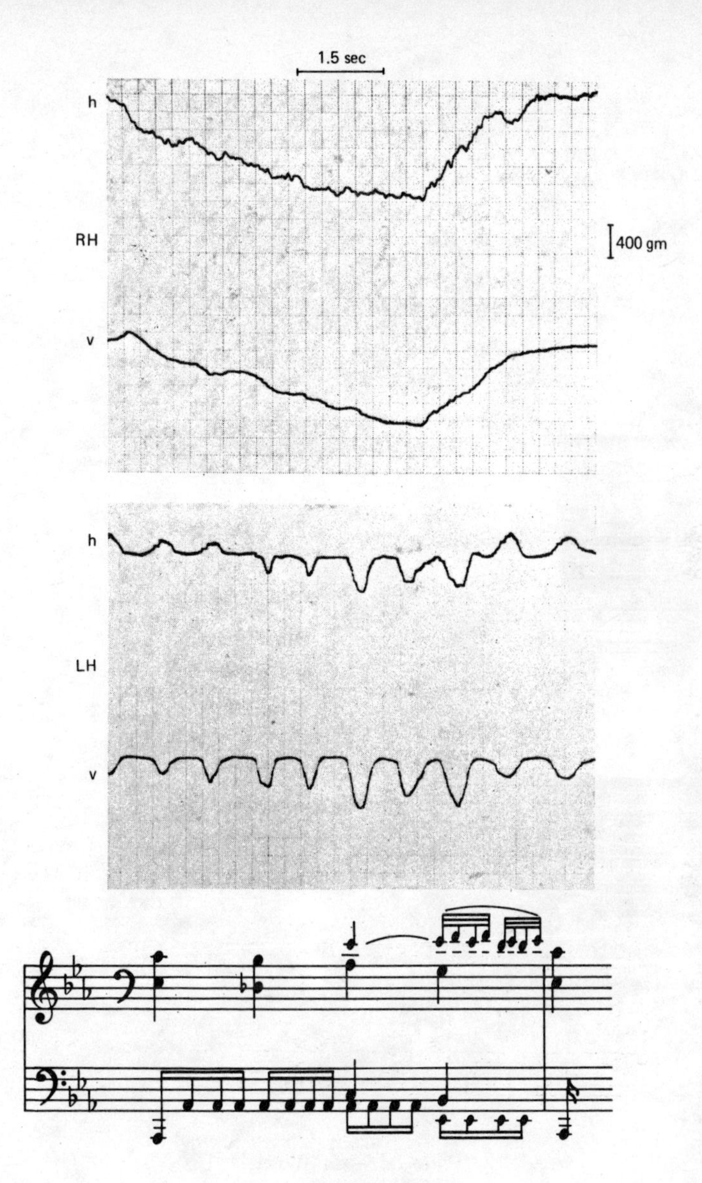

Plate 13. Example III

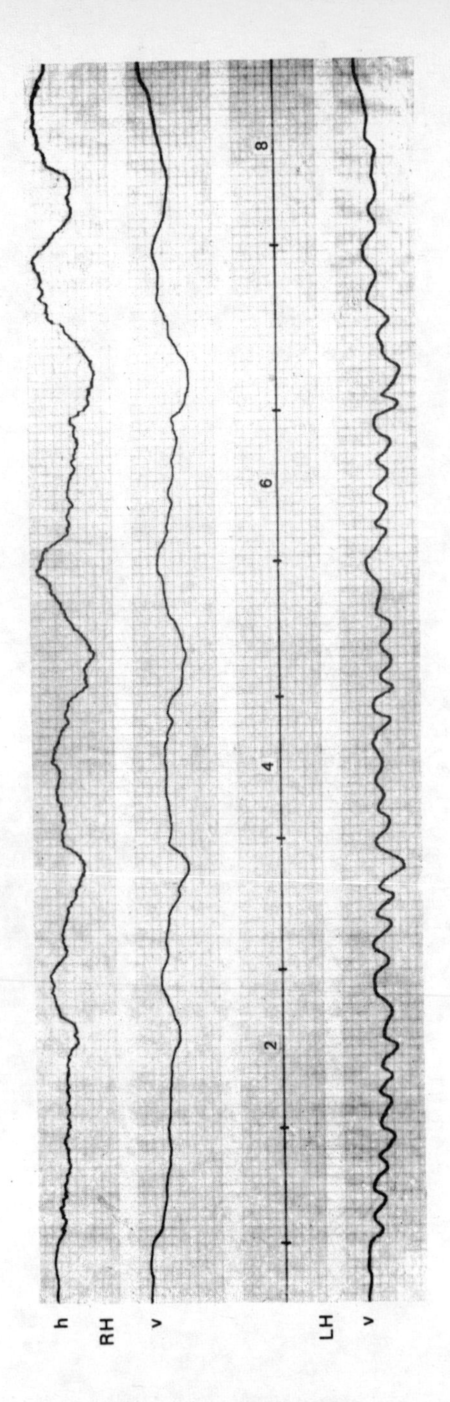

Plate 14. Example IV (a)

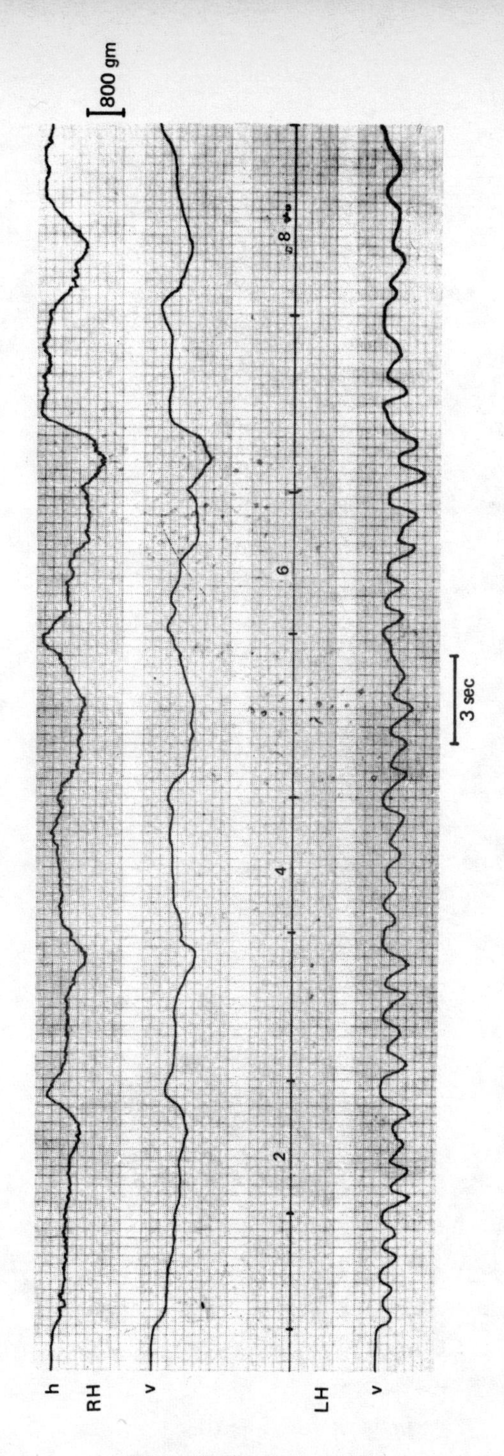

Plate 15. Example IV (b)

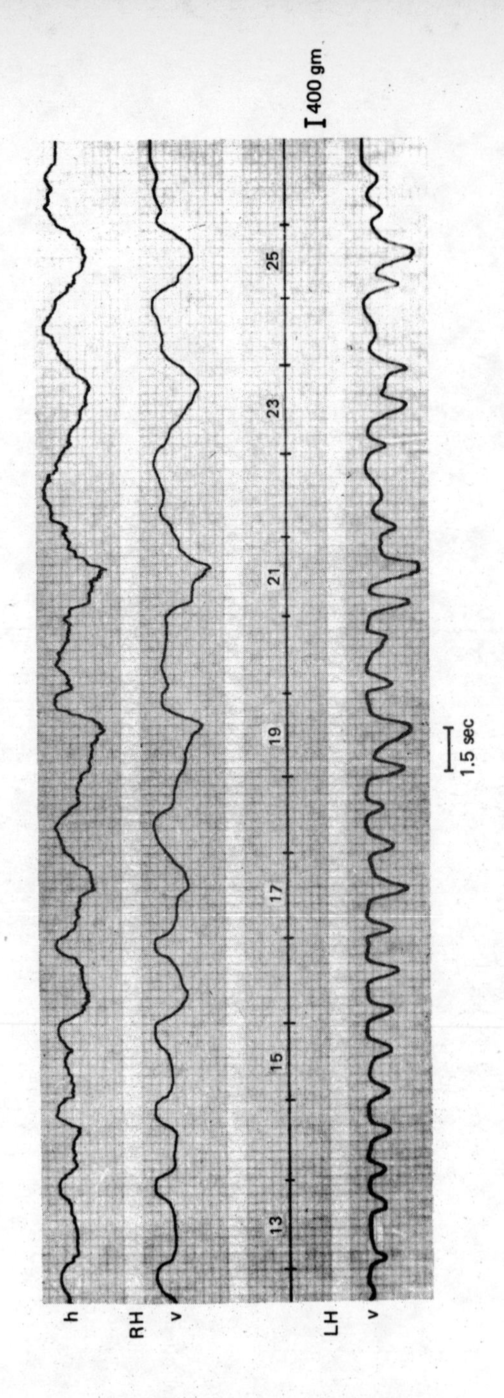

Plate 16. Example V

lightness of the upper body, warmth in the back of the head and back of the neck, and heightened feelings of serenity and "enoughness." This lasted from late afternoon until bedtime.

L.D., M.D. (Psychoanalyst and Psychiatrist, Female) Age 49

First Session (1/9/73) Two Cycles

Experienced emotions as "paired" and opposite, e.g., grief and joy seemed opposed and very intense. More so than other emotions. Felt good for twenty-four to thirty-six hours. Sex was paired with some grief in second cycle.

Second Session (1/15/73) One Cycle

Cycle was unexpectedly interrupted and left me with some tension. I returned to it and released tension. *Cried* when I got to grief and felt rage very intensely. Had two significant dreams after this experience which I could analyze for myself quite well because of *focus* and clarity.

Third Session (1/22/73) One Cycle

A feeling of boredom at first. Partly due to being tired at night. Then a peaceful and "into it" feeling with timelessness in which I seemed to *play* with all the emotions quite calmly and to enjoy it. Slept well. No dreams. Woke feeling well. This day had been one which started with a lot of anger and irritation. So can rate this experience as an excellent one.

M.J. (Psychiatrist and Psychoanalyst, Male) Age 50

First Session (1/15/73) Two Cycles

Noted particularly with emotions of hate and anger there was a repeated need to swallow and, especially with hate, a very severe burning sensation in the throat. The second time around with hate, there was an opening up in my throat and in my breathing for a period of time and an awareness of a passageway of air that I had never really experienced before except once or twice with Al Lowen. The first time around of anger-hate, love-sex, joy, and reverence I felt the strongest feeling, at first with anger. I noticed my lips quivering, something that I've never been aware of before. It also happened with hate, though hate seemed to be a more profound feeling and somewhat colder. The first time around I felt fear with anger and hate. With hate in particular I noticed that what I would do is begin to, at certain points, put myself down for not being as good as other people and that would cut off the feeling and I could see from the experience how putting myself down is really just the reverse of feeling and expressing anger and hatred, particularly hatred. I also noticed that anger was a feeling that I was blocking somehow by not feeling in my arms and my fingers and that I was cutting off and detaching my feelings. Once I became aware of this, I could allow more of the feeling to go into my arms. The flow of energy is something I was quite aware of throughout the whole experience.

Grief seemed to be centered down in my lower abdomen, and it was the hardest of all the emotions to reach. Somehow I got the feeling that it was the one deepest buried in me. I grieve, but I'm afraid to allow myself to feel the grief because then I will feel the hurt and allow myself to be exposed to hurt again, which is, of course, what I need to do in order to fulfill my life.

The experiences I least had confidence in feeling were joy and love. The one that I experienced least the first time around was sex, simply being some pretty girl in the room, but very strongly the second time around with tremendous heat throughout the whole lower part of my body. Then when love came up (I don't remember which came first, now) it was something that was experienced more in the upper part of my body, my shoulders, my chest, and into my heart, and I realized that there was a split, a cutoff between those feelings in my pelvis, the grief in my abdomen, and the love in my chest, and suddenly they all seemed to flow together.

Somehow reverence was the easiest for me; it was just a very quiet meaningful experience in which I was in touch with something which I could not name. Occasionally there were images of the country, where I live, possibly of animals, but primarily it was a contact with something very deep inside me and if it went in any direction, it was upward. I'm also more aware of an attempt to control my feelings, order them, to grasp onto ideas and to force feelings out and to let them flow. I have a real need to be in control of these feelings, rather than to let them control me, or to, at least, let me live them.

One of the physical experiences, the tension of my jaw, at the present time I feel remarkably relaxed, as much as at any time in my life, though there is the sense of the grief inside and the question as to what I can do about it, about reversing everything that I understand that makes for this grief. I think I feel calmer than I've ever felt before in my life.

D.F. (Female) Age 27

Fourth Session (12/2/73)

No Emotion—Mechanical.

Anger—Pressed finger rest very hard. Fantasy of throwing globs of paint at a canvas. Anger phase seemed long.

Hate—Again pressed finger rest hard but had no particular thoughts of hatred. Seemed very, very long and just concentrated on pressing finger rest. Started to look forward to love and joy.

Grief—Same motion as before, pushing down and across—sometimes stroking. Felt sad but peaceful. Tried to think of a way of depicting grief. Started to really get into that but phase was over.

Love—Felt good, caressing finger rest. Thought about children, swinging, laughing. Gentle swaying.

Joy—Also felt good. Finger hopped, light motion. Thought about running, playing, sunshine, and happiness. I am beginning to feel more joy.

Sex—Again, the same rubbing motion. Thought about my body as a whole, sensual object. Thought of paintings of nudes without feelings of disgust but of a natural thing.

Reverence—I am really enjoying reverence more. My finger moved lightly across button, almost a combination of love and joy. Thought about nature—snowing, still and quiet—watching each snowflake fall.

I did the sentic cycles very early in the morning before everyone else was up. At first I didn't feel much except a calmness but I didn't feel tired or drained. Later I felt very happy, peaceful, and sat for a long time looking out the living room window into the back yard. The yard seemed especially beautiful. The only fear I had was that this feeling would go away. I thought about doing the sentic cycles and what the real purpose was for doing them. I felt for the first time I had a glimpse of what was really happening. I felt like my soul had been "tapped" and wondered how incredible it was to have this feeling. Also wished I could feel like this always. I had visions of people walking across my yard and me going out to greet them with warmth and love. I particularly enjoyed the morning—playing with the children, listening to music, reading to them, which was unusual because most of the time I feel annoyed by them.

Several hours after doing the cycles. I still feel good but not as I felt earlier. It is hard to describe how I feel now—almost fearful that I won't feel the same again and a little fearful that I felt so good and peaceful.

In a way, I feel a little silly about my feelings. Also, I am trying to judge them—whether they were good or bad, right or wrong, and whether or not they are appropriate feelings for someone like me (at my age). I started to get the feeling of the tremendous responsibility of these feelings—normally I don't feel responsible for my feelings or I am not aware of my responsibility.

Sixth Session (12/8/73)

Anger—Not much at first but then started to get angry at helpless feelings and anxiety.

Hate—Both in anger and hate I was caught up with my feelings of inadequacy, helplessness, and how I hated to feel that way.

Grief—Can't remember much about grief except the general feeling of grief. Felt very sad and almost like crying but I couldn't.

Love—I don't remember at all what I felt other than feeling frustrated during this cycle. I try to concentrate just on the feeling of love and I can generally get it when I think of the children. I feel rather empty during this cycle—not that I feel unloved, but I feel like my own love for others is thwarted. I realize more and more the difficulty I have in showing, feeling, and expressing my love, but I know it is there. Sometimes I do feel love but it is rare—I wish it could be spontaneous again.

Sex—This phase is getting better all the time! I am getting more and more sexual feelings. Very nice—I enjoy it.

Joy—Thought of warm sun shining on my face—felt good, comfortable. A song was going through my mind. This cycle is also getting a little better, but I keep thinking I should feel more joy like I used to.

Reverence—I started to think about a blade of grass—so simple yet so beautifully created. I started to pray but very differently than before. I seemed to move out of the focus of attention in not asking just for help for myself but asking God to help me understand and see the needs of the people I care for and to help me show my love for them; just to actually look at other people and not only at myself and my problems. It felt so good.

Before I did the cycles I felt nervous and uptight. I noticed my hand was shaking when I started but stopped. Afterwards I felt peaceful and felt that way for the rest of the day. The day was a pleasure—really enjoyable!

G.R. (Female) Age 29

First Session (9/22/72) One Cycle

Have lots of questions. Couldn't stop my mind from working. Weird experience.

Very peaceful—dazed. I'm sort of like in a state of—the Reverence thing got to me. My first image was church and how high the ceilings are, and being a kid, and how it was a sacred place. Then a lot of space above me—enveloped me—almost like drowning, but it was beautiful, comfortable.

No Emotion—I was just being mechanical getting a little bit anxious, but it wasn't controlling me.

Anger—After a while was getting a tingling sensation in my finger. I was very very scared, also very angry. But it gets into a hate thing when it got connected up with a person.

The only time I felt the time was too long was in joy. I wanted to give up, wanted to stop and cry. I couldn't conjure up any joy. I didn't want to.

It wasn't difficult to express anger. Didn't have any specific person's face there. When hate came in I thought about my mother, but anger itself (was not associated with) imagery. Just came out.

It's dangerous to express anger. I'll be hit. I was hyperventilating.

HATE—My first feeling hate was one of every part of me going into some middle part of me, and seething. Almost as though image I had was of looking at someone. I hate, and every part of me is feeling the hate, but not expressing it. Almost like an absence of feeling for person. That's what true hate is. Then anger came in. To me it connected up with a person—my mother. It was just anger afterward.

GRIEF—Right before grief I started feeling very—like the anger was spent. It started waning and I started to feel very sad. When grief came on I wanted to fight the feeling of grief and fought it the whole way. I could feel myself trying and I didn't want to try.

LOVE—During love . . . I just got feeling about people I like, have feelings of love for, one after another, different people. D., he was just holding me and stroking me, just being cradled, and I rocked back and forth. The image of the sun—a lot of warmth—being bathed in warmth. It went in the direction of abandoning myself to the sun, to a person, letting it come in. More receiving than giving.

SEX—I was questioning that love was connected with sex. I resisted. Got in a block. My image was of a man kissing my breasts and caressing me. Then I got the image of a penis coming into me, and I resisted, and then there was a whole image of being forced against my will in a sexual situation of a man trying to make love to me. I think I was trying to get away from my own sexual feeling. I might really get turned on by rape fantasy. Resisted it. Then I started feeling very sad.

When I heard the word joy, I thought, My God, there is no joy. I started thinking of ice cream. Picture of me and my mother. I'm holding on to ice cream cone. Made me very sad that no joy connected with sex. Felt very barren.

I was starting to cry. At one point I tried to get joy through crying, but wasn't feeling it particularly.

REVERENCE—My first image was of a church and God and altar. Gothic image of everything being much much bigger than I was.

Then of infinite space—coming down and enveloping me. How peaceful death must be. Then image of drowning in water and very warm liquid, just as though death was going to rescue me.

Then I felt very very calm.

Second Cycle (*Done separately, on same day*)

Feel really good. It was a different experience, this time, totally. Much more loving and warm. It was just a transition of feelings that carried along. Last time I tried to compartmentalize. This time I just stayed and went along, and experienced an organic kind of transition from one feeling state to another.

NO EMOTION—Just thought of something like "Star Trek." Someplace way in future where I was sitting in a big chair and looking all around me passively. My fantasy was that I had been programmed not to feel any emotion and I was playing that part.

ANGER—I thought of it as my mother trying to slap me or hurt me in some way. It got to be a real struggle. At one point I felt I couldn't get away from being hurt, but I tried to assert myself. Click, she was trying to hurt me and I reacted against that.

My anger was to stave off an attack, to scare person away with my anger. That session seemed very long to me.

HATE—I didn't want to hate. I pictured my mother and I pictured R. I didn't want to hate them because I felt it was a loss on my part, in some way I was the loser. I went into the imagery of when I was with R. the last time and I had been aggressive sexually and he had not responded. I felt I had made a total fool of myself.

Extreme anger and hatred for being made a fool of.

Tremendous effort, in the beginning, to feel hate. Element of my hatred not having an effect, a feeling of helplessness.

GRIEF—Not active at all. Very passive grief. I felt helpless, abandoned, very drained. I felt so helpless that I couldn't even feel grief. Left, like a desolate, empty space. Nobody going to care. Nobody going to come. No point to expressing feeling because no one would come. Effort to push finger rest.

LOVE—I experienced again this image of being rocked, of being cuddled and rocked and stroked, and swaying back and forth. Images of the group I work with coming over. Mostly connected with the group, that was the first place I really allowed myself to feel love.

I could have just swayed on the finger rest button.

Sex—This time it was different. I was resisting feeling sexual. It was almost like an innocent sexual thing. My fantasy was that D. was stroking me in an innocent way. Then it turned into a sexual thing. But my feeling was it was O.K., he wouldn't hurt me. I wouldn't have to give anything in return.

Concentrated on feeling sensations in my vagina. Felt safe down there. Didn't feel it was being violated, felt it was being loved, a very gentle, quiet sex. Not much feeling in my breasts. It was really an evolution of the love segment.

Joy—Was continuation of the sex. Like I got an image of myself looking up into a loving man's face and just feeling good and safe and unthreatened. Started getting images of rolling around on a bed with this man, in slow motion. A very loving, tumbling image. Like it never stopped moving. Very free-flowing, like a free fall. Nothing got in the way. No sharp objects. Warm air cushioning everything. Very loving, protective, receiving.

Reverence—I got an image of being—it was very early in the morning. Sun wasn't up yet, but it was light. Big meadow with trees around. Very still, except for the sound of birds. I felt I could have stood there for a very long time, just being part of this quiet scene. There was nothing to fight. I could just have laid down and looked at the sky—at one with my surroundings.

There was a house somewhere, and the man would still be there. It was O.K. to be alone, because there was love.

Many of these reports are of the very first sentic cycle session ever done by the subject, following only a few minutes' instruction. The depth of experience and satisfactions made possible by the simple, yet profoundly affecting meditative rite of sentic cycles continues to astonish users well after their initial experience. With their finger rests and sentic cycle tape they can do sentic cycles at home, whenever they feel the need, whenever they wish to affirm their sense of belonging. For many it is an opening of a new and better world, a door to security for which they have received the key.

Sentic Cycles and Psychosomatic Stress

Each sentic state is accompanied by specific somatic experience.* For example, a person who experiences anger may have a sensation of limbs tending to be torn apart and of certain abdominal tension. But the nature of repressive processes makes it possible to repress some aspects of the sentic state, while experiencing parts of the somatic experience (or "virtual body image"). A person may remain aware of only part of this total phenomenon while no longer knowing that it is part of his anger, nor what specific situation may have given rise to it. Such partial, incomplete virtual body images may also appear from time to time in a person's awareness, as a truncated form of his original experience.

Another way in which a suppressed sentic state continues to function, without the individual's being aware of its cognitive connection, is by a specific physiologic shunting that concentrates on selected aspects of the virtual body image. (Selected portions of the virtual body image may be transformed into specific physiologic consequences—e.g., specific body tension such as stomach cramps, tics, and the like.) Virtual body images are quite specific and differ even for the various shades of the sentic states, and so particular psychosomatic symptoms in effect may be seen as somatic traces of the specific character of the sentic state from which they arise. Chronic set posture and facial expression also may be considered often to result from similar dynamics.

Longer-Range Effects of Doing Sentic Cycles

The expression of these sentic states during sentic cycles tends to free the individual from these unaware, accumulated somatic memories. Although each sentic state experience has a temporary effect, alleviation through sentic cycles is cumulative over a period of time. The associated fantasy processes appear gradually to be effective in reorganizing the dynamics, so that a new integration can take place. These processes include elements of catharsis, of abreaction, of

* We consider some aspects of this characteristic experience a "virtual body image" and describe the phenomenon in the following chapter.

desensitization, and of forming new associations. This makes it possible for sentic cycles to be helpful in cases of phobias, in addition to the alleviation of non-specific anxiety.

Long-term results of sentic cycle experience show facilitation rather than habituation of the effects. Instead of requiring greater and greater doses for a given effect, the effectiveness of sentic cycles persists, and may even increase. Thus, Mrs. D.S., a thirty-eight-year-old nurse who learned to do sentic cycles at the NYU Nursing School, writes after two years that her tape broke, and asks for a replacement. She adds, parenthetically almost:

> My usual pattern is to play the cycle on two consecutive days each week. This is what I have been doing irregularly for the past year. Obviously there have been some positive results for me while doing sentic cycles. I pay particular attention to my posture before starting the tape. The most persistent personal change not altered by intermittent use of the tape has been my ability to experience the emotions without fantasizing. The over-all feeling I experience after each cycle is relaxation sufficient to fall asleep accompanied by an awareness that I have energy to do any tasks that I may want to.
>
> The general effect on me personally is an ability to experience the emotions more fully, or quickly, as they are triggered in day-to-day living. I feel more at ease with people and less tense in stress-producing situations. I have more arguments, but also more orgasms. These effects diminish when I discontinue the cycles.

A particularly interesting case involves a paralyzed subject who has been doing sentic cycles every day for over two years. Because of the theoretical interest of this case, we shall describe it in some detail.

Mrs. C.N., who lives in Denver, contacted me in May 1972 expressing her desire to experience sentic cycles. It was not she, however, who wrote, but her nurse: Mrs. C.N. had been paralyzed from the neck down for many years, suffering from multiple sclerosis. The letter posed a problem we had not yet encountered. With her arms and legs paralyzed, how could she possibly do sentic cycles?

If the sentic theories are correct, then it should not matter which part of the body is used to express the essentic forms, as long as the movement has sufficient degrees of freedom (the number of dimensions in which movement is free to occur). So I designed a chin rest for Mrs. C.N. (she could move her chin and neck) to be used instead of the finger rest! During a trip to California, I stopped in Denver to give her this chin rest and to instruct her in its use.

Mrs. C.N. was in such an advanced state of the disease that in addition to her bodily paralysis her two eyes rolled independently of one another. One eye had to be covered by a patch to avoid double vision, and even then her uncovered eye moved largely uncontrollably. Now in her late forties, Mrs. C.N. has been suffering from multiple sclerosis for over twenty years. She is totally unable to move her body below the neck, and has to be positioned and carried from place to place. At night her husband must turn her over every one and a half hours, which he has dutifully done for many years. At the time of my visit, the emotional state of Mrs. C.N. was poor, not surprisingly. She had previously attempted suicide through an overdose of pills. A tracheotomy had been performed to allow her to breathe during the drug overdose coma, and as a result, she had lost a good deal of her voice. Her paralyzed condition left Mrs. C.N. with little opportunity to express her grief, frustration, and anger in the way other people can.

In less than an hour Mrs. C.N. learned to express essentic form with her chin on the chin rest and found it quite natural. Her first experience of sentic cycles was a truly spine-chilling experience for me. When she expressed anger and grief there was such concentrated, powerful intensity in her expression that I could hardly continue. But when it came time to express joy she said, "I cannot do joy, there is nothing that gives me joy." For some moments, I did not know what to answer, but then I said, "Imagine you are perfectly well and you are playing outside in the sunshine, and express that!" Mrs. C.N. tried, and found that it worked: she could do this. The next problem was with reverence. The patient said, "The only thing I can feel reverence for is my husband, he has been so good to me all these years. As far as any outside force is concerned—God or nature—I can only feel intense anger and resentment at the injustice of my affliction." With some reluctance, I agreed that she might think of her husband in terms of reverence and Mrs. C.N. finished her first cycle. She had cried during grief and said that this was the first time in many years she had been able to experience some of these emotions. Thereafter, Mrs. C.N. has kept a regular schedule of doing one sentic cycle at ten-thirty every morning. Her nurse puts on the tape for her and positions her with the chin rest, and she has been doing this every day for over two years.

Even within the first two or three weeks a change occurred in her personality. She became less resentful, more calm and cheerful and outgoing. After three months a transformation had taken place in her relationships with her family and others. She became more interested in them, and smiled and was talkative when her husband came home at night from work, instead of complaining and being resentful. She looked forward to her half hour of "sentics" every day and would not allow any disturbance to interrupt her routine. I saw her altogether only three times during the first year. On one visit I was told by the new nurse (who didn't know who I was) that Mrs. C.N. was doing her sentics and could not be disturbed! As the year progressed the improvement continued and became more pervasive, so much so that it came to be a real pleasure to be in Mrs. C.N.'s company; a radiance seemed to issue from her that affected others who came in contact with her. She now could enjoy music, and although her paralysis had not diminished, she slept better, suffered less from pain, and could tolerate it more easily when it occurred. She also required considerably less supportive medicine. Near the end of the first year she had a serious accident. She had been positioned improperly and toppled from her chair, smashing part of her upper jaw, tearing her lip and breaking some teeth. Doing sentics during this time allowed her to get over the psychological effects of the accident with little emotional trauma.

Six months later, she was asked whether she was not getting tired of doing the same set of emotions every day. Would she not like additional ones, such as envy or hope, or substitute them for some of the others. She said, "I am satisfied with doing these. I already *have* hope through doing the others so I don't need to do hope." A year later she still feels the same way.

One of the benefits Mrs. C.N. says she is getting from her sentic cycle experience is that it lets her cry in a gentle way during the grief phase, without the violent spasms that used to wrack her without giving her any real emotional release. She is able to cry in this fashion every day and enjoys the experience. Interestingly, she changed her manner of expressing love within the first few months. Initially, she had been asked to express love, as she would the other emotions, with an opening movement of her jaw. But she discovered that she preferred expressing love with a turning to and fro of her neck, moving the jaw sideways over the chin rest in a caressing manner. Of course, there was no reason to object to this; it was a mode of action she also chose for expressing reverence. In these ways we were learning from her.

The experience of Mrs. C.N. demonstrates the continued long-term effect of sentic cycles and the ability of the incapacitated to benefit from their experience. In changing her own expression and personality, Mrs. C.N. also changed the family atmosphere dramatically and brought an increased enjoyment of life to all around her. To quite an extent, Mrs. C.N. became aware that although her body was not functioning, her mind and her person were sound; her disease could not really touch that part of her that was most herself.†

† In some ways it may have helped her to discover these aspects of her person more than if she had been healthy. She had the advantage of being able to stick to a schedule that allowed for a daily sentic cycle experience. Healthy individuals seldom would be willing to submit themselves to such a stringent schedule.

TEN

The Nature of Sentic Experience: Further Elaborations of Sentic Theory

In this chapter we shall consider further aspects of the development of sentic theory and experimental findings. We will examine aspects of the nature of sentic experience, the physiological processes associated with it, and verifiable predictions that sentic theory can make concerning that experience.

Satisfaction

Traditional psychology has encountered difficulties in studying the precision of emotional communication also partly as a result of its attempting to view and grade its qualities of experience in terms of a single dimension—a single "gray scale" of pleasant/unpleasant. But there is no equivalent shade of gray to which emotional pleasures can be meaningfully reduced by ignoring other important dimensions of quality.* Pleasures vary in their degree of pervasiveness (the

* As is possible, for example, with the phenomenon of color. The range of all colors may be projected into a single black and white scale by ignoring hue and saturation and by preserving an equivalent intensity (brightness).

capacity of some pleasures to satisfy a range of urges for various durations and to cause other urges to abate), and they vary also in the type of satisfaction that follows them. They selectively exclude and include other satisfactions and pleasures as part of their process. Thus pleasures may enhance or inhibit other pleasures, and other needs and urges may be stimulated or suppressed.

How to compare the excitement of an amusement ride to the peace of a Bach cantata, the pleasure of a sunny morning to the beauty of storm, or the joy of color to the majesty of the starry night? Each has its time and place, and, outside of this, its effective quality changes too. Each has its time and place also in the context of man's life. The very concept of quality gives pleasures an order that depends on other dimensions than that of intensity. What are these dimensionalities?

Among the many words and concepts of natural language giving rise to confusion in regard to natural brain processes, few are more enigmatic and unresearched than the notion of "satisfaction." The concepts of beauty, goodness, and justice have given rise to whole fields of inquiry, but the concept of satisfaction has not received similar attention from philosophers. Perhaps for this reason, the unclarified concept is acting as a rampant weed in our culture. Psychologists, as well as Freud and his followers, have not given it a large measure of consideration, nor have the physiologists. Perhaps the worst thing that one can say about a concept is that everybody assumes he knows what it means. The study of sentics and of the effect of sentic cycles, however, may help clarify some of the dynamic principles of satisfaction.

The word itself has the Latin roots *satis* and *facere*, "to make sated." If we inquire further as to the meaning of "sated" the dictionary refers us to "the 'satisfaction' of hunger or of desire," or "to quieten"—a circuitous route! But if we consider examples of the experience of satisfaction, we notice that when hunger is satisfied there exists a feeling that is not merely the absence of hunger, but a distinct feeling of its own. And when we complete defecation there exists a feeling that is not merely the absence of the urge to defecate but also has a quality of its own. Indeed, after we have emptied the bladder, sneezed, or scratched in response to an itch, there is in each case a feeling of satisfaction that has a quality of its own and lasts for a period of time, fading into nothing before a new build-up phase begins. At the end of orgasm, too, there are a number of sensations that have a quality of their own.

"To make quiet" is an insufficient description of what these processes have in common. They do share some dynamic properties of what are called relaxation "oscillators," and the fact that such distinctive qualities of sensation of "satisfaction" occur at the end of the discharge period. That these phenomena do occur at those times in the cycle implies a bimodal neuronal organization, since the "satisfaction" sensation is not coincidental with the discharge phase but follows it.

On the other hand, there is another type of satisfaction. Many sensations and qualities can give satisfaction without a build-up period and discharge phase—for example, lying in the sun or savoring the greenness of grass. The sight of the ocean or of a snowy mountain peak or of the starry skies—not replaceable by looking at reproductions—these qualities appear to be integral functions of our nervous system programming that require the dimension of space itself.

In earlier chapters we have talked about the satisfaction of expressing essentic form. If we now consider the organization of them into sentic cycles, we observe that the specific new satisfactions provided by sentic cycles indicate the presence of elements of both types. The experience and expression of emotion provide one aspect. Its own quality of peace, if it affords it, is itself a satisfaction, lasting for some time. And the memory of that peace is another kind of satisfaction, that tells one that it is there "for the asking."

Sentic Theory and Freud

Let us compare the principles of sentic theory with some views of Freud. Freud tended to shy away from experience of generalized emotion, emotion that he could not verbalize in terms of associations. For example, in *The Moses of Michelangelo* Freud writes:

> Works of art do exercise a powerful effect on me, especially those of literature and sculpture, less often of painting. This has occasioned me, when I have been contemplating such things, to spend a long time before them trying to apprehend them in my own way, i.e. to explain to myself what their effect is due to. *Whenever I cannot do this, as for instance with music, I am almost incapable of obtaining any pleasure* [my emphasis]. Some rationalistic, or perhaps analytic, turn of mind in me rebels against being moved by a thing without knowing why I am thus affected and what it is that affects me.

And in *Civilization and Its Discontents* he states:

> It is not easy to deal scientifically with feelings. One may attempt to describe their physiological signs. Where that is impossible—I am afraid the oceanic feeling, too, will defy this kind of classification—nothing remains but to turn to the ideational content which most readily associates itself with the feeling.

Such a constrained attitude of unwillingness to free the emotions from the content-bound personal and social setting seems part of a certain rigor of Freud's own personality. Yet with his perspicacity, in *The Relation of the Poet to Daydreaming* he is well aware that

> Many things which if they happened in real life could produce no pleasure can nevertheless give enjoyment in play—many emotions which are essentially painful may become a source of enjoyment to the spectators and hearers of a poet's work.

Faced with an apparent paradox, he amazingly resorts to the word "technique" as a rescue:

> You will remember that we said the daydreamer hid his fantasies carefully from other people because he had reason to be ashamed of them. I may now add that even if he were to communicate them to us, he would give us no pleasure by his disclosures. When we hear such fantasies they repel us, or at least leave us cold. But when a man of literary talent presents his plays, or relates what we take to be his personal daydreams, we experience great pleasure arising probably from many sources. How the writer accomplished this is his innermost se-

> cret; the essential *ars poetica* lies in the technique by which our feeling of repulsion is overcome, and this has certainly to do with those barriers erected between every individual being and all others.

Indeed, we may say so now, if the "technique" includes empathy, being faithful to pure essentic form—abolishing inanimate artifice in favor of the precise attentive passion of inwardly listened to and communicated living forms.

It seems that, for Freud, in real life the self-protective dynamics predominate over the dynamics of giving† and over the seductive contagion in emotional communication. Concerning the principle "love thy neighbor as thyself" he says in *Civilization and Its Discontents:*

> If he is a stranger to me and cannot attract me by any value he has in himself or any significance he may have already acquired in my emotional life, it will be hard for me to love him. I shall be doing wrong if I do, for my love is valued as a privilege by all those belonging to me . . .
>
> When I look more closely I find still further difficulties. Not merely is this stranger on the whole not worthy of love, but to be honest, I must confess he has more claim to my hostility, even to my hatred. He does not seem to have the least trace of love for me, does not show me the slightest consideration. If it will do him any good, he has no hesitation in injuring me, never even asking himself whether the amount of advantage he gains by it bears any proportion to the amount of wrong done to me. What is more, he does not even need to get an advantage from it; if he can merely get a little pleasure out of it, he thinks nothing of jeering at me, insulting me, slandering me, showing his power over me: and the more secure he feels himself, or the more helpless I am, with so much more certainty can I expect this behavior from him towards me.

† Expressing an emotion is a form of giving—the concept of "giving" and its ramifications in sentic theory as related to satisfaction are very significant. A kiss, for example, has potentially a "giving" component that transcends the mutual sensory excitation involved. Sentic "giving" is also contained in a blessing and in a curse. "Giving" in relation to sentic experience shall be treated more fully in another book.

As we read this we may have a curious bifurcated response—we can see an obvious rightness in these rather mole-like remarks, whose view leaves the initiative to the other fellow, but we may feel strongly that, in a different context, they are quite wrong.

Perhaps if Freud really heard Beethoven's last works, for example, he would have valued the mutual reality of generalized emotions (and the function of pre-sentic control) as dimensions additional to the personal and social realms of which he was a master. He could not readily tap that intrinsic source of joy, belonging, and happiness, nor could those millions who followed him exclusively. If he could have done so, the concepts of being "worthy of love" and "love valued as a privilege" would have seemed meaningless to him in that context. Sentic studies demonstrate how human beings, regardless of race, sex, and, to a large extent, age, can experience sentic states and their relationship as a part of human heritage.

Cognitive Aspects of Generalized Emotion

In a quite special way, emotion and knowledge are not as mutually exclusive as is commonly supposed. Knowledge of emotions is more than an acquaintance with their special character. Each sentic state, generalized or not, seems to imply almost a world view as part of its nature. Such a view may not be formulated in specific terms, yet it seems to be implicit. (Actually, we frequently confuse the cause or recipient of an emotion with the state itself as a cognitive influence.) It may most clearly be seen in the experience of generalized emotion.

An important aspect of the special experience of sentic cycles is that corresponding to the various sentic states that make up the cycle; one experiences a succession of attitudes. That is, with each successive state one experiences the particular world view of that state. To know these attitudes intimately and clearly is to be conscious of aspects of human nature which we usually call "intuitive" or "instinctive." Recognizing these as cognitive sentic processes helps to clarify the concept of the "intuitive": attitudes and distinctions implied are not so much the result of specific situational content, but seem to be part of the nature of the quality itself, experienced in its generalized form.‡

Some cognitive distinctions can be related to the nature of the horizontal component of the essentic form. The horizontal component may be strongly away from the body, or only slightly, or may be toward the body, implying rejection or acceptance, and what lies behind these words.

Another such cognitive implication is reflected in the experimental observation that in certain aspects the essentic form of *hate* does not have its formal opposite in the essentic form of *love*, but in that of *hope* (See Plate 9): the opposite of hate, in terms of essentic form, is not love but hope! If we think about this, we may recognize that there is a sense of destroying life or killing in hate; but hope implies an engendering and nurturing of life. Another example is reflected in the essentic form of guilt which generally has a strongly aggressive component directed toward the body. (It appears somewhat like hate directed inward.)

Particularly significant are cognitive aspects of the experience of certain states of bliss, in which the state itself appears to give knowledge of interrelatedness.

These cognitive aspects also ensure that, although hope, for example, may be irrational and irreducible, the irrational can become rational on a different level of integration: sentic states are used rationally in sentic cycles or in music.

But precisely because of the cognitive aspect, the negative emotions (generalized or specific) such as hate, even in subliminal forms, also produce the familiar "emotional bias." We cannot do without the "knowledge" of emotion because we cannot do without emotion (conscious or repressed).

A clearer understanding of the distinctions between generalized versus specifically directed emotion, the Apollonian and Dionysian experience of the state, and the actor and spectator point of view

‡ There was a strong interest in the nineteenth century in these matters, e.g., the cognitive relationship of joy described poetically by Schiller in his "ode to Joy": brotherhood is seen to be a result of joy—not the other way around, as is often presumed.

would make it easier to find rational, enriching ways of integrating sentic states and their cognitive implications into our lives.

Sentic Afterimages

We regard sentic states as a special class of qualities. One of the known characteristics of *sensory* qualities is that they have afterimages. (For example, after looking at a bright light, we can see an image of it if we close our eyes.) We might expect, therefore, that the experienced qualities of sentic states could also display analogous phenomena—that there should be sentic afterimages, or, to use a seemingly more appropriate term, sentic "after-experience" as distinguished from satisfaction as such. (The term "afterimage" however does refer to all forms of sensory stimulation, not just the visual.)

Afterimages must not be confused with the memory of the experience itself. Some forms of afterimages appear to persist in the same quality as the original stimulus; other afterimages sometimes indicate the opposite quality of the originating stimulus. (Thus, the afterimage of a bright light is a bright image, but the afterimage of purple is green, and vice versa.) During afterimages, we are generally less sensitive to the same stimulus—an aspect of refractoriness.* (For example, a loud sound raises the threshold of hearing.) Some sensory modalities such as temperature sensors include after-sensations that may not be easy to separate from the other bodily sensations that accompany them (e.g., the glow felt after a warm bath).

The nature of *sentic* afterimages is not yet fully understood. It is clear, however, that the order of sentic states experienced in sentic cycles has a considerable effect on the specific experience of each state. For example, the relationship between Grief and Love is such that Love is facilitated after Grief. In the reverse order, however, the specific experience of Grief is also affected—but not facilitated—by the immediately preceding state of Love. Each state appears to cast its shadow on the following ones in a way that needs more study.

* A refractory period is that period of insensitivity to a stimulus that follows excitation.

Hormonal and other bodily changes accompanying each specific state produce a distinct cumulative pattern for every sentic state sequence. This happens because hormones secreted into the bloodstream as one state is established are not removed immediately upon generation of the next state. This is another example of unidirectional rate sensitivity (URS) applied to sentic state systems.

The duration of sentic state afterimages is generally several times as long as the corresponding sentic state experience within the sentic cycle. One of the difficulties in the study of sentic afterimages is that we have no words to denote their specific sensations. We need also to distinguish between the gradual self-extinction of the sentic state and the phenomenon of the afterimage. Pronounced afterimages require stimuli of strong intensity. The same may be said to be true of sentic afterimages; very mild sentic states may produce negligible afterimages.

Afterimages can help us to understand the nature of opposites, as programmed within our nervous system. For instance, a purple afterimage is produced by a strong green light because the dynamic balance between green and purple in terms of inhibition and excitation has been disturbed by habituation to the green stimulus.

Similarly, sentic afterimages may help us to clarify the nature of the sentic spectrum to determine which sentic states might be considered as opposites. The ability to generate sentic states in the laboratory, repeatedly and reliably, by the method described, makes it possible to discover the dynamic meaning of opposites in regard to sentic states and to enlarge on and clarify these problems.

Virtual Body Images

As each sentic state is actually experienced, generated by our method, one's body becomes very quiet. This makes it easy for subjects to observe the bodily sensations that accompany each sentic state, sensations that are quite apart from the experience of each separate expression. We call them "steady state sensations," meaning thereby that they are experienced as part of the state iself, and not specifically with the transient expression. The sensations are quite different for each state. For love there tends to be a sensation of flow appearing to come from within the torso, flowing outward to the limbs and through the neck. There is a steady sensation of flow, without a sense of diminution of substance at the region from which the flow appears to originate. There seems to be no actual physiologic process of the body giving rise to this body image; changes in blood flow do not correspond to this feeling. And, of course, there is no substance that actually flows in the way that is felt.

Similarly, with joy there is a specific sense of lightness and floating. The characteristic sensation of anger feels as if the body is tending to be torn apart. The induced heaviness of grief, or the sense of loss of boundary of the body in reverence—all these do not correspond to physiologic visceral processes, yet are very specific and consistent. Our method of repeatedly generating sentic states makes it possible to oberve these body images with a special focus, since the rest of the body—apart from the exertion of finger pressure—becomes very quiet. Our observations lead us to conclude that these images are programmed projections of the nervous system. What does this mean?

To project a sensation into space is a normal, though highly remarkable, function of the sense of hearing and of vision. (We do not sense *at* the retina, or normally *at* the eardrum.) We do not feel photons hitting the eye (as we would expect to sense a small fly hitting it) or sound waves hitting the ear, but automatically project that they come from some outside region of space. We "sense at a distance," unlike the sensing of warm or cold, of touch, or of taste. (The projection takes place monocularly and monaurally as well, of course.)

This capacity is available to other sense modalities under certain circumstances, as has been demonstrated by G. Bekesy. Bekesy was able to produce a sensation of touch five to eight feet away from the body by phasing two vibrators placed on the chest some distance apart in a manner similar to stereophonic hearing of the two ears. (He could make the sensation of touch move about in space outside the body by adjusting the relative phases of the two vibrators.) And, of course, the phenomenon of the plantom limb is a well-known example of a different kind.

We propose that the characteristic sensation of flow for love and other specific sensations characteristic of each separate sentic state are projected virtual body images, specifically programmed into the nervous system.†

In addition to the virtual body images, there may of course be sensations of actual physiologic changes such as abdominal tension, crying, changes in the sexual organs, and so forth. Some of these changes also can be perceived differently, depending on the sentic state within which they occur. For example, tears during the state of grief have a very different sensation from the tears produced by an irritation of the eye. But, as has been pointed out by the critics of the James-Lange theory (the theory that emotion *is* the experience of bodily changes that occur when you have an emotion), these actual physiologic changes are not synchronized in time with the initial emotion state and their perception cannot in itself be taken to represent the nature of the emotion.

The theory of virtual body images for specific sentic states in some ways appears to reconcile the different viewpoints of traditional theories of emotion, as represented by the polar opposites of the James-Lange and Cannon theories and their offshoots. (The Cannon theory holds that emotion is experienced centrally by the brain and that experience of emotion is possible without sensations of or from the body.)

For every sentic state there is a programmed virtual body image which includes specific "virtual" sensations along with specific posture, and motor activity. These sensations are "virtual" only in the sense that there is no directly corresponding physiologic realization of the sensation e.g. of "flow" for love, or lightness for joy, etc. But of course, they are very real experiences.

Each emotion appears to have its characteristic sensory projection gestalt. If we speak of waves of anger coming over us, the lassitude of grief, gut reactions of hate, the lightness of joy, these are more than figures of speech; there appear to be clear, separate virtual images that correspond to each specific emotion.

We may distinguish between the actual body behavior that is kin-

† These images, in fact, include the direction and magnitude of gravitation (e.g., the "lightness" of joy and "heaviness" of grief). See Chapter Fourteen.

esthetically sensed, such as contractions of abdominal muscles during the emotion of hate, or crying during grief and associated respiratory behavior, on the one hand, and sensory projections which are experienced but have no direct observable body motor activity. Further, the abdominal muscle contractions accompanying the expression of hate are sensed very differently from similar muscular contractions related to tickling or to preparedness before jumping. In each case, when muscle changes are driven by a different sentic state, there is an entirely different sensation.

The ability to generate emotion through initially focusing on a concept may be considered in relation to the studies on "cognitive labeling" of Schachter and Singer. Their well-known studies have indicated that injection of epinephrine, producing an arousal state, tends to predispose an individual to be in an emotional state, but without specifying what state; then an additional influence is required to induce a specific emotion, an influence they have called "labeling." Our studies however show that it is possible to begin by "labeling," and then produce sentic states which may in turn have hormonal consequences.

Electric Activity of the Brain in Relation to Sentic States

The changing observable electric behavior of the brain is related to conscious events like the tip of an iceberg to its mass. Two distinct aspects of electric activity in the human brain can be recorded from the scalp at various sites, both of which belong to the iceberg as much as to the tip.

The first method involves measuring the pattern of electric activity accompanying *a particular event* such as a perception, an expressive movement, or a specific experience retrieved from memory. These patterns of electric behavior are confined to a few seconds or less and can be observed at various sites. During this time one can observe contributions to the activity from various regions of the brain. These regions come into operation sequentially, in general, and the sequence is characteristic of the particular event. The timing

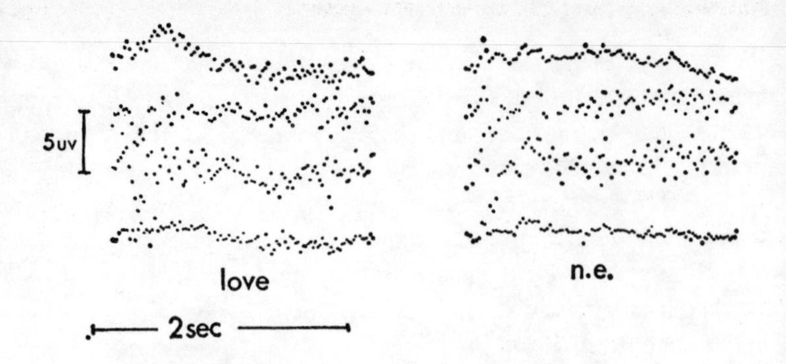

Figure 26. Average changes in electric brain potentials during the expression of love and also during the expression of no emotion. The essentic form of love is reflected in the top trace, representing the left frontal lead, while other occipital and frontal leads do not show this form. Early activity especially notable in the occipital leads includes auditory response to the click. Note that the form bears a resemblance to the essentic form of love as measured through the finger pressure transducer. The response on the right is shown for comparison, as a control, with the absence of the love-modulated E-acton. (Leads are left frontal, left occipital, right occipital, and right frontal; all leads are referred to a common vertex lead. Average of one hundred actons.)

and the sequential nature of the response from each region are precise and give us information relating to the event. (See Chapter One for responses to color and visual form.)

This kind of electric activity, however, represents only a very small, hidden part of the total electric activity of the brain at any one moment. There are always many other events occurring in the brain, which obscure the specific one in which we happen to be interested. In order to measure the "hidden" activity, called "evoked potentials," it is necessary to observe the activity during many such similar events and average the responses. By doing this, activity that is not related to the event tends to be averaged out, and, conversely, activity related to the event is reinforced. Often as many as two hundred repetitions may be necessary to obtain sufficient and accurate measures of evoked potentials. Figures 26 and 27 illustrate aspects of the electric activity of the brain related to the production of essential form.

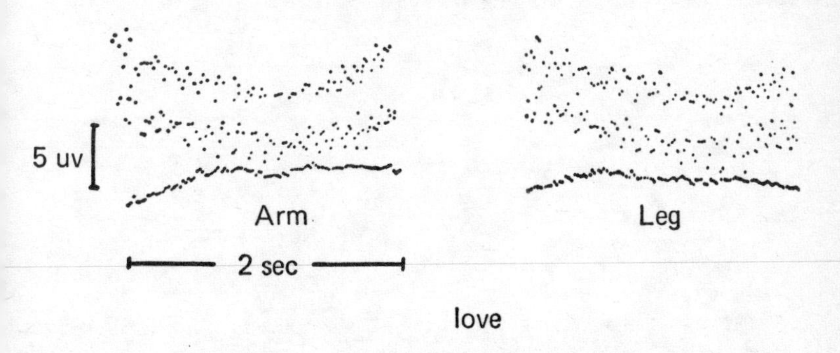

Figure 27. A similar response as in *Figure 26* in another subject, but this time comparing essentic form produced by the finger pressure with that through pressure of the foot. The similarity of the shapes observed illustrates the independence of essentic form from the output modality chosen to express it.

The second aspect involves measuring the total *ongoing* electric activity of the brain at various sites on the scalp and observing changes in time. This total recorded ongoing activity is known as the EEG or electroencephalogram. The character of this activity varies at different locations and changes according to the state of the individual. The well-known alpha, delta, and theta waves are examples of components of the total brain activity. Not only the presence or absence of such components but their relationship between various regions of the brain—front to back, right to left—may be considered significant. Considerable changes also occur in the degree of synchronicity between different portions of the brain.

All these aspects are found to change during experience of different sentic states. Each sentic state affects the brain's electrical activity in specific ways. It is possible to use such changes to constitute an index, and the index may even be used as a bio-feedback measure. The best bio-feedback, however, is the experience of the sentic state itself—an inherent feedback. Specific changes in electric activity of the brain during sentic states are shown in Figures 28–30. Much work needs to be done to study these changes further.

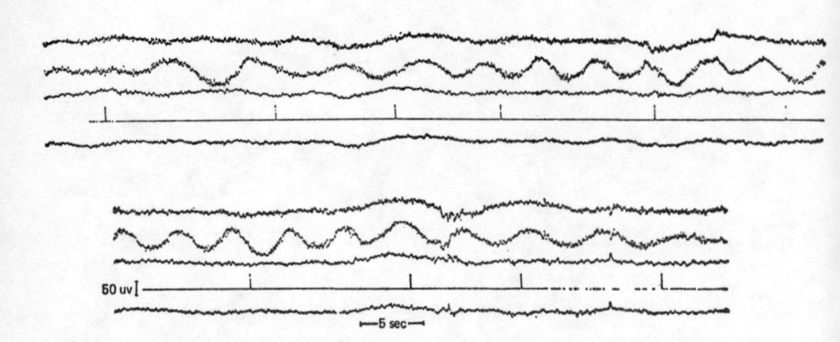

Figure 28. Very large slow waves observed in the second trace (left occipital lead) during the phase of reverence. Such slow waves are not normally encountered in the observed electric behavior recorded from the scalp. These remarkable waves persisted for over one minute, and have a period of 4–5.5 seconds per cycle and an amplitude of over 100 microvolts. The pulse on the fourth trace indicates the soft clicks initiating the E-actons. (Leads from top to bottom: left occipital, right occipital, left frontal, right frontal.)

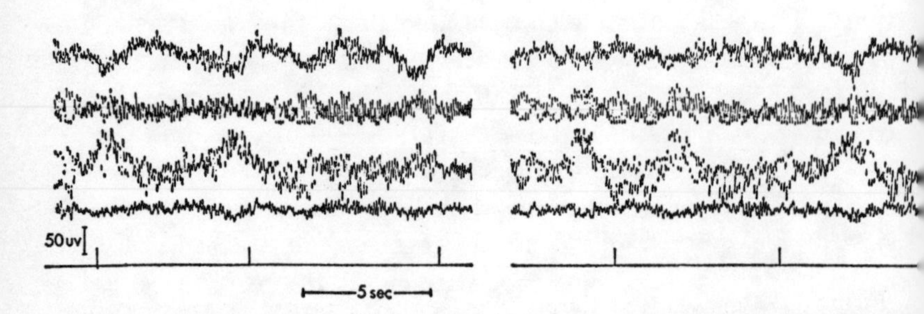

Figure 29. Selective presence of large slow waves on the right occipital lead primarily (third trace from the top) during the love phase.

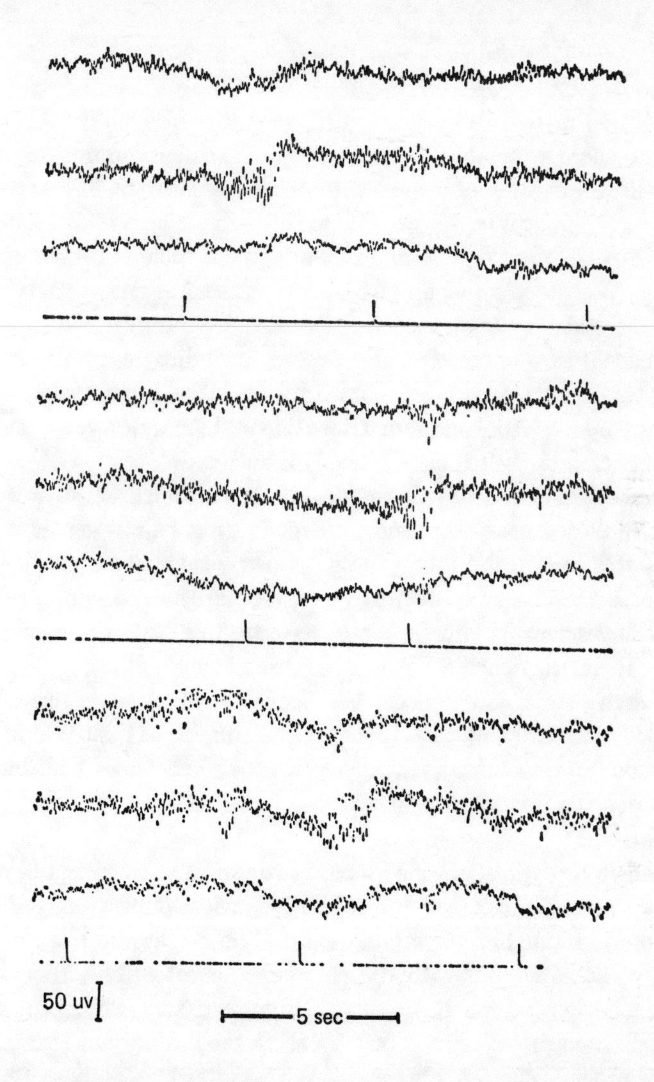

Figure 30. Shift bursts as shown here are often observed during anger, in single leads and sometimes in two or more leads at a time. These shifts in the base DC level are of considerable magnitude and persist for some time after the burst associated with it. (The second trace of the top example demonstrates such a shift most dramatically.) This type of behavior is observed quite frequently and sometimes at a regular periodicity. The bursts do not seem to be phase-related to the individual actons. (Leads as in *Figure* 29.)

An Objective Sentic Measure of Intensity

Sentic theory is concerned with the identity of qualities. There is a one-to-one correspondence between specific essentic forms and corresponding qualities of experience. However, essentic form as such does not define the degree of intensity—the dimension of intensity of a quality is *not* represented in a one-to-one manner by the essentic form. We noted in Chapter Seven that the intensity with which a specific state is experienced is influenced by the degree of openness of perceptual and conceptual processes, including repression and the process we have called the "point of view." The intensity and modes of experience (Apollonian or Dionysian) which accompany the state are affected by conscious and bodily influences.

How then does sentic theory deal with the dimension of intensity? We can, of course, ask a subject experiencing fantasy-generated sentic states to rate the intensity of his own experience according to a scale, say from zero to five. As we in fact do this procedure, subjects rate themselves for each separate state on this scale about one hour after their experience. The average score of such self-ratings across all the states for 2,500 subjects has been 3.8. Such subjective scoring provides an index of how involved the subject has become in each specific state, and can also indicate when subjects have had difficulty experiencing particular sentic states. Nevertheless, it is a subjective evaluation.

Sentic theory, as we have seen, has been able to cross the chasm between the subjective and objective, with respect to the communicative function of certain qualities. So far, however, we had not been able to do this with the parameter of intensity, although this deficiency may soon be overcome. Sentic theory has recently provided an objective method of evaluating the intensity of sentic states as a numerical score obtained essentially without subjective judgment of either the subject or the experimenter. Moreover, this method of measuring intensity is intrinsic to sentic communication theory and does not rest on the measurement of psychologic bodily responses, which are well known to be highly variable.

How is this done? To measure the intensity of a sentic state we make use of the dynamic properties discussed in earlier chapters concerning the timing of E-acton initiation. As noted, in order to build up the intensity of the sentic state the E-actons must be initiated at quasi-random intervals, that is, not in a predictable, regular rhythmic pattern. A *regular* rhythmic repetition (if at an appropriate rate) will not build up the sentic state but on the contrary will tend to *discharge* it. By selecting a suitable repetition rate, this discharge can be controlled.

It becomes possible, therefore, to measure the intensity of a sentic state at a particular moment by switching from a random type initiation to a regular rhythmic initiation. This will cause the intensity to be gradually discharged. But, the greater the intensity, the greater number of repetitions it will take to discharge it. Accordingly, the subject merely indicates at which moment he no longer feels the state, it is necessary then only to *count* the number of repetitions it took to discharge the state, from starting when the initiation rate was switched from random to repetitive. This number provides an index of the intensity of the state at the moment concerned. We thus have the elegant possibility of a numerical index related to intensity derived from the dynamics of expression alone, self-contained within sentic theory!

Interestingly, after we had discovered this method of measuring intensity, a very well-known pattern of behavior appeared in a new light: the action of tapping or patting a person on the back repeatedly in order to quiet his passion and emotions. This kind of patting is effective only when it has a certain rhythmicity and may be used under various circumstances. A woman can use this repetitive patting to cool sexual excitement in a man (or vice versa, in today's world). It can also be used to stop a child or an adult from crying, to assuage grief, or even to calm anger. In each case the pattern of movement results in a decrease in intensity of the emotion, but only when the patting is performed with a certain rhythmicity. At least three taps are desirable for the effect. If the third tap occurs after a markedly different interval from that between the first two, the effect tends to be lost. (The rate of patting is at approximately 0.7-second intervals.) This specific dynamic form of patting is done intuitively and with specific intent, by many, perhaps by most people. Thus, we see sentic theory illuminate an ancient act of touch communication.

Prediction of Acton Theory: Blocking of Phase Shifted E-Actons

Our studies of sentics differ from most approaches to the study of psychologic factors in that they are not primarily statistical. Even a single instance of a contradictory result would serve to throw sentic theory in doubt, and would require changes in the theory! We are dealing with some of the processes and entities concerned in the manner of hard science: we can make predictions that are capable of being confirmed by experiment, predictions that will involve *new* experiences. Since there is existential coherence between essentic forms and their qualities of experience, any new predictions would also concern corresponding specific experience.

Sentic theory can make predictions about the timing of expressive actions executed simultaneously, and about the conditions of blocking, as we shall see in the following.

We have seen that only one sentic state can be expressed at a time and that a single expressive action, or E-acton, has a definite duration and course. As pointed out, we cannot express anger with one hand, and at the same time joy with the other, and experience them both. We cannot do this, even if we attempt to express the second state not simultaneously but a little later, during the course of an E-acton already begun. If we try to do this, there is blocking.‡ The coherence between the expressive form and the corresponding experience is broken. An E-acton once begun must be completed before another one begins.

These properties of E-actons can be used to predict a rather unexpected property of the dynamics of expression even within the *same* sentic state—a prediction about expressing E-actons through different output modes. Let us take the example of a person expressing love. Once a love E-acton is begun with one hand (a caress), we can predict that another such E-acton could not be initiated with

‡ The experience of the state ceases quite abruptly and one experiences instead a sense of irritation, of frustration. In a specific sense, this blocking is also a kind of repression. An incomplete acton tends to result in an unpleasant sensation, regardless of the nature of the state expressed. It is as frustrating to interrupt an anger or hate acton as a joy or love acton.

the other arm during the course of the ongoing E-acton, without blocking.

This prediction is readily confirmed and applies to other sentic states with equal validity, for example to anger or to grief. It also has an interesting and significant corollary: one E-acton can join in the expression of another in some other part of the body without blocking if it does not start at its beginning but is executed as a fraction of an E-acton—corresponding to the remaining fraction of the ongoing E-acton—so that the two E-actons finish together in parallel! (See Figure 31.) For example, a phrase such as "I love you" must be said with a different tone of voice if it begins in the middle of an E-acton caress than if it starts together with the caress, if blocking is not to occur. Since the minimum duration of love E-actons is approximately 2.1 seconds, this means that separate love E-actons cannot be initiated with different output modes during 2.1 seconds without blocking.

This specific, unambiguous prediction has significance for understanding how people communicate with each other. It permits one to understand that emotional blocking occurs, under certain circumstances, as a natural phenomenon—and is *not* a mental disturbance, or symptom of disease. It helps to avoid miscommunication, and distinguishes between natural and unnatural patterns of communication.

Such a finding is significant for music also, as it makes it clear that the effectiveness of essentic form communication does not increase with an increasing number of E-actons beyond 2.1 seconds, i.e., there

Figure 31. Diagrammatic illustration of free and blocked expression involving more than one E-acton.

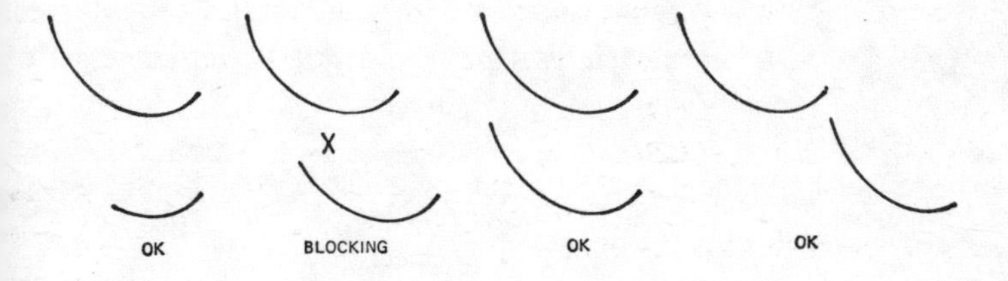

is no sense of producing more than one love acton in 2.1 seconds—it only causes blocking. (This knowledge would prevent many music students, and musicians, from playing some music as if squeezing the last drop of juice out of a lemon: it defines exaggeration and its failure to communicate, in this particular aspect.)

ELEVEN

Sentography and Personal Relationship Profiles

Because essentic forms are stable, as we have seen, we can proceed to study an individual's sentic relationship with his human and natural environment using our methods to obtain his sentic responses to personal and impersonal relationships. In a sense, this is the opposite of generating and measuring generalized sentic states—we are interested in a person's sentic responses to particular features of the environment and to particular people.

Since we know the essentic form for specific sentic states, however, we can attempt to interpret the sentic responses in terms of the known forms and sentic states. The known forms can be used as a kind of template to reveal the sentic relationship of the subject with a particular individual or an aspect of the environment.

The measurement techniques used in this method are similar to the ones described earlier. The sentograph and voluntary expressive pressure of a finger is used. Instead of expressing a particular required sentic state, however, a person is asked to express his re-

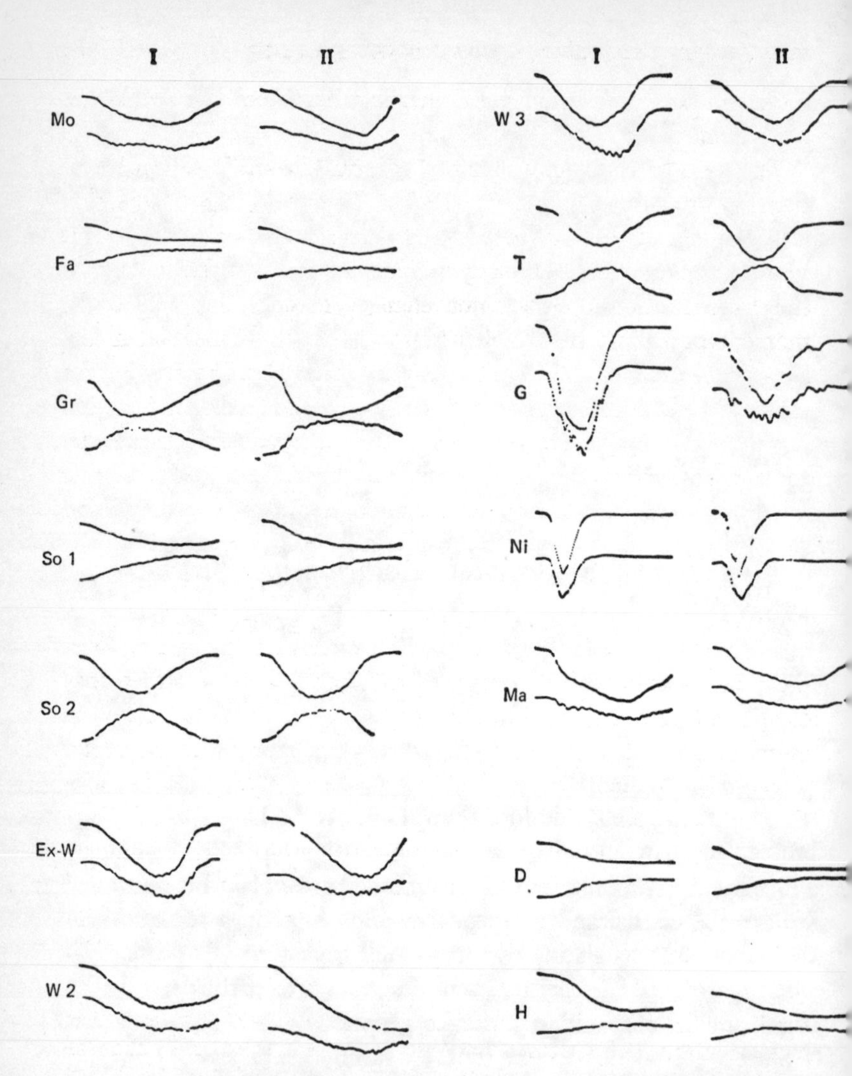

Figure 32. A Personal Relationship Profile for a male subject, forty-five years old, comprised of sentic responses to person idiologs on two different occasions. Sentograms shown are the average of ten actons in response to such words as Mother, Father, etc. Each name is repeatedly pronounced a few seconds apart by the experimenter, ten times in succession. Note the characteristic shapes introduced on two separate occasions (two weeks apart) for each person idiolog, and compare them with the basic essentic forms given in Chapter Four. Note the resemblance of the sentogram for Father (Fa) with the essentic form of love, with its inward horizontal component. The sentogram for Mother, on the other

sponse to the name of suggested people with whom the person has a relationship.

The series of sentograms obtained constitute a sentic personal relationship profile of the subject (PRP). The sentogram of the subject's fantasized reaction to each particular individual, such as his mother, father, etc., has a distinct character and is stable as long as the basic relationship does not change. It does not reflect the momentary feelings toward that person as much as the underlying, longer-term relationship. A man may be irritated with his wife, for example, but his sentogram for "wife" would show not the irritation but an expression of the relationship at a deeper level. These sentograms acquire special significance as we relate them to the essentic forms for specific emotions. Such a comparison often is revealing and significant in a way that verbal expression of feelings cannot be.

The figure shown (see Figure 32) comprises the collection of sentographic forms of the PRP for one subject. The sentogram can be compared with the established essentic forms for specific states previously measured. For example, the sentogram for father may closely resemble the essentic form for love as in the figure; and, the essentic forms of anger, hate, or sex may be observed in particular sentograms produced by the subject as an expression of his relationship with specific individuals.

Other stable sentograms may clearly differ from any of the established essentic forms. These are especially interesting in a different way. They may express "mixed" states, i.e., combinations

hand, has an outward horizontal component. In fact, all female sentograms in this PRP (Mother, Ex-Wife, Woman 2, Woman 3) show an outward angle of pressure, whereas sentograms to Grandfather (Gr), Son 2, and male friends (D, H) show a marked inward horizontal component. The sentogram for Woman 3 may be compared with the essentic form for sex, while that for Richard Nixon (Ni) resembles the form for anger and that for the subject's "business enemy" (G) is suggestive of the form for hate. Other sentograms are clearly different from the simple essentic forms so far measured. The element of "inscrutability" present in this subject's reaction to Mao Tse-tung (Ma) confirmed by the interview is also subtly reflected in his attitude toward Mother. (In the interview the subject indicated being awed by his mother and not really understanding her.)

of basic states. Or, they could represent basic states we have not yet investigated.

Measuring and Interpreting a Personal Relationship Profile

In measuring an individual's PRP, the experimenter in an initial interview with the subject selects names of individuals with whom the subject has, or has had, significant relationships. Generally included are mother, father, wives or husbands, brothers and sisters, children, grandparents, lovers, boss, subordinate, and/or other significant individuals. Figures of national prominence, such as the President, may also be chosen, if the subject has a significantly developed sentic attitude toward them.

The subject then sits in a chair without armrests and places his arm on the finger rest in the standardized position, and is asked to express his sentic response to the person mentioned by the experimenter with a single transient pressure. For each person chosen the name is repeated five to ten times at random intervals of several seconds apart; as he hears the name pronounced, the subject expresses his sentic attitude on the two-dimensional pressure transducer. Five to ten responses are usually sufficient to characterize the form quite accurately; using more than ten responses for one fantasized person tends to blunt the sensibility of the subject.

In choosing the sequence in which the names are presented, it is better for the subject's relaxation to avoid repeated violent contrasts in attitude from one name to the next and to proceed in a gradual sequence as far as is feasible.

When asking a subject to express his sentic reactions to how he feels about the individual concerned (and not to how he feels about what he or she might have done that day), the subject is quite easily able to avoid expressing reactions to a temporary event of that day, and is aware of this distinction without any real difficulty. Aspects of the totality of the relationship determine the form, and not a particular incident. Yet there can be incidents that have a deciding effect on the total relationship. In such a case a change in the form will be observed and may persist after such an incident.

The PRP can be used diagnostically and as a particular sentic ex-

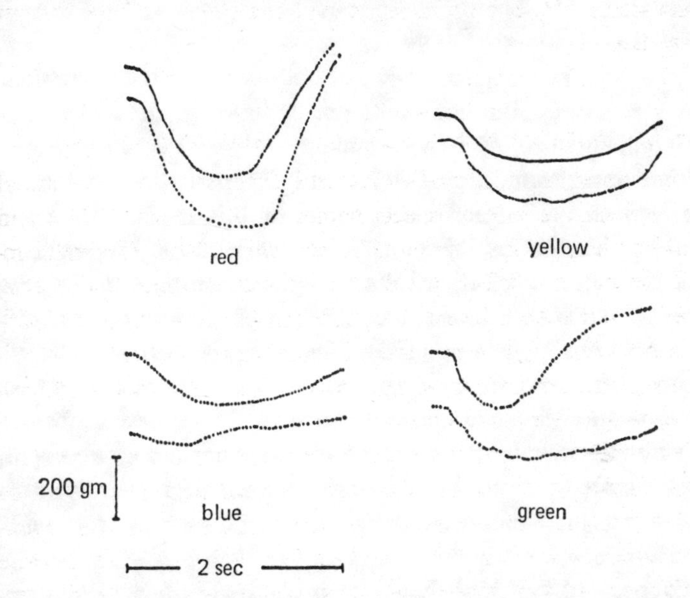

Figure 33. Sentic reactions to colors as measured with the sentograph. Note the distinctive forms for each color. The excitement of red is shown by a strong outer-directed response. The calm of blue is reflected by a small inverted horizontal component, i.e., the absence of an outward thrust. Yellow has a more sustained response form than red and the response is outward with a sustained energy. Green shows a compound motion outward and also upward in the second phase. (Because of this response, it was necessary to use a modified transducer setup that permitted a negative vertical pressure to be recorded.) Curves shown are valid for the particular subject and particular hue only. Shapes are relatively sensitive to minor changes in hue and saturation.

perience, as well as providing insight into the subject's relationships, for the therapist and for the subject himself. Also, taking a PRP can be a valuable emotional experience in itself.

In a similar approach, a person's sentic reactions can be measured by various factors of the environment, such as color (see Figure 33) or shapes, either singly or in combination. This tells us something both about the character of environmental factors and about the subject himself.

"Mixed" Expressive Actons

So far we have mainly considered and measured the expression of basic sentic states. But how are the many subtle shades and combinations for states expressed and communicated?

Some sentic states appear clearly to be "mixed"; that is, they contain elements of several sentic states. In this respect sentic states resemble the spectrum of colors. Thus, while red and yellow cannot be sensed in terms of other color sensations, orange is clearly sensed as being a combination of red and yellow. States such as melancholy and envy seem to be compounded from several others. How does the essentic form of these states represent their components? It is clearly *not* through a simple algebraic addition of the separate forms—such an addition would interfere with the demodulating process that functions according to the recognition principle of a key-lock manner. Such a summation would also tend to confuse quality and intensity.

It appears instead that the problem is solved in biologic design by the ingenious method of combining portions of separate E-actons sequentially. The essentic forms are "telescoped" together to form one combined form. For example, melancholy (which may be regarded as a combination of love and sadness) appears to be expressed by an E-acton which begins as a love acton that cannot complete itself and after approximately 0.6 second changes into a sadness acton. The combined "telescoped" form results from a *single* initial preprogramming and does not involve a separate decision of stopping and starting the second acton in midstream, which as noted earlier would result in blocking. The love component beginning the acton is sufficiently long to be recognized as such, and the termination of the acton in sadness is also recognized; nevertheless the melancholy acton is expressed and recognized as a single entity.

The dynamics of mixed expressive actons are still being investigated, and we have just begun to discern which emotions are the result of mixing elements of the basic sentic states. It will be quite some time before we can distinguish with full adequacy the basic and mixed states of the emotional spectrum.

PART THREE

Sentics, the Individual, and Society

A surface of grace
Bounds fluid motion
Myriad nerve-channels, like parachute chords
Connect surface movement to the moving thought—
—Essentic form is born

And the moment's true surfaced expression
Seems one graceful line
To a point of powerless power
Giving
Weight to weight,
Time to time, continuity to experience

Asleep or awake, I too, sometimes seem
A point of nothing

A point of contact of living breath
With the multicolored, evanescent scene—
Giving form to surface.

TWELVE

Essentic Form and the Transformation of Sources of Energy

Emotions Stored in Memory

Qualities can be remembered as such, regardless of specific situational content, as the experience of sentic cycles shows. A person who has done sentic cycles can remember sentic qualities he experienced, regardless of what fantasies he may have had while producing them. In fact, he may tend to forget these fantasies while still remembering the quality of experience. Thus, it seems, the experience of the quality itself is stored in the memory engram. That is, there may exist a chemical representation of the memory of a specific quality, such as anger or love.

In his paper "The Unconscious" Freud sees an apparent contradiction in the term "unconscious affect."* Although he conceives a

* Freud writes, "It is surely of the essence of an emotion that we should feel it, i.e. that it should enter consciousness. So for emotion, feelings, and affects to be unconscious would be quite out of the question. But in psychoanalytic practice we are accustomed to speak of unconscious love, hate, anger, etc., and find it impossible to avoid even the strange conjunction, 'unconscious consciousness of guilt' . . .

repressed *idea* as being unconscious, he sees a contradiction in the concept of a repressed unconscious *affect*. This view implies that an affect cannot be stored in the memory as such, as an entity. It denies an affect the existential attribute which is given to an idea.

Freud's distinction appears to have as its roots a notion that the very existence of an affect is linked to bodily processes, while, on the other hand, ideas occur in the brain. Such a distinction is misleading. The *quality* of pain, hunger, redness, of a musical experience can be *remembered*. And if we may recall a quality, we may also choose *not* to recall that quality, that is, to suppress that aspect.

What happens to the memory of an expressed sentic state? What is the difference between a memory of an expressed sentic state, as compared with one that has remained unexpressed and incomplete? A crucial difference seems to be with respect to energy dynamics.

Incomplete states stored in the memory continue to demand expression, to require fulfillment. To discharge this, a scanning process may allow us to complete them selectively as opportunity arises for expressing that emotion. (For example, a twenty-two-year-old female student, whose dog had died six months earlier, cried bitterly during the Grief phase when doing sentic cycles for the first time, at last being able to mourn for her dog.)

Alternatively, expression of a dormant sentic state may depend on reactivating that state, not through memory alone, but through newly created situations. However, the experiences of anger from one cause may not always be helpful in discharging stored anger from other causes.

It is observed in our studies that the quality of the experience of a

---

"In every instance where repression has succeeded in inhibiting the development of an affect we apply the term 'unconscious' to those affects that are restored when we undo the work of repression. So it cannot be denied that the use of the terms in question is logical; but a comparison of the unconscious affect with the unconscious idea reveals the significant difference that the actual information is in the system Ucs [the unconscious] whilst to the unconscious affect there corresponds in the same system only a potential disposition which is prevented from developing further. So that, strictly speaking, although no fault can be found with the mode of expression in question, *there are no unconscious affects in the sense in which there are unconscious ideas* . . . The whole difference arises from the fact that ideas are cathexes—ultimately of memory-traces—whilst affects and emotions correspond with processes of discharge . . ."

sentic state can be transferred from short-term to long-term memory storage, like other entities of memory. For this to occur, a person should have a period of relatively undisturbed sentic condition following the experience. If the short-term memory storage relating to sentic states is undergoing too rapid and continuous change, the experience cannot settle in terms of long-term memory. (Thus, in our lives, after any significant experience, we should leave adequate time —one hour or more—for the experience to sink in, and not divert our sentic state immediately afterward by distractions. This seems advisable for any valuable experience.)

Rhythms of personal interaction are related to the dynamics of essentic form. When people are "in harmony," their essentic form productions are interlocked in a unifying time pattern. The phases augment rather than cancel or block each other. The choice between genuine and cathartic expression and of repression or blocking is often effected by the interpersonal timing in the exchange of essentic forms.

Essentic Form in Dreams

There appear to be no significant differences between our experience of essentic forms in dreams and our experience of them in the awake state. Smiles, gestures, musical phrases, tones of voice, etc. all function in dreams much as they do in real life. Yet we are able to generate these "unconsciously" in our dreams without confining ourselves to the expression of our "own" sentic states. In a dream we may experience love expressed by another, the anger of two or more others toward each other, and so on, on a practically limitless dramatic stage. What gift of fantasy we all have in our dreams!

The need for dreaming appears related to sentic states that need to be expressed. Dreams provide ways for satisfying expressive demands, as well as for experiencing relationships with more insight than in the awake state.† We need to separate satisfaction of the re-

† In considering the sentic structure of dreams, an important distinction between the concept of wish and the sentic state of hope must be made. The essentic form of hope is readily measured. It may exist without a specific object that may be hoped for. Hope is open-ended; it is a generalized sentic state. "Wishing," on the other hand, needs an object.

pressed demand for expression from the pleasant or unpleasant quality of the sentic state experienced in the dream. If nightmares represent the expression of suppressed fears, they may be in that sense "liberating" and attempt to discharge a situation which demands expression.

In their analysis of dreams, Freud and his followers have emphasized the importance of affects as constructive influences of the dream. With each scene of the dream a particular affect occurs. As one remembers a dream, one also remembers the corresponding affect. (In fact, it is through this affect that we gain confidence in remembering more and more details of the dream.) It is the cement, so to speak, that binds the various details together within that particular scene of the dream. In the construction of the dream as a whole we may experience a succession of affects.‡

Dreams often sum up the present condition of the individual in terms of his life situation. Potential interaction between sentic states of various individuals and their needs contributes to the particular "wisdom" revealed in the dream. Our sentic discrimination and experience may be more acute in dreams. When dreaming we often are better able than when awake to experience requirements of others in addition to our own needs to experience empathy.

Like dreams, sentic cycles make it possible to enjoy the expression of states which one might not be able to do in real life. Providing these safety vents, sentic cycles also tend to modify the dream content and unconscious driving forces of the personality. (Such reliefs may also act temporarily to unbalance the drives of the individ-

‡ The time course of experience in dreaming appears to be highly accelerated. However, it may be possible to relate the minimum duration of a particular sentic state to the duration of single expressed essentic form. One can speculate that possibly, scenes may be collapsed in time so that many actions are projected into the time of one essentic form. There is a unitary, specific, sentic experience for each section of a dream—the quality of the sentic state is maintained throughout this portion of the dream. The shortest period of this maintained state may be related to the duration of essentic form. Certainly experience with sentic cycles suggests that during the expression of a *single* E-acton frequently several scenes concordant with the expression flash within one's fantasy—even if only for a fraction of a second. Images appear and disappear at rates that may occasionally approach the duration of a single moment (0.2 second). This phenomenon is significant in relating the function of sentic cycles to the function of dreams.

ual, and he will at times have a strange sensation of missing his familiar neurotic urges. However, a readjustment readily takes place in which the more creative aspects supplant the missed destructive elements. A proper measure of sentic cycle exposure is necessary to achieve this. Too much exposure may cause too great a dissipation of the incentive to act.)

Biological Aspects of Expressive Satisfaction

A repressed sentic state may be said to have the urge for expression also stored with its memory. On the other hand, if a satisfying expression has occurred, the memory also incorporates that satisfaction.

From a systems point of view, there is some correspondence between the demands of a spontaneously generated drive such as hunger, and demands of unsatisfied repressed sentic states. But while an individual is clearly aware of the method of satisfying hunger—namely eating food, and more particularly, through *specific* kinds of food—the demands of repressed sentic states become known to the individual only under selective attention.

If a person with repressed anger finds himself in a situation, which, for other reasons, provokes him to anger, he may at the same time discharge some of the unexpressed, repressed anger. He may not be aware of this. This well-known phenomenon has bearing on the study of generalized sentic states and their relative independence from the specific situational content.

Let us consider the dynamics of a particular biologic satisfaction, say that associated with urination. We may ask ourselves to what extent is the drive itself related to a desire to obtain the sensation of satisfaction? We may observe that the sensation urging one to urinate does not urge us toward the particular sensation of satisfaction we experience upon completion of the urination process. Urination would take place regardless of whether this final satisfaction would be experienced. But during the process of urination the urge undergoes a transformation. Even though there is no satisfaction until the completion of the act, information is nonetheless received by the nervous system; the ongoing process of urination has had an effect on the urge to commence it.

An unexpressed sentic state provides an urge to express. During expression there appears to be a modification of the felt urge so that one inherently relates the act of expression to its previous requirement, and finally, the feeling of satisfaction is experienced additionally, as a bonus, so to speak, not as a component of the urge. Although the satisfactions are in themselves pleasant, it is not the desire for these pleasant experiences that urges us to act. The urge itself has an aspect of blindness with respect to these satisfactions. (We desire sexually not in order to experience the satisfaction one feels after a sexual act, but for its own sake. The satisfaction that follows is an experience in itself.) The expression of each sentic state has its own particular satisfaction. The satisfaction of experiencing anger may, at times, be more pleasant than that of expressing love.

Although one might say that obtaining food and eating is an "expression" of hunger, it is not so in the same sense as applies to the "expression" of sentic states. An infant, a young bird, or a dog communicates the desire for food by specific cries recognized by the mother or attending person. These cries express a sentic state. Acts resulting from hunger have communication characteristics of the state. The usual action pattern of eating acts to a certain extent, if remotely, like an expressive motor pattern in being contagious and in providing satisfaction.

But this is only one aspect of its nature. No one has been able to compose music about hunger, or for that matter about eating. Expressive patterns associated with hunger do not lend themselves to musical portrayal. Why is this so? The sensation of hunger is specifically related to food only. There is no way of satisfying hunger through any other sensory modality. To communicate love, however, a caress or tone of voice or a gesture are all possible modes that can satisfy the need to express. But no sounds have ever been invented to satisfy hunger and no gestures will satisfy an empty stomach.

Nervous system signals and body images for hunger are thus specific; yet, generalized sensory input communication and experience of sentic states may affect the dynamics involved. Under emotional stress, we may lose appetite and starve ourselves, or, under repressed emotion, overeat.

It is interesting and remarkable that during sentic cycles hunger is sharply attenuated or disappears (this also happens during sleep). The fantasy experience provided by sentic states appears to fill the sentic domain, and displaces the sensation of hunger.

Sexual Satisfaction and Relationship Idiologs

If we compare sexual desire and function, and its drive, with the hunger drive, we note in each a repeated generation of desire, with some specific goal-direction or cognitive aspect that may result in an action pattern.

Merely chewing and swallowing without eating gives some satisfaction (e.g., chewing, and spitting food out before swallowing and *then* swallowing—a good way to reduce weight!). But the demands of hunger include also recognition and specific selection of food; if we eat three pieces of cake, for example, we no longer want to eat cake even though we may not be satisfied, i.e., are still hungry. Further subtle body images are brought into play. We do not know how that selection and imaging process works—its functioning is clearly unconscious—but it is essential to satisfaction.

Consider the nature of the satisfaction of the sexual drive, and masturbation. When a person touches himself on the nose, say, it is a neurophysiologically different experience than if someone else touches him, since in one case intention, motor action, and touch perception are integrated, and in the other they are not.* It is clearly a mistake to identify the sexual drive, its experience, and satisfaction with the physiologic processes of sexual excitation and orgasm. The spontaneous generation and perception of essentic form in mutual sexual communication increases the level of excitement, and changes the quality of experience and of satisfaction. The generating action of essentic form combines exciting and seductive aspects. (To generate these forms freely, the sentic domain must not be filled with anxiety or fear.)

* As also in massage, compared with self-massage.

If we love the other person, and there is desire to merge with the other individual, then how we integrate that image (or idiolog of the person) with the sexual impulse is very important. The inability to integrate these may become a source of sexual problems.† In fact, experience with experimenting with the order of the phases of sentic cycles shows that the phase of sex when coupled between love and joy has an entirely different function, than when it is positioned between other sentic states. The kind of satisfaction obtained from it may vary greatly according to the sentic states associated with it (an example of the "loose coupling" of qualities referred to in Chapter Nine). The sexual drive shows itself to include more than so-called "physiologic gratification." It, too, comprises virtual body images and cognitive aspects (in the sense of Chapter Eleven). Combining or divorcing ardor, joy, and love in relation to sexual experience, we alter its dynamic function both as to unconscious and conscious experience.

Orgasm—as well as a tickle or a yawn—includes a wide range of experience (which should have better verbal description) that includes the *image of relationship*. Not only does the *intensity* of the experience vary greatly with these relationship images, but certainly also the qualities and consequent satisfactions.

The sentic function of the relationship image is definite and real, but adequate words do not exist yet to describe its range and depth. This makes it most difficult for us to be clear about the sentic meaning of relationship. (Words such as "brother" mix up relationship concepts with genealogy.) In terms of sexual experiencing, the sentic meaning and function of relationship cannot be constrained to fit the established word categories such as "lover," "mother," "father," "friend," and so on. The extent to which the person or person idiolog encompasses a range of conscious and unconscious possibilities—as *potentialities* of relationship—controls the degree of satisfaction and quality. Although we have no words to denote these potentialities we can clearly sense their sentic function. Distinguishing types of relationship as "nourishing" and "draining" is an example of going in the right direction toward finding verbal equivalents for a

† The effect on the dynamics of the unconscious processes is very different, depending on the idiolog consciously experienced.

better differentiation, but these are still very inadequate compared to the richness of the phenomena of relationships.

Thus, paying greater attention to the virtual body images associated with the sentic state of sex and to its own cognitive aspect (see Chapter Eleven) should allow us to discriminate better within the range of sexual experience and its energy balance (as has been explored to a considerable degree by the Reichian schools of therapy). The large role of fantasy in governing the quality of sexual experience, recently brought to social attention through current popular magazines, has been systematically cultivated, however, in a different context in Tantra Yoga, as mutual fantasy. Fantasy acts both to create idiologs of essentic form repeatedly and in combining the sexual with other sentic states.

Energy capacities released by good sexual relationships are perhaps the most unused and unrealized potential source of psychic energy and human resources. Regarding sexual functioning largely mechanistically, however, is a dangerous mistake to make in an effort toward making these resources available. If our evolving current concepts of sexuality (and the prevalence of various levels of pornography) seem unfulfilling steps that appear to have truncated the essential nature of this drive, it seems to be because sentic relationship (except paradoxically perhaps for S-M) has not been given its proper fantasy function as part of the sexual experience itself.

As the reader may have noted in the reports of subjects on their sentic cycle experiences, these experiences may at times help to integrate the sexual drive with personal image idiologs and prevent the truncated shadow of one interfering with the other.

There are some immediate practical applications of sentic methods to sexual problems. For all too many individuals, sexual activities are associated with specific, traumatic memories. These associations often interfere dramatically with the natural spontaneous enjoyment that the experience has to offer. Anxiety, guilt, fears of impotence and of homosexual fantasies, phobic feelings, and anger—these are examples of some of the processes that may occur against the will of the individual. Sentic cycles can be used to redirect these fantasy processes by offering new associations, and by providing enjoyable experience of the emotional spectrum.

This method, acting in part somewhat like Wolpe's desensitization method (a technique of behavior modification which works by repeatedly and gradually associating the quality of an unpleasant experience with pleasant contexts), consists of deliberately and briefly bringing to the subject's mind the negative associations when he is established in a positive generalized sentic state—for example, love or joy. In this way, habitual fears of sexual inadequacies may also be replaced by repeatedly establishing positive associations during the sex phase of sentic cycles. As the specific stimulus giving rise to fear is thought of in a positive sentic state, the fear-provoking stimulus becomes less potent after sufficient repeated association, and assumes some of the character of the state in which it is presented. In this way, it can be possible to abolish the fear of snakes, for instance, and perhaps even induce a love of them. One should be careful, however, that the positive state is well established first, before the negative fantasy is presented. (Otherwise the subject might end up with a fear of love, instead of a love of snakes!) In practice this is not difficult to avoid.

Not surprisingly, the reduction of non-specific anxiety produced by sentic cycles, can be helpful in problems involving impotence and frigidity. (Where possible, it is desirable that both members of a couple partake in sentic training.)

Aggressiveness, Peace, and Energy

The expression of emotions affects the drives which urge toward expressive behavior. A key problem is to gain insight into the relation of emotions and drives to psychic energy. Psychic energy and aggressiveness are often and falsely equated. The all too vague concept of "aggressiveness" appears to fall into several distinct categories which have separate functions. These various types of "aggressiveness" may be noted in the behavior of animals.

For example, a hungry animal will hunt for food and may kill another animal in the pursuit of this goal. But psychobiologists (for example D. Ploog) have found that such behavior does not appear to be associated with anger or hate. The animal kills its prey to satisfy hunger.

Another aggressive, "angry" behavior is observed as an animal endeavors to secure his "territorial rights" and to fight off rivals, in order to protect his property, relationships, and family. This self-protective behavior does not usually involve killing.

A third form of behavior we also tend to call "aggressive," even though it is not directed at any other being, is the "aggressive" pursuit of constructive activity and exploration. A female turtle single-mindedly buries her eggs, ants labor untiringly in concerted action, birds build their nests, and other animals hoard their food in anticipation of later consumption. (In humans this activity is exemplified by the engineer, the inventor, and the builder.)

Some ethologists are of the opinion that certain aggressiveness is a continuously generated and periodically discharged urge (like the sexual drive), which operates dynamically like a ramp function or sawtooth configuration. (See Figure 34.) Also, it has been found to be possible to breed animals genetically according to specific types of aggressiveness, demonstrating that the intensity of their sexual drive is not necessarily correlated with the intensity of other aggressive drives.

The hostile behavior that one observes arising from the frustration of drives can be clearly differentiated in animals, as well as in humans, from the constructive forms of aggressiveness. The latter involves not attacking another individual, but rather a problem, and energies are spent not fighting others but on the solution of a problem or the execution of a plan.

On the whole we may admit with Freud that in humans, creativity is more like excretion than like ingestion. But in creativity

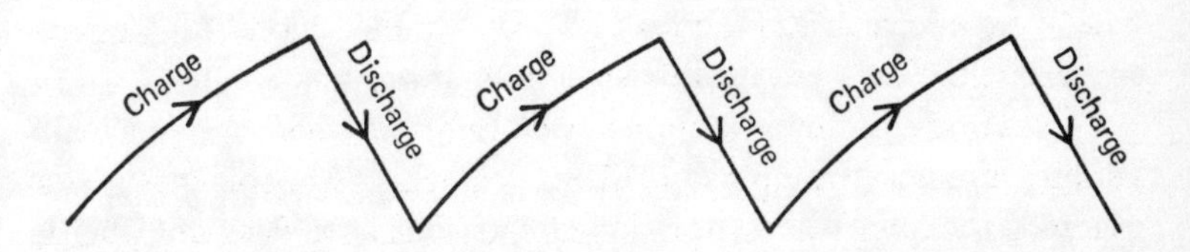

Figure 34. Ramp function illustrated by sawtooth configuration corresponds with the dynamics of some periodically discharged urges.

there is also an element of ingestion. Ideas and expressions are received.‡

The concepts of aggressiveness and of psychic energy overlap, like many other concepts of natural language. The problem is to understand distinctions between emotions, drives and their relation to psychic energy. But the concept of psychic energy itself is diffuse. Do we equate the energy of anger to that of joyous excitement? For many, anxiety is the driving force behind aggressive action and psychic energy. In more disturbed individuals there is no longer an awareness of the goal which would remove anxiety; that is to say, anxiety becomes non-specific. Eventually such anxiety may no longer produce activity. A drive based on the urge to remove anxiety is also a drive to remove the blocking which anxiety produces. There comes a point, however, when an individual no longer recognizes the blocks and restrictions, and is ready to forget that he indeed does have a drive which is being so blocked. The person increasingly represses both the manifestations of the drive, as well as its blocking, until gradually he becomes resigned, gives up, and becomes one of Eliot's "hollow" men.

A crucial difference between energy based on anxiety and creative energy seems to be that in the latter instead of trying to *get* something, we experience both giving and receiving—although not necessarily from or to specific individuals. Being connected to the source of receiving is at the same time a feeling of strength and peace—that is, energy. A balanced, hemeostatic equilibrium takes place as a result of the knowledge that in giving "there is more where that came from"; the source of riches seems much greater, in fact, than we are capable of receiving. The feeling of peace and security which accompanies this realization is stronger than any other.

The form of psychic energy which results in spontaneous generation is frequently and clearly seen in the play of young children. Play may have its rules, but they serve to allow freedom of choice and of

‡ At times, one experiences the dynamics of being a mere "vessel" for receiving ideas and forms that appear to come to one. The processes of being obsessed by a drive seeking to purge one, or to excrete, or literally "express," is joined by another, conjugate experience of being a vessel for receiving that which comes. This requires not suction, but a clarity of emptiness, like a clearly focused telescope erected onto the black sky, open to receive the light of an unsought star.

action to exist. For older people, using that source of psychic energy may represent a change in attitude toward being itself. Many of us do not feel a spontaneous joy and gratitude for life. According to his autobiography, even Bertrand Russell, in spite of his gifts, his insights, his success, and his sensitive nature, did not experience this until late in life. Deeply ingrained anxieties and resentments appear to prevent one from experiencing this. But if these can be removed, the forces of regeneration can be set free.

In generating qualities of experience, we know that for some sensory qualities the nervous system has developed a two-channel communication system so that the *absence* of the stimulus has a quality of its own. Darkness is not nothing. When one experiences black, certain neurons in the retina are stimulated by the absence of light. (This happens because receptors that are stimulated by light to inhibit these are now inactive.) Using the design principles of excitation and inhibition, the nervous system can create unique qualities through the *absence* of a specific stimulus.

This is not to suggest that peace is darkness. But when influences of other sentic states, which by their mode of action often are inhibiting influences, are absent, the inhibition is absent too, and peace may be experienced as a spontaneously generated continuum. In the sphere of emotions, interactions also seem to occur in a way so that some emotions and qualities may be only experienced provided they are not inhibited by others. Through sentic cycles' discharge of accumulated emotional needs for expression, inhibiting influences are removed. This appears often sufficient to experience the spontaneously generated well-being and enjoyment of existence as such, even the specific ecstasy which we call by the word "peace."

This kind of peace is not the peace of dreamless sleep. It is not the peace of lassitude or of laziness or of lethargy or of inactivity. It is accompanied by gratitude and a surge of energy, no longer directed at the removal of anxiety or at some goal set for the satisfaction of a drive, it is energy which joyfully embraces what the world has to offer.*

* The combination of the experience of calm or quietness with increased psychic energy, an apparent paradox, is paralleled by the experience associated with meditation. In fact, sentic cycles may be regarded as a unique "active-quiet" form of meditation, which includes considered experience of emotion.

THIRTEEN

Sentics and the Sources of Ethical Being

The Sentic Source of the Ethical Impulse

As we have seen, essentic forms tend to fall into two groups: those which are expressed strongly away from the body and those which tend toward incorporation. This distinction makes it possible to correlate some of them with concepts of rejection and acceptance. Thus, we naturally enter the realm of ethics. How are ethical considerations related to the qualities of sentic states? Can love exist without an ethical aspect, or hate without an unethical one? Do the qualities of grief and joy have innate ethical aspects?

These questions are not solely philosophic, but also have an experimental basis in the light of sentics. For most philosophers, emotions are largely seen as interfering with ethical judgment and behavior. Even Spinoza, whose treatise on ethics concerns itself with emotions in systematic detail and whose great insights in many ways anticipate our findings, was mostly concerned with eliminating emotional attitudes which appeared to him to promote bias and obscure ethical thought. On the other hand, it is clear to us that empathy, as we have described it, is entirely in harmony with ethical objectives.

Through the practical distinction between Apollonian and Dionysian emotional experience and the ability to cultivate empathy, sentics may clarify the relation between the sentic basis of the ethical impulse and the sentic states that hinder its realization.

Let us consider the biblical ethical principle, "Do unto others as you would desire them to do unto you" (or "Love thy neighbor as thyself") and Schweitzer's "Reverence for life." Such ethical principles denote attitudes, plans for action. As we have seen, sentic states also place characteristic constraints on possible action patterns. An individual under strong emotion becomes more predictable in some ways. His actions tend to be constrained to the demands of the particular emotional state. Moreover, sentic states continue in time according to their own inertia. Accordingly, a man in a sentic state responds to the requirements of the moment with an emotional filter. The question is how the constraint of sentic states relates to the constraint of ethics.

In fact, the ethical principles we have quoted above do not eliminate sentic states. On the contrary, they specifically *include* the experience of reverence and desire: *reverence* for life, and, in good will toward others, the *desire* for the nurturing of life. Clearly, it would seem, regardless of our approach to ethics, *sentic states serve as a basis for the ethical impulse* and thus its principles.

The sentic states that serve as a basis for the ethical impulse in man seem to appear to some degree in the lives of animals. Thus, many species of animals display behavior that implies that doing good to others may bring them satisfaction. I. Eibl-Eibesfeldt calls this the "altruistic" behavior of animals. Parents labor hard to feed their offspring; animals come to the rescue of others when they are in danger. (It would seem that we are often less "humane" than animals!)

Such evidence suggests that we may look for a natural harmony in ethics by considering the natural qualities of sentic states, their interrelation, and their dynamic properties, including sentic afterimages. These properties are not yet fully understood. If we consider sentic states as ordered merely according to a single dimension of pleasantness, as is often attempted, we necessarily find many contradictions. For example, so-called "unpleasant" sentic states such as anger may be very satisfying (and thus "pleasant" in a different sense) under the appropriate circumstances. Research into the unique dynamic system qualities of sentic states is required for understanding their relevance to ethical thought.

Thus, if, as it appears, ethical principles are inherently connected with and derived from certain sentic states, we may study how the application of these principles is reinforced by some sentic states and modes, and hindered and prevented by others. Sentics can contribute toward social ethics by making the application of ethical principles more natural—it can allow the ethical impulse to be frequently regenerated. It can help to avoid the distorting or brutalizing sentimentalities and injustices that result from an insufficient empathy/sympathy ratio.*

Social Significance

A practical problem of social ethics is discovering how to integrate these new findings and experiences into the social fabric. The knowledge of essentic form will give rise to numerous applications in communication with others and in environmental design. These possibilities will necessitate increasing discrimination to encourage socially desirable applications and discourage exploitative ones.

Further, the practice and experience of sentic cycles introduces a new element or input into probing of relationships. When people practice sentic cycles, especially together, they are made aware of the human qualities they share—through their own direct experience, not merely intellectually. This tends to make them more accepting of each other, and to develop an intimacy that is not easily come by in other ways. Sharing their experience and fantasies afterward can further add to mutual understanding and trust. People will thus be

* Although ethics is not justice, the concepts of justice and ethics are interwoven in our culture, in a way of which we are not fully aware. (For example, Mercy is an ethical concept, not an arm of justice, yet is used judiciously.) Love indeed is never just: more than just, it is a gift—both to the giver and to the receiver. Nurturing and giving of life commanded by the ethical principles has love as its source.

less dependent on chance circumstances in meeting the "right" person in order to experience the empathy that arises from intimacy. The recognition of the universal quality of sentic states is an ethical input, and the way a society may react to this input will be a significant clue to its own nature.

Considering sentic states in terms of the acceptance-rejection quotient as indicated by the horizontal component of the essentic form, we may prefer to cultivate a set of sentic states that are accepting, inclusive, incorporating, and that engender energy without destructiveness or hostility. An ethical educational approach derived from the biologic basis of sentics could lead us to educate the young at an early age in the elements of sentics, teaching them in practical terms how every individual has the ability to experience and communicate these states. Their relationships could gradually be transformed to include many individuals who previously might have been rejected and disliked. Through an enlightened cultivation of essentic forms for communication, and the enjoyment of sentic practice, many of them would no longer be quite as "ignorant of what they are most assured." Through sentic education we may hope for a greater sense of brotherhood, and in turn for less deprivation and isolation. The practice of sentic cycles tends to diminish prejudice by increasing our range of empathy. By discarding the timeworn notion that emotional qualities are vague and only matters of personal opinion, we make room for the natural roots of emotional communication that bind people together.

Our dislike of individuals is often based on our dislike of their sentic habits, which have developed in them as a result of their education and experience. (Some of these are "defense mechanisms" in Freudian thought.) An object of sentic training is to minimize the need for rigidified defense mechanisms, and to develop a sense of openness and trust. We shall always have much sorrow and pain, and also injustice; but the former could be borne better with sentic training, and constructive psychic energy could be increasingly provided to reduce the latter. We have seen in the past how hate breeds hate, contempt breeds contempt, and anger breeds anger. Allowing the expression of these in non-destructive sentic cycles, we may free ourselves from their chain of necessity.

Personal Relationship Idiologs and Ethics

Let us consider the question of how generalized emotions relate to those involved in a personal relationship with a specific individual. If one can experience generalized sentic states, it might seem that specific individuals might not seem important to experiencing sentic states. This would be a misconception, however, because the arc of communication from one individual to another is not complete unless it includes the final point—the point of both individuals' unique existence. A caress applied to the skin only is incomplete. In closing this arc, there is an inevitable commitment made. The time relations of this commitment are part of the sentic dynamics, the non-verbal cognitive aspects of the state. (Having accepted one another "in one's heart," one expects to stay there at least for some time!)

As we have seen, the sentic domain can elogize—hold images—of loved ones. Without such an image (not necessarily visual, of course), love that may be felt is not directed specifically at one person. There is what may appear as an essential sacrament in the bond between two people that exceeds simple sentic experience. This bond is formed, in effect, by the creation of an elogized sentic receptor in ourselves for every individual we care about. These elogized receptors are not interchangeable but unique. We may like dogs, but our own dog receives a special place, not only because of our sense of responsibility, but because we *know* that dog. To know in this sense does not mean to be introduced socially, or even to have a full psychoanalytic knowledge of that individual's case; but is rather a simple statement of the existence within us of that individual as an elogized, unique sentic receptor.†

If in our daily lives we may often tend to interpret Jesus' ethical principle as "love your neighbor, except for your neighbors," this reflects that the intellectual good will we might feel toward the unknown millions of the world is different in an important way from the love of those we know intimately. It is true that there is a similarity through understanding the generalized sentic state and the consequent sense of the "brotherhood" of man. But the communication arcs in those two situations are different. With individ-

† This is another instance of the cognitive aspects of qualities of emotions.

uals we know personally, a reciprocal relationship in the present is possible, communicated through essentic form. No such communication is yet possible between the distant millions.‡

Sentic Diet and the Environment

Application of the universality of essentic forms shall help us also to create environments that will favor the sentic states we desire.

Our society has already discovered how to do this for sex—though imperfectly. In fact, our culture is inundated with attempts to use the essentic forms of sex as a seductive tool. With the philosophy that everyone likes sex, a technology has been created in which visual and auditory essentic forms of sex are used to attract and excite as large a segment of the population as possible.

Such mono-sentic stimulation, however, tends to fixate people and leads to sentic impoverishment instead of achieving balanced sentic fluidity; this is all the more so when this form of sexual stimulation cannot lead to adequate resolution. It *is* very important to be aware of the pure forms of sexual communication. But it is important to cultivate our awareness of the pure essentic forms for the generation and communication of other sentic states as well.

Sentic hygiene would demand that we include in our environment adequate stimulation through the pure essentic forms of love, joy, reverence, and other related qualities. The power of these essentic forms to transform the state of mind is quite comparable to that of the essentic form of sex, although it may not be so for individuals who have become habituated addicts, so to speak, of sexual communication. The socially pervasive essentic forms of sex tend to produce a dependence on seeking this form of stimulation, often leaving little opportunity for seeking other sentic experience.

An important part of human nature is that a balanced experience

‡ Perhaps someday there will be a way of integrating essentic form communication, so that love flowing at a given time from one individual toward many others can be mutually felt at a distance. In music and the other arts, there are partial attempts at this, but reciprocity to a large extent is not really possible, although a concert performance can include elements of reciprocity. The possibilities in our society of sentic communication among large numbers of people—not in a confused, chaotic state, nor as simultaneous response to only one sentic stimulus—need exploration.

of sentic states allows each one (including sex) to be experienced more fully than exclusive concentration on one state. A degree of variety is essential in human life. The best food, the most beautiful scene, the most lofty sentic state experience palls if not interspersed with other experiences.* Failure to recognize the need for variety as a basic data processing requirement of our nervous system vitiates much of our planning, and of the realization of the principles of social ethics.

Our need for sentic variety is well pointed out by dreams. Each dream may be constructed around two or three sentic states, a state persisting for a large part of the dream. With a series of dreams a fairly comprehensive idea of an individual's sentic requirements is portrayed. They may well include most of the spectrum of sentic states; but specific omissions may be significant. The need for varied sentic experience, as evidenced in dreams, may be a better indication of our needs for a balanced sentic diet than the comparatively vague notions and rationalizations we are able to conjure up in our awake state.

It is especially significant that we find indications that *reverence* (one's relationship to an existence larger than oneself) also appears to be a natural ingredient of a balanced sentic diet. Our balanced daily diet might well include the experience of the essentic form of reverence. Indeed, it is amazing to see, over and over again, how the intensity and enjoyment of that phase increases in the course of just a few experiences of sentic cycles in subjects to whom reverence is initially rather meaningless. They spontaneously come to discover its importance in their lives. The wordless implications of the state are understood and function in them. They sense their need for this state.

It seems that many of those millions who are apparently devoted to the cultivation of sex have highly repressed desires for the satisfaction of their spiritual hunger!

* The physiological phenomenon of adaptation based on rate sensitivity holds also for sentic experience. The range of adaptation time constants involved needs to be further experimentally determined and certainly will vary for different sentic aspects, over a range of hours, days, to months.

The Sentic Principle of Non-Equivalence of Individuals

The new techniques of communication that have been practiced at such centers as Esalen often enable individuals more readily to experience love and other sentic states and to express these freely toward one another. After experiencing them, one soon realizes that these forms of communication have an element in common with the free communication of a musician, even though they may be directed at specific individuals. Successful participation in such groups may allow one to feel love toward practically all participants.

Such experiences are very real. Yet, they are incomplete in one respect. In such a condition of "love," it tends to be possible to substitute one individual for another without a corresponding experience of loss. To exaggerate the point, if one participant were to drop dead and a new member to take his place, one could relate to the new member (given a similar amount of time) in much the same way as to the missing member.†

Such relationships, however, leave out an important part of the communicational link. The communication channel of love must find its way to the *unique* elogized image of the particular individual —we must, in common parlance, "care" for that individual.

Sentics appears to be able to make a contribution to this problem in clarifying the distinctions involved. Sentic theory suggests that it is *not* because of individual differences that we regard individuals as unique. In fact, it is a consequence of sentic theory that paradoxically, *individuals would be unique even if they were identical to one another.*

To illustrate the distinction involved, let us consider a conversation I had with Pablo Casals some time ago, in which we talked about sentic studies. Having discussed implications of sentics for a time, Casals rejoined, "I am a philosopher too," and continued, "Tell an eight-year-old child that in the whole history of the universe no individual ever has been just like him, nor will there ever be another individual just like him—that he is a unique experiment of the

† While each individual may be different, those differences are more like the "spice" than the "meat": one relates primarily to their essential humanity and secondarily to their specific differences.

universe, a unique participant! If the child understands this, how can he ever kill or commit the atrocities we find around us?" That is, Casals implied, if a person is aware of his participation in the universal process as a unique link, he will feel responsible, and have a natural ethical desire, a sense of belonging participation in the universal process. His "uniqueness" is given by his particular constitution and corresponding natural gifts, which have never occurred before, nor will ever be duplicated again in this specific way.

But we need to proceed one step further. We need to recognize the essential uniqueness of each individual, *regardless* of his specific individual differences. It is not these differences that make him unique, but the facts of his being *an entity capable of being elogized.*

Any part of the entity of a molecule can be replaced by substituting an equivalent atom. All atoms of the same element are equivalent. In a relationship between people, however, such equivalence does not exist. The difference lies in the imaging or elogizing function of fantasy processes which constitute an indispensable aspect of empathy. We shall try to formalize this more precisely.

Let us consider a relationship between two individuals. A and B. If one were to substitute, in theory, an exactly similar individual A′ for one of the people (A), two possibilities may exist. If the other individual is not told of the substitution he would be deceived and would regard the substituted individual A′ as the one replaced (A). If he knows however that two individuals were involved, two separate images will be elogized in his sentic domain, one for each of the two individuals. Empathy will allow him to experience the absence of one individual as a *loss.* Such a loss is in no way canceled by the presence of the new, second elogized entity. The second entity may mitigate one's sense of loss and be a compensation for the loss, but would not allow the individual literally to forget the loss of the first entity. A loss followed by a gain, even of the identical entity, does not cancel to *no event* (this is an application of unidirectional rate sensitivity and rein control to living systems). The situation is different from that of a molecule in which one atom has been replaced by another, equivalent atom. The state of such a molecule in no way reflects that a substitution has taken place.

The knowledge of twoness acts as a branch point that provides for the separate images in the data processing scheme of the nervous system. Without that knowledge, the processes of empathy could not function adequately: the result is that there are two elogized images, not one. This constitutes a sentic ethical principle of nonequivalence. We may state it formally thus:

> Individuals are elogized as unique entities regardless of how similar they may be to one another. They cannot be substituted and are empathy non-equivalent, i.e., ergodic substitution is impossible.

The process of elogizing individuals results in a one-to-one correspondence between an individual and his elogized existence in the person with whom he has a relationship. Accordingly a substituted individual is a contradiction in itself. Love permits no substitution. This is in fact so, no matter how closely similar the two individuals may be. The similarity may make it quite difficult to form coherent distinct images but this is an unessential difficulty, giving rise to some confusion at worst.

Generalized love and love for a particular individual differ in that for the latter a specific individual is elogized and forms a living image in the person who loves. Such an "elogy" of an individual, like a thought, cannot be "unthought." It (and its recall) can only fade —for good or bad, as it may be!

FOURTEEN

Sentics and Space Travel

Insight into the relationship of sentics to ethical principles may help us deal with some of our problems with our earth environment.

However, when we venture out of the earth environment into space, the very nature of our biologic programming may bring us into a new source of conflict, the nature and potential danger of which can become clear through sentic considerations. In this chapter, we shall consider the effects of space travel on our earth-made biologic emotion communication systems. This may prove to be instructive in thinking about our emotion communication design in the larger frame, as inhabitants of the universe.

About fifteen years ago Dr. N. S. Kline and I developed the concept of the *cyborg*, which denotes how a man may extend his regulatory processes to suit the environments he may choose to live in. The cyborg concept suggests that a man traveling in space should not be constrained to take an encapsuled earth environment with him; rather, he should use his intelligence to redesign his bodily regulatory processes, supplementing them with artificial automatic homeostatic devices, to allow him to exist more naturally in a "foreign" environment. Such a man, redesigned by himself to fit the environment he chooses, is a cyborg. By analogy, if a fish wanted to live on land, he should not surround himself with a bowl of water, but, as a smart fish could, design himself special gills so that he could breathe air.

We proposed then that man has enough intelligence to begin to redesign his systems in just that way. Wherever possible, he would do far better to redesign his physiological regulatory systems so that he could, in the new external environment also, near optimally regulate his internal environment without his conscious attention. Today, insights contributed by sentic theory have significantly altered our understanding of the problems involved.

Experience with sentics has disclosed that specific modes of emotional expression are related innately to the direction and strength of gravitation. Space travel changes man's ability to express emotion, and also affects his need for it. The ways in which these changes occur suggest some new ways in which his needs may be satisfied.

Maintaining Emotional Health in Space

Man's exploration of space has been successful from the technical point of view during the last decade, but emotional exploration of his new experience and environment has not been spectacular. It may be too much to expect astronauts to provide us with a fully communicated view of their new enlarged experience. The exigencies of piloting their vehicles necessarily make great demands on them, and so we must be satisfied with the language of "wows" and "man-oh-mans's" and similar expletives, whose implications we can only guess at from their contexts on earth. But communicating new emotional possibilities is only part of the story that remains to be developed. The other part—perhaps in the long run more important—is to provide for the emotional needs of astronauts who are together confined to such small spaces for such long periods of time, often without significant emotional contact with human beings, other than their fellow astronauts.

To plan for extensive space travel adequately we need to understand man's psychological drives, needs, and qualities of satisfaction, as well as to provide for physiological homeostasis. We could call this aspect his "psychological" homeostasis, but that tends to be misleading, since there is an indissoluble connection between his mental and physiologic functions. And of course, we are more advanced in understanding the process of physiologic homeostasis than those that include psychologic homeostasis. How can man be "authentic" in space?

Some outstanding components of the astronaut's emotional experience are exhilaration, boredom, and anxiety. Exhilaration is fine, although at times it could provoke dangerous recklessness, but one wants to avoid the deteriorating effects of boredom, and at times of anxiety. The build-up of explosive needs, unsatisfied through long periods of deprivation, needs to be avoided.

The problem of the astronaut is not so very different from that of the inhabitants of earth. Man has a need for both order and variety. Nature has provided both, but in his trip into space he may well suffer from too much order and not enough variety.

There is a strange technological imbalance between man's development of his tools and machines for the penetration of space, and his lack of progress in cyborg technology, even in the most obvious modifications of his own nature for the environmental goals that he sets. The first thing man needed to do on achieving the tremendous technological feat of landing on the moon was to sleep for eight hours! Of course, we do not know why man needs to sleep. But if the spaceship had such pervasive unknown needs, it surely never would have made it to the moon!

An essential part of sleep is to allow man his necessary dreams. Every man when he dreams has at his disposal an extraordinary faculty of imagination and fantasy. Even the "dullest" man, when he dreams, produces plays that he casts, directs, and acts in—and for which he even designs the costumes and sets. But the quality of those dreams in a prolonged space trip could become nightmares.

Sentic cycles enable a person—in space or on earth—to undergo a highly pervasive and integrating emotional experience. As noted, the sentic cycle experience affords the calmness combined with a sense of well-being and energy—it is not the calmness of a tranquilizer.* Hostile aggression is attenuated and there is a sense of belonging and of satisfaction in simply being. Although sentic cycles can be emotionally draining if done to excess, in proper measure no boredom sets in. Remarkably there is a collapse of the sense of elapsed time; a one-hour sentic cycle experience is often judged to be only some twenty minutes long.

All these attributes make sentic cycles interesting for possible use in space travel to provide for emotional stability and to prevent boredom.

The paralyzed subject in Colorado (Chapter Nine) has experienced conditions in some ways analogous to those of space travel. Because of her paralysis many of the sensory inputs available to normal individuals are eliminated for her. Even her sleep pattern is affected by the necessity that she be turned over every hour and a half throughout the night, which her husband has been doing for all these years! The fact that sentic cycles have made her life not only tolerable but even pleasant is relevant to the conditions facing the space traveler.

The Changed Nature of Emotions with Altered Gravity

As noted earlier, the expression of emotions takes place very differently in the absence of gravitation. Experiencing the virtual body images characteristic of sentic states shows that the position of the body and limbs in relationship to the direction of gravity is an integral part of the entity of the sentic state and of the essentic form. Virtual body images are closely linked to the force and direction of gravity. Reviewing aspects of them, we may note that for joy, for example, there is a sense of lightness, of bounce. As illustrated in Chapter Four, the essentic form of joy contains a rebound overshoot corresponding to a floating sensation. Grief, on the other hand, is ac-

* Sentic cycles may also be preferable to the use of various drugs, not only because the drugs may have side effects, but also because of the length of time it takes the body to recover from the administration of drugs. A suitable combination on sentic cycles with appropriate drugs may well be possible, however.

companied by a sense of heaviness of the limbs. There is also a tendency of the head to be tilted downward and to one side; for joy, the head tends to be tilted upward. The expression of anger has a strong downward component. Courage, also, is expressed directly in relation to the direction of gravity.

Expressing love with a caress normally tends to be with palms downward; the pressure exertions necessary to carry out a caress with the palm pressing vertically upward are foreign to our programmed forms of expression, tend to feel unnatural, and, if attempted, may block the feeling of the emotion associated with it.†

Furthermore, we may remember that in the introduction to this book we briefly discussed a specific emotion, which we have called being Apreene, that may be a prerequisite for the discovery of new ideas. For this emotion the head tends to be tilted slightly to the side and slightly upward, the body feels light, and there is no anxiety and fear, but an enthusiastic and yet a still eagerness, which waits to receive; the face has a characteristic openness and intentness, a rapt kind of attention, and there is a characteristic sensation in the forehead between the temples. This emotion too involves gravity! Does this imply, then, that the combination of lightness and strength experienced with this emotion (a feeling of not being totally earthbound—cf. "the flight of the imagination") will no longer provide us with the sense of newness, of being taken out of one's pedestrianism, in space travel where lightness is habitual?

Such questions really ask to what extent those inherent body images will be felt as missing in space travel, and to what extent they might be altered or retrained. If there is no gravity, how can the heaviness of grief find its expression? Will it no longer be heavy, or will it simply not be possible to express and even experience grief? Experiments in water tanks reveal the difficulties resulting from removal of gravitational forces on the ability to communicate and ex-

† During the Apollo-Soyuz flight, there was a memorable moment when the Russian cosmonauts shook hands with the astronauts. An especially memorable aspect, from the point of view of sentics, was that the Russian vigorously shook the astronaut's hand "vertically downward" with respect to his bodily orientation, and then having moved the receiving hand about four inches "downward" stopped at that level, holding the hand still. A firm, friendly, "manly" handshake, with a measure of commitment—this is how it appeared from the earth. But how did it actually feel, without gravity's confirming guide?

press emotions. When floating in water, the dynamics of gestures are modified not only because of the resistance of the water but because of the altered kinesthetic experience. In fact such an experience is a good illustration of the sentic principle of partial reciprocity. Floating in water tends to be pleasant in itself: the absence of heaviness tends to counteract possible bodily images of grief and related sadness, and is in accordance with virtual body images associated with joy. Much of the exhilaration of the experience of weightlessness appears related to this characteristic of the essentic form of joy. The experience is presaged in the experience of those who dream about flying with their own bodies. This is a very common dream. One pushes off with one's legs and then floats while usually looking down on the scene below with a delightful feeling.‡

The ability of dreams to provide us with a precise perspective of feeling and to create pre-verbal concepts for us is a crucial human function. How will conflict between virtual body images of emotion in astronauts' dreams be reconciled with their waking experience in space?

How do we account for the lightness of joy? What is it about joy that links it with lightness indissolubly? If on earth the shape of a caress has to be the way it is to express love, while a sexual caress, say, has a very different form, how might these forms be different in different parts of the universe? If each emotion has its own specific spatio-temporal form and if we should encounter some new emotions among beings living elsewhere, what might their essentic forms be? Clearly, emotions which we regard as the highest developed on earth may well be surpassed by more developed beings—it is not merely in intelligence but also in the spectrum of emotions that evolution proceeds.

The emotion-generating function of our dreams uses the essentic forms and the innate virtual body images that include the magnitude and direction of gravity. In the weightless condition of space, as also in conditions of different gravity, the traveler will find his accus-

‡ The author once had occasion to ask astronaut Cunningham if he had ever dreamt of flying in this way. He said he had done so, on a number of occasions. "And how did that feeling in the dream compare with your experience of weightlessness in space?" I asked. "Come to think of it, it was just like that feeling," Cunningham replied.

tomed emotional virtual bodily images at variance with experience. To what extent the essentic forms would be modified in prolonged space travel can now be investigated. Instrumentation necessary to do this is simple and light. Thus it appears the opportunity should not be missed in coming space flights to conduct these simple tests.

A specific question is whether the virtual body images—which involve gravity and appear to be genetically programmed into man's nature—would be affected by prolonged weightlessness. There is a direct correspondence—or coherence—between the expressed form and the felt experience. If there is an alteration in the form, the felt experience also changes. If the exigencies of space travel alter the expressed form, our built-in nervous system integration of that form would also alter the quality of the corresponding emotional experience. In other words, it is possible that disassociation may occur between gestures and experience even in the awake state. This would present a serious problem for the emotional stability and long-term viability of the astronaut's mode of life. Expressing essentic form with finger pressure and sentic cycles provide a possibility both to study this condition and to ameliorate it if it is a serious problem.

The ability of man to express his emotions in accordance with his nature is indispensable for a prolonged existence in space. In a weightless condition, can man's emotional nature function in an unaltered manner or—like a ballet of Mendelssohnian elves—will the dance of space necessarily require him to transform his emotional nature?

Virtual body images associated with each emotion have an unconscious origin. They are not willfully created by each individual—they represent human heritage. So do essentic forms. This unconscious heritage travels with us into space. But the autonomic and the unconscious meet, and so by understanding our unconscious sentic heritage consciously, we may be able to teach our autonomic systems to live in harmony with our old heritage, as well as with our new exploration of outer—and perforce inner—space.

FIFTEEN

Sentics and Natural Order: the Evolution of Sentic States and the Generation of New Ideas

Concerning the Existence of Emotion

We are in the habit of considering entities as "things," objects of matter in space. But we are not used to thinking of entities in time as existing in the same sense that things exist. In this book, we have tried to point out the error in this kind of thinking. Even in considering elementary matter, such as a photon, time cannot be left out: the frequency of the photon is an inherent part of its nature. Without time a photon could not exist. Quantum mechanics extends a similar concept to the nature of all forms of matter. The nature of matter depends on the existence of time. Without time, matter cannot exist.

In our language, however, we have become accustomed to distinguishing only forms in space as existing, as if forms in time did not exist. The concept of a "thing" literally embodies this attitude. This is reflected in the historical quest for an answer to the question

"What is emotion?" Thus, for example, we find McDougal saying, "emotion is not a thing," while other psychologists claim, "if emotion is not a thing, it is in effect nothing." Between the categories of things and nothing, much is excluded! On the other hand, others like Sartre, impressed by the "magic" of emotions, conceive that magic as equivalent to the "supernatural." If emotion is not a thing and yet is an entity (as seems to be sensed by Sartre), we would seem to be dealing with an apparently magical phenomenon!

However, if one recognizes that entities may exist in time, as well as merely in space, at least part of the magical aspect of the communication of emotions becomes "natural" magic rather than supernatural. That two magnets a distance apart attract each other is as magical as anything that we may observe. In that sense the communication of emotions is still magical. But we no longer need to regard it as supernatural, as unconnected with the order of nature.

What, then, is the nature of this connection? How do the entities of emotion derive their existence from the order of nature? We may again consider the two possibilities we raised in the early section of this book. The first is that they are the result of genetic mutations produced by chance, without any pre-existing conditions for their existence. That means that it would have been impossible, even in theory, to predict that these entities would arise.*

The other possibility is to consider these entities as among those which potentially exist in the order of nature, like specific molecules: i.e., that the potential existence of these entities is implied by the universal laws, and that their actual realization depends on the chance interaction of the processes of mutation (the pinball machine analogy). The quantum levels of molecules exist potentially whether or not a particular electron is captured. Likewise the entities or qualities we are considering may exist as potentialities, and become realized through chance processes of interaction.

In considering these two possibilities we should realize that if we

* This view can lead to attempts at synthesis such as the book by E. O. Wilson, *Sociobiology*, in which the qualities of emotion and experience appear as arbitrary byproducts of the DNA's program of producing more DNA (Wilson compares this process to a chicken being "an egg's way of making more eggs"); paradoxically, in this "synthesis" the elements of experience are not considered fundamental natural entities.

favor the first, then we must be prepared to accept the existence of two different kinds of entities: those that pre-exist like molecules, and those qualities that arise at random without any necessary basis in universal order. We then have to consider how the latter may exhibit the degree of stability and precision which we observe. The infinite precision of the existence of a molecule is not the precision of a machine.† A man-made machine has the freedom to make errors. No two mass-produced items are *exactly* alike. A molecule, however, can never make an error. It can never malfunction. The concept of accuracy is meaningless to it; it has no freedom to be inaccurate (this is regardless of the Heisenberg indeterminacy principle, which is itself highly determinate).

The stability of the phenomenon of red, or of love, across the centuries can be accounted for by genetic stabilities. But a crucial question is whether predispositions exist for the mutations involved in their development. Is it possible that some molecular combinations have an inherently more probable existence, and that these specific combinations are genetic language elements resulting in the specific spatio-temporal organization characteristic of those qualities? At present there is little direct evidence on the molecular level that this is so. Mutations may appear to have an equal chance for occurring regardless of their "constructive" aspects; we regard their continued existence as largely determined by natural selection. There is mounting evidence, however, that such a view is inadequate to account for what may appear as design choices.

It is simplistic to believe, a priori, that higher molecular organization is completely free in the sense that the organization of a hydrogen atom is not. It is conceivable that certain combinations of the elements of the genetic code form "words" that have a pre-existing "meaning." That is, the stability of existence of these configurations would not itself be of random nature, although their actualization would be the result of chance.

† A machine implies a specific function—a human design that determines the function of the machine (for example, a machine that makes bicycle parts). Such a human design is not rooted in natural law. An artist, on the other hand, may feel some compulsion to be faithful to an inner form he senses to be in accord with an aspect of natural order. (Such a constraint, rooted in the nature of qualities, is different from the constraint of "copying" from nature.)

This second alternative implies that such entities cannot arise from nothing, although they may arise by chance (in the same sense that the hydrogen atom does not arise from nothing). This would mean that a series of entities potentially pre-exist waiting to be realized through chance interaction. Clearly the qualities so far realized in our own development would represent only a fraction, and perhaps a very small fraction of entities existing in potentiality. A chance process of evolution would determine whether one or another pre-existing quality would become realized first. The order in which qualities come into existence would be subject to chance (though it may be that certain qualities have to exist first before others can come into being), as well as the time at which they come into existence. But the number and possible nature of the potential entities would be a predetermined function of natural design, implicit in the genetic code.

There is growing evidence of various kinds for this second alternative. Studies of enzyme structure have discovered that enzymes which have evolved separately, within totally different organic functional systems, nevertheless turn out to have similar structures—evidence for the "pinball machine" theory. Further, similar specific, highly ingenious solutions to environmental problems in totally different parts of the world are found in both the plant and animal world.‡ Language, too, may have arisen independently among separate human groups. Thus, on various levels we see nature displaying "preferred" solutions. We may try to account for these through purely statistical considerations, but there is growing difficulty to avoid concluding that some design choice is implied in the relative stabilities of some of the DNA molecule configurations in the genetic apparatus. We shy away from the concept of "design" if we regard it anthropomorphically, as intelligence having to make certain *new* choices. But we are well satisfied that there is design in the universe with regard to atoms and molecules; physicists admire the "elegant design" implicit in natural law—*that* in fact appears to be a source of its beauty, as well as of the awe and wonder which physi-

‡ For example, certain algae plants have adapted themselves to live at geyser temperatures of 170 degrees F. by similar "unique" means in Yellowstone Park and at Russian geyser locations.

cists often experience. Why then should we not permit ourselves to accept the possibility that design may be implicit in the more complex molecular organizations? Ultimately all universal design principles tend toward the simplest and yet encompass all of the complexities of the real world: there is no contradiction here, since experience of the entities of qualities is essentially simple while the circumstances bringing it about are highly complex.

Concerning the Evolution of Sentic States

The evolutionary processes that give rise to qualities can also be considered to give rise to the special class of qualities of sentic states. Different sentic states thus may have developed at different stages of evolution. Our observation that the electrical activity of these specific states influences different regions and orientations of the brain is in accordance with this supposition.* P. D. MacLean's concept of the "Triune Brain" also supposes different types of emotional experiences at various levels of brain evolution.

However, advances in genetic engineering may make it theoretically possible that the next sentic state to be evolved might not have to await a random event for its actualization. If the nature of the relative molecular stability of the genetic code pertaining to specific sentic states is known, it is conceivable that it should become possible to produce a new sentic state by the actualization of another such stable configuration, assuming, of course, our speculations concerning the genetic bases of the evolution of sentic states are correct. It may even become possible to predict the nature of the next essentic forms to appear, provided a fully comprehensive mathematical theory of essentic forms can be formulated.

Thus, the main underlying hypothesis for these considerations is that *the evolution of qualities and of sentic states represents the gradual actualization through random influences of potential exist-*

* That does not mean, however, that specific sentic states are associated with specific centers of the brain. It is clear that in any sentic state a large part of the brain is involved and not just a localized region. Nevertheless, it does appear that the electrical activity is modulated in specific ways in different parts of the brain for each sentic state.

ence inherent in natural order (in a way similar to the evolution of molecules).

The striving of the individual may be seen as an attempt to actualize selective potentialities. In this perspective, his own selection may in some ways seem to parallel the selection of evolution: sentic qualities most recently developed by evolution may promise the most potential "growth" for the individual, communication of the "highest" sentic states, as an element of culture, seems to be in accord with the direction of evolution. In this way, men like Beethoven who consider their function to be messengers of a higher *Geist* may also pioneer in evolution.

Concerning the Source of Order in the Process of Fantasy. Evolution of Ideas: BEING APREENE

As we noted, in the creation of dreams the sentic state appears to act as a generating matrix into which specific details of the construction of the dream fall. This "falling into place" of specific details when a given sentic state is established similarly is an important part of the creative process. When we try to recall someone's name from memory, an aspect of our awareness goes blank for some seconds, while some unknown process "searches" our memory, within a certain "set," until we "remember" the name or item for which we search. Likewise, it seems there is a specific sentic state which acts as a receiving template, as a "catcher" of new ideas—a state in which one is ready to receive the details pertaining to the set, like an aspect of the process of dream creation. Being in that appropriate state, a concatenation of ideas will naturally occur.

We have no conscious understanding or even experience of this organizational process and no word has been developed to denote it. Yet it is one of the most important functions of the brain. This state allows certain freely operating processes to occur, even though we do not consciously experience the details of these processes. We merely experience a general state of readiness, an openness to receive. Yet in those moments, searching combinations are taking place without pressure, without binding concentration, without conscious logical thought restraint. Such thinking, however, represents elements of logic also, but the logical thought appears to be the result of brain function rather than that of a "rational"—i.e., conscious examination—of each element of thought. In this sense rationality may be said to be inherent brain function: an unconscious rationality not subject to learning as syllogisms but simply exercised and available to be freely used. (The use of rationality to avoid inconsistency and self-contradiction is only a shadow of its real function—a secondary rather than primary aim of the creative reasoning process.)

In thinking of new ideas we need to place confidence in our creative reason, much as we have confidence in the creative dream process—a deep confidence "to let it happen." After the connections have been made we may test them for inconsistency, and reject an idea. *But we must not reject ideas before they are born.*

How do we reject ideas before they are born? By not providing suitable conditions to allow the birth of new ideas, we in effect abort them, or prevent their conception. In the introduction we have described a state that accompanies their conception. We shall call that sentic state, which nurtures the quest for new ideas, "being apreene." This sentic state, like others, has particular concomitants of body posture, facial expression, and a virtual body image. As we have described it, the head tends to be tilted slightly to the right and slightly upward, the body feels light, and there is a characteristic sensation of sideways expanding pressure in the forehead between the temples. Inhalation takes place slowly and steadily, while expiration is rapid. It is a specific intellectual fervor, an openness, receptivity, enthusiasm, a readiness to receive.

New creative ideas occur probably mainly through the sentic state of being apreene. Without that state, ideas that are found may well never exceed the pedestrian. In an apreene state new ideas appear in an unexpected manner. They employ reason, but not what is taught as "reasoning" in school. The unexpected ideas surpass those that can be obtained through conjecture. In this state, the quality of ideas is transformed—the unconscious processes appear to be involved to a much higher degree. We stand there with "a net," in readiness, waiting for "the fish to be caught."†

† Some of the concepts that form the basis of this book presented themselves to the author in such a way and in dreams, and he was forced to follow their consequences whether he wanted to or not. In the state of being apreene, ideas may present themselves with "demonic" power—the result of an agency outside the willful direction of the individual.

Having identified its essentic form (see Plate 10), we see that being apreene is a sentic state that can be elogized, practiced, and cultivated. And to have named it makes it easier to do.

The state implies also a total absence of fear and a willingness to accept whatever may come without fear of its implications. This may be a factor why certain types of creativity are so rare in totalitarian states. To be armed with courage and *thus* not afraid may require a mental set which can be inimical to creativity. Rather, the unafraid searcher needs trust. Trust that whatever may come into his awareness is worthy to be well received and even treasured. Indeed, we may even say that the processes of fantasy contain a "whole" or "holy" aspect which man may tap. When he has found this, a man knows it, and this is part of the apreene sentic experience. As Hermann Hesse phrased it, "Be a window to let the light in."‡

To be apreene is a concomitant to the unconscious processing that takes part in creating new ideas. Having named and identified the state, it has become more amenable to consciousness. Like the verb "to think," it remains a mystery, but now we can, through the word, evoke the state—and through its essentic form, practice it.

‡ We should be very careful to differentiate between the apreene state which is focused on the receiving of new ideas, and the state of empathic involvement that encompasses the drama of personal existence and its emotions. Being receptive to ideas is not the same as being sensitive or "listening" to people.

SIXTEEN

A New Form of Laughter: A Prediction of Sentic Theory

In the preface we alluded to recent, exciting findings of sentics concerning laughter. It seems fitting to approach the end of this book with a short chapter on laughter. What an extraordinary existence laughter is—how important in our lives—and yet, how little do we know about its functioning!

Laughter, like speech and crying with tears, is found on earth only among humans. Although some birds and animals, such as the laughing bird and hyena, can produce what sounds to us like laughter, these sounds are not associated with any apparent sense of humor. And though other animals in turn seem to display degrees of what appears like a sense of humor, they do not laugh. The combination of laughter with the sensation of "funniness" seems a specifically human development. We should thus expect the sentic study of laughter to be a particularly interesting example of communicating specific qualities through expressive dynamic patterns.

There are, of course, many kinds of laughter. A particular laughter combines in its expression aspects of both the individual's character and the particular situation that gives rise to it. An individual's spontaneous manner of laughing contains sentic information about his person. The sentic significance of the subtle shades of one's tone of laughter reveals one's present sentic state but also one's "point of view." We can recognize a person by his mode of laughter almost as well as by his speech. In part, this reflects the characteristic configuration of sound produced by the individual's particular resonant structure. But to a great extent, choices of sentic use of inflection and subtleties of dynamic voice changes are also personal characteristics of the individual.

Like the subtleties of relationship of tones in music, the tones and inflections of the countless possible gradations of laughter reveal more and more, the closer one listens. As one listens attentively, the precision of laughter as communication, more than almost any other single form of behavior, can afford direct, intimate knowledge of the individual. Laughter is able to transmit various sentic states implicitly, as a "sentic carrier." There is joyful laughter, malicious laughter, sardonic laughter, embarrassed laughter, spiteful laughter, and so on.

Like other essentic forms and sentic states, laughter can also be experienced as a generalized sentic state, without either a cause or recipient.* In the most common experience of laughter, an urge to laugh (which may be suppressed) is provoked by a particular situation, perception, or idea. As one laughs, this urge is satisfied. After a certain duration of laughter, there is no further urge to laugh. (But there is an aftereffect on the sentic state and an afterimage.) The urge to laugh and the dynamics of its expression and satisfaction are also affected by the prior sentic condition of the individual. Like orgasm, sneezing, or sobbing, laughter is a repetitive biologic pattern.

At times, one experiences paroxysms of laughter, in which the laughter keeps triggering itself. Less and less of the provoking stimulus is required to maintain laughter. This experience is close to laughter without a cause. But most commonly, we recognize what it is we are laughing at. There is usually a cognitive aspect to the initiation of laughter; that is part of our notion of a "sense of humor."

* There have been devices available from time to time that produce sounds of laughter. These can make one laugh, in sympathetic resonance, without other "reason."

How Laughter Is Provoked Mentally

A sudden perceived incompatibility of two idiologs of sentic significance is involved in provoking laughter. To induce laughter, the two incompatible idiologs have to be viewed with detachment from a point of view in which both idiologs are contained in a higher synthesis. The suddenly discovered integration is: "Order I" and an element of disorder with respect to Order I are viewed with detachment from "Order II," the point of view of the person who laughs. From the point of view of Order II, the element of disorder has become only an apparent one.

When we are tempted to laugh at ourselves, we recognize incompatibility between two elogized views. A child who is running may fall and cry, but the same fall may cause him to laugh if he has at that time a spectator-like, detached point of view, which allows him to discover the sudden fall as only an apparent element of disorder in a larger sense of belonging. The late Alan Watts often used to start meditation with a characteristic deep laugh, continued for some time—an image of cosmic laughter, which clearly illustrated the disparity between the world and our possible ideas of it.

But not all incompatibilities of idiologs are automatically conducive to laughter. What distinguishes these is our attitude or point of view—another instance of the influence of the point of view on the quality of experience.†

If a dressed-up man walks along the street and suddenly falls into a ditch, we may think it funny if we have a "spectator" point of view. Sympathy would prevent one from laughing: one would respond with a similar sentic state to the person concerned (e.g., being mad at the construction company which neglected to cover up the ditch).

The integration of laughing may, however, sometimes involve empathy. This power of laughter is used successfully, for example, in the art of Charlie Chaplin. By dressing himself as a tramp, he creates two incompatible idiologs: his dress as opposed to that of the rest of

† In terms of other aspects of sentic theory, we can also distinguish between Apollonian and Dionysian laughter, each with corresponding virtual body images, and between laughter directed at an event remembered from the past, or at a present situation, or in anticipation of the future.

society. But this is funny in itself only because we are able to subsume both idiologs in a larger human integration: a recognition of the artificiality and vanity of dress. Chaplin induces empathy involving the condition of man. It is not a question alone of resonating in sympathy with the plight of the unfortunate. This is no laughing matter. His achievement lies in requiring from us a higher integration in empathy in which we may laugh and also be compassionate.

The New Dynamic Form of Laughter

Although much has been written on *what* makes us laugh (by Freud, Eastman, and Bergson, among others), the physiology of laughter, amazingly, has received only the scantest attention. Laughter contains two distinct action patterns: (1) a breathing pattern and (2) a voice pattern. Both the breathing and voice patterns have a characteristic "chopped" nature. Breathing consists of a series of expiratory puffs or bursts (or "step functions," in control theory terminology). These occur at the rate of about five per second. If there is no more air left to be expelled, a fast, gasping inspiration is taken, and the expiratory bursts are interrupted only to allow the necessary inspiratory gasps to take place, until laughing stops.

With each expiratory burst, there is also a muscular activation of the vocal cords, in a similar chopped manner. Both processes operate together in the expression of laughter.

We have seen that in the expression of a particular essentic form many different motor output modes can be used (Principle of Equivalence). Using finger pressure is one such example. According to the theory, therefore, the voice component in laughter may be regarded as one of a number of possible motor output modes. Thus, we may predict that, maintaining the respiratory component, it should be possible to *replace the vocal component with another equivalent motor output*. If this motor output has sufficient degrees of freedom and is activated in a dynamic pattern similar to the voice component it replaces, the experience of laughter should be realized.

This means that it should be possible to replace the voice component by a repetitive finger pressure—a finger pressure recurring at the same rate as the chopped character of voice would have, and related to the *simultaneously maintained* chopped breathing pattern. This would not produce the same sounds of laughter, but it should permit the full quality of laughter to be experienced.

In fact, it is readily possible to do this. As one tries, one senses the experience of funniness "locking in" with the new expressive pattern, and one becomes clearly aware that he is laughing. The sense of funniness "locks in" only when the pattern is done the "right" way—at the right frequency, phase, and angle. This voiceless "touch" laughter also produces the same paroxysms as the familiar laughter, and it is often difficult to stop laughing in this way, once begun. It may even be easier to laugh in this manner without a particular cause. A similar release of tension is achieved by this new form of laughter as that experienced with the usual laughter. It is enjoyable, and can be maintained for considerable periods of time.‡

No subject has failed to experience laughter in this new way. The frequencies of repetition are approximately five per second, corresponding to the frequency observed in customary laughter. The mean frequency observed in twenty subjects was 5.03 per second with a standard deviation of $\pm$ 0.18. If the reiterated finger pressure is stopped, the laughing stops also. If the frequency is significantly faster or slower than five per second, the sense of funniness is lost.

A second interesting observation concerning the new laughter is that the vector *angle* and wave form of finger pressure turn out to be related to the specific sentic quality associated with the laughter; joyful laughter, for example, tends to be vertically up and down, similar to the angle exhibited by the essentic form of joy. Malicious laughter on the other hand tends to be strongly away from the body, like anger and hate; while sardonic laughter is toward the body somewhat like the expression of guilt.

Thus it is possible to distinguish between joyous, merry laughter, malicious laughter, sardonic laughter, and gradually to characterize

‡ On one occasion, the author was laughing in this way during most of a rather boring lecture at a recent meeting. He was sitting in the last row of the hall, thinking that no one would be disturbed, as he did not make any sound. At the end, a lady sitting next to him asked, "What were you laughing at so much during this lecture?" She turned out to be the wife of the chairman of the meeting!

other forms of laughter that shall define themselves, much as the essentic forms have defined themselves in the course of the work outlined here. By presenting different types of laughter-provoking stimuli to subjects—jokes, pictures, cartoons, or sounds—and letting them express laughter on the finger transient, it is possible by observing the vector angle and the dynamic characteristics of pressure (as with the inner pulse of a composer) to obtain measurements that may be related to the subjects' point of view, their possible sadistic or masochistic tendencies, and various other aspects of personality.

The new laughter is useful in itself, but its greatest importance is that it *independently confirms the existential coherence between expressive form and experience.* This coherence is not learned, but is part of the dynamic program of human nature, implied in the genetic code: a coherence existing as a bridge between the subjective and the objective.

The new laughter has existed, potentially, like a molecule exists potentially before it is formed. It was just left to chance for us to think of realizing it. The correspondence between the expressive dynamic pattern and experience, as a unique entity, appears to be an aspect of our being in touch with reality (as it defines itself to us). Because of it, we can ask questions concerning dynamic expressive forms in ways similar to questions we ask concerning the form of a particular molecule.

But what is it that determines the correspondence between a particular expressive form and a specific quality of experience? How is it that love and laughter have the particular essentic forms they have? If we can answer that, we may be able to find new forms of expression for new sentic states beyond the range of our present potential for experience.

Epilogue

As I write this, I seem to hear a kind of cosmic laughter, laughter at our feeble efforts to understand—laughter provoked by the incompatible idiologs of our efforts and the enormity of the task —the seemingly deliberate need for comprehension *beyond* human capacity inherently required.

Beyond this, I feel the need to express gratitude, a sense of responsibility, and awe for having been allowed to explore a little of that expanding island of the unknown in the ocean of the unknowable—an island that is expanding more and more as the answer to every good question raises several others in chain reaction.

Every such question partakes of both fantasy and reality, as we have seen. And as we endeavor through sentics to see more reality in fantasy, and more fantasy in reality, we may also progress in clarifying thought—as we become more aware of the dynamic anatomy of emotion in ourselves, and in the world around us.

Man, the breeder of questions, may he find his Blessing—answer to no question.

and he said
with a smile,
"The Kingdom of heaven
is also
Where fantasy and reality
meet."

APPENDICES

I. *Biologic Design Principles for Sentic Communication*

1. A *sentic is a single-channel system; only one state can be expressed at any one time.* (Exclusivity Principle; see page 18)
2. A *sentic state may be expressed by any of a number of different output modalities.* (Equivalence Principle; page 18)
3. *Regardless of the particular motor output chosen to express a sentic state, its dynamic expression is governed by a brain program or algorithm specific for that state which shall be called essentic form.* (Coherence Principle; page 18)
4. *The production and recognition of essentic forms are governed by inherent data processing programs of the central nervous system, biologically coordinated so that a precisely produced form is correspondingly recognized. The recognized form in turn generates a sentic state in the perceiver.* (Complementarity Principle; page 18)
5. *The intensity of a sentic state is increased, within limits, by the repeated, arrhythmic generation of essentic form through E-actons.* (Self-Generating Principle; page 25)
6. *Sentic states may be experienced and expressed as pure qualities or identities, without reference to specific auxiliary relationships to generate or receive these qualities.* (Experience of generalized emotion; page 43)
7. *The power of essentic form in communicating and generating a sentic state is greater the more closely the form approaches the pure or ideal essentic form for that state.* (Communicative Power as a Form Function; page 53)

II. *A Glossary of Sentic Terms*

Acton The simplest elementary unit of voluntary action: the brain action decision together with its execution, such as a simple single finger or eye movement.

Apollonian "Point of View" A point of view compatible with empathy from which emotions are experienced and savored as existential entities, rather than as ego-functions, implying a contemplative, somewhat detached, yet very aware and discriminating condition with characteristic Apollonian virtual body images for each emotion.

Being Apreene The state of eager expectancy in searching for ideas, which includes an intellectual ardor and openness. This emotion is accompanied by a sense of lightness and quiet in the body, the absence of anxiety, and trust that ideas received will be worthy. Its virtual body image is further characterized by a slight tension across the forehead, a slight inclination of the head, and initial inspiration of breath—an "inspired" waiting for an idea to come.

Blocking A phenomenon that occurs when an essentic form is not permitted to complete itself. A blocking of experience felt as a deadening, an inability to experience further, a frustrating feeling that is similar regardless of the nature of the essentic form left incomplete; a love acton, or anger acton, or joy acton not allowed to complete themselves all result in blocking and frustration. Blocking is related to repression.

Cognitive Aspects of Generalized Emotion Generalized emotion does not need a specific cause or recipient to be experienced, yet its experience influences the way we relate to the environment, the way we view ourselves and others. When we experience a specific sentic state, it also affects the way we know relationships, and our functions in a direct manner. Thus, for example, joy engenders brotherhood, anger fighting and violence, grief isolation. The state of bliss, in the same sense, has been regarded by religious leaders to impart cognitive relationships and understanding. The experience of sentic cycles itself has cognitive functions that change one's point of view and manner of relating for some time after doing them.

Dionysian "Point of View" The experience of specific emotions with full bodily involvement, as ego-function, accompanied by specific virtual body images: lightness, heaviness, sensations of flow, being "torn apart," and so on. Focal experience is centered lower in the body than with the Apollonian experience of the same emotion.

E-Acton An expressive acton, an element of communication-action whose form is modulated by the state seeking expression. The more precisely effective the modulating process, resulting in essentic form production, the more powerful the communication.

Elogize A word denoting the act of imagination, but not specific to the visual sense or any particular sense. One can elogize a specific quality (red, sour, warm) or a specific emotion (joy, anger, love, sex, reverence) or a particular form of movement (throwing, jumping, dancing). The term denotes the same process as the word "imagine" stripped of its visual bias.

Empathy The faculty of imaging another person in oneself, in his or her essential totality as a living being. Such an image importantly includes potentiality. It is always accompanied by good will.

Essentic Form The form that has developed biologically for the communication of a specific emotion state or quality. It is a spatiotemporal form, with a clear beginning and end, that can be expressed by various motor outputs: a smile, a gesture, the tone of voice, etc. In each case it is the essentic form that carries the emotional message as a precise dynamic form. It is the biological arc that bridges the isolation between individuals. Essentic forms are produced and sensed by symbiotically developed nervous system programs. They also serve as the emotion communication elements in music and art.

Generalized Emotion This is a term used for the experience of the quality of an emotion, either Dionysian or Apollonian, as experienced in itself without reference to particular causes or recipients. With our grammatically conditioned use of words, we normally say we are angry *at* someone, but not that we joy *at* someone; or, we love someone, but we do not anger or grieve someone (that in fact denotes causing anger or grief in the *other* person). In the experience of generalized emotions, these various grammatic references are dropped. In experiential terms, sentic cycles (as well as our experience of music) readily makes it evident that pure qualities of emotions can be experienced in themselves, without recourse to specific situations, causes, or recipients. Laughter that is generated by laughter itself, and other contagious means of emotion generation, constitute familiar examples.

Idiolog An imagined quality of experience (sensory, affective, or motor) together with its physiological brain process concomitants. One may have an idiolog of red, warm, joy, anger, a tone, a particular movement, etc.

Mimicry Expressive action that imitates essentic form without corresponding sentic experience. It is detached and disconnected from its affect.

Orthoessentic Form The ideal, true dynamic expressive form for a particular basic emotion.

Personal Relationship Profile (PRP) A collection of sentograms representing a person's sentic reactions to various individuals with whom he has relationships, such as mother, father, husband, wife, siblings, children, sweethearts, social friends, boss, subordinates, etc. In interpreting the PRP, these sentograms can be compared with the known sentograms of specific emotions. PRP sentograms are helpful in revealing the nature of relationships, and change markedly only when the nature of the relationship changes.

Present Moment Although the present in terms of physical science is infinitely short, in terms of human experience the present moment has a finite duration. In terms of the ability to make separate decisions and experiencing "chunks" of experience such as syllables, the minimum duration of a "present moment" is approximately 0.2 second.

Pre-sentic Control The ability to change one's sentic state voluntarily, freely generating each state in a condition of sentic fluidity without repression of another state. This ability, essential for great musical performance, is important in relationships with others and with the environment. It in no way conflicts with the simultaneous experience of inner peace, but in fact strengthens it.

Quality An irreducible element of experience that is not translatable in terms of any other element. Salty, sweet, red, joy, warm, and itching are such qualities—unique entities of experience whose existence is biologically programmed. Qualities are the transducers of experience; we are constrained to experience life through them. Their existence is highly stable.

Recognition A basic function that has meaning on many levels of existence, from that of elementary particles that relate to one another characteristically; to the recognition of molecular shape; to genetic programming through macro-molecular recognition and genomes; to immunologic recognition of antibodies and antigens; to the recognition of food and sexual mates; to the recognition of qualities and essentic forms. It is a reflection, a re-cognition of pre-existing relationship or existence.

Relationship Image The image of a characteristic relationship, such as "brother." It includes the potentiality of possible interrelation. "Mother," "father," "sister," "brother," "lover," "friend" are accepted names for such relationship images, although their existence as distinct or as interpenetrating images comes about within the person through their sentic significance.

Sentic Afterimage The experience of a distinct quality following a sentic state, which would not have occurred without the prior experience of the state. Not to be confused with the memory of the state and its recollection.

Sentic Cycles A specific succession of sentic states generated and experienced by a person in a quiet sitting position, through expressing the sentic states repeatedly with transient finger pressure on a nearby finger rest at intervals given by timing signals on a sentic cycle tape (or record). The timing signals are characteristically different for each sentic state in the cycle (No Emotion; Anger; Hate; Grief; Love; Sex; Joy; and Reverence), and are derived from the biologic timing of each essentic form. Doing sentic cycles is easily learned. The experience of thus traversing substantially most of the emotional spectrum in thirty minutes is cumulative and results in over-all significant effects lasting from three to twenty-four hours or longer, generally involving increased psychic energy and specific insight.

Sentic Fluidity Not to be confused with emotional instability, sentic fluidity is the condition of being ready to experience any sentic state appropriately, either in the Apollonian or Dionysian manner, and being able to switch from one state to another largely effortlessly, without compulsion, repression, or undue attachment to any one state.

Sentic Rut The opposite of sentic fluidity; the helpless attachment to a sentic state from which one is unable to free oneself. Frequently and often damagingly prevalent with anger, hate, and resentment.

Sentic State A state of emotion; a state encompassing a quality of experience linked with the motor system in a unique way that makes it capable of specific communicative expression.

Sentogram The graph of essentic form, or of sentic reactions to the environment or to other individuals as measured on the sentograph, consisting of traces of the vertical and horizontal components of an act of expressive finger pressure.

Sentograph The instrument that precisely measures the forms of the vertical and horizontal components of transient pressure on a finger rest as functions of time. May or may not have averaging capability.

Sympathy As contrasted with empathy, in our usage sympathy denotes co-resonance with the sentic state of another, the wave of contagion of emotion that spreads from one individual to the other. A chief method of contagion of emotion is through essentic form; one could say that essentic form is its biologic medium.

Virtual Body Image Every sentic state has its specific bodily sensations, such as the lightness of joy, the heaviness of grief, or the sense of flow of love. These sensations appear to be projections of the nervous system, rather than perceptions of physiologic changes as such. These projections seem to be characteristic of the sentic state, and programmed functions of the nervous system. They need to be distinguished from the experience of the actual body changes, tensions, relaxations, and breathing efforts that accompany the specific state. This concept strikes a balance between the concepts of the central (Cannon) and the peripheral (James-Lange) experience theories of emotion.

III. *Mathematical Appendix*

The generating or transfer function as given in the equation stated in Chapter Six:

$$\frac{U(s)}{I} = b\left(\frac{\tau_1\tau_2\tau_3 s}{(1+\tau_1 s)(1+\tau_2 s)(1+\tau_3 s)}\right)\left(\frac{\tau_4 s}{1+\tau_4 s} + \Omega k_p \frac{\tau_5}{(1+\tau_5 s)}\right)$$

is composed of two parts. The first part is similar in form to the "human operator" transfer function:

$$K\frac{s\,e^{-\tau_3 s}}{(1+\tau_1 s)(1+\tau_2 s)}$$

as determined for tracking tasks, for example, with the addition of another time constant. The second part is the sum of an adaptive and a unidirectionally rate sensitive term. The adding of two separate channels is primarily utilized by the passionate states, and is an expression of a special late-developing function.

This generating function is restricted to have meaning only for impulse inputs, related to the decision to express. The equation has physiologic significance.

The generating function includes a unidirectionally rate sensitive

Figure 35. Analog computer circuit for simulating essentic forms.

term; it is thus non-linear and multiplication is non-commutative; the input to the transfer function in the second bracket is the output of the transfer function in the first bracket, and not the reverse.

An analogue computer circuit for simulating essentic forms according to the equation is given in Figure 35.

The decision to express is expressed by the input impulse function. The output of the linear portion of the equation is represented by a sum of four exponentials, as functions of time with t=o at the time of the input. (These have independent time constants but interdependent amplitude coefficients.) The non-linear aspect of the equation has no known analytic solution but is easily computed on a

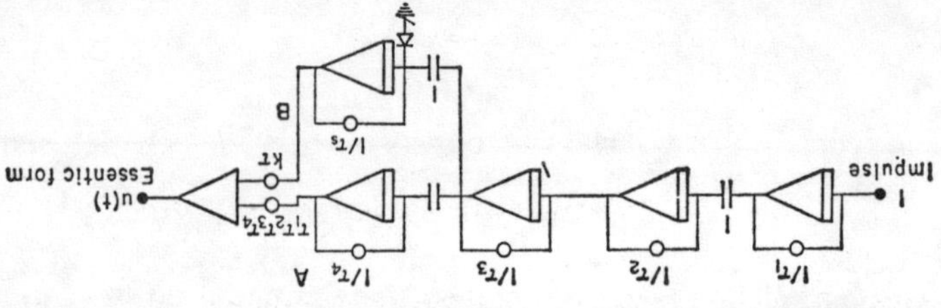

computer.

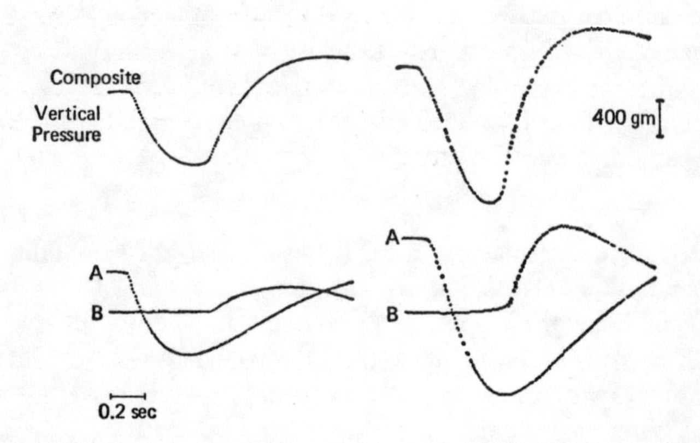

Figure 36. Components of computer essentic form simulation showing separate contribution of portions A and B of transfer function. B represents effects of late-acting muscle group.

As to the question of uniqueness, we may appeal to Occam's razor, or maximum simplicity, and to the possible physiologic significance of this formulation. And we certainly should look at this formulation, according to our present state of knowledge, as hopefully subject to greater refinement in the future.

Communicative Power as a Form Function

The theory that essentic form acts more powerfully the more closely it represents the "true" form may be formulated by the following form function relationship:

$$P_c = a(1 - e^{-\lambda/u-\nu})^n$$

where $u = \mathrm{u}(t)$ the pure essentic form
$\nu = \mathrm{v}(t)$ the actual essentic form
λ = a sensitivity constant
t = time
$n = 3$ at our present state of inquiry.
a is the maximum attainable value
$e^{-\lambda/u-\nu}$ represents the effective impurity factor.

This formulation takes into account that communicative power increases rapidly as the ideal shape is approximated; *u-v* in the exponent is taken as the time integral of the absolute value of the instantaneous difference between the actual essentic form and the essentic form required. This is a tentative formulation; it weighs departures from essentic form according to amplitude. A more comprehensive formulation would have to include frequency and time selectivity with respect to effective errors.

IV. *Music Appendix*

We shall here give a few examples of particular essentic form (rather than the inner pulse as described in Chapter Eight) and sentic experience embedded in music. The examples given may also be thought of as samples of sentic music analysis.*

To understand precisely how essentic form influences the communicating power of music, one needs to hear the music, inwardly or actually, as played with the various shades of expression engendered by selection from the living essentic forms. Those who can hear inwardly from reading the printed score and are familiar with the musical examples chosen will find it quite easy to follow the examples. Others may wish to hear them on records, and thus reconstitute the feelings, expressed sentographically in the illustrated examples, in order to obtain insight into the process.

In the examples that follow we are using a further extension of our methods for the analysis and measurement of musical expression. This recent development allows simultaneous independent measurement of the phenomena of essentic forms, as separate from those of the inner pulse. Two sentographs are used simultaneously, one for each hand: the right hand expressing the inner pulse; the left

* The reader may wish to consider the relationship of this mode of analysis to analysis in terms of tension and line, such as Schenkerian analysis (which treats music's unifying structure in terms of extended tonal tensions and resolutions). Sentic analysis is more specific about the nature of the tensions involved, and is able to observe and record them in detail.

hand expressing the essentic form (without the pulse), in a manner similar to our music-less method of expression of emotion.

The method of expression is somewhat like the movements of a conductor who may give the pulse or beat with the right hand while expressing special sentic aspects with the left hand. (It is not always easy to do. The recorded pulse of the right hand naturally tends to carry indications of the essentic forms implied as well as the inner pulse. However, it does permit the recording of the essentic forms without the pulse, while maintaining the framework within the living pulse structure.) In all these examples of particular interpretations, no sound was used; the expressions are produced as the music is inwardly thought.†

EXAMPLE I

Bach, Prelude in F minor, Bk. II, Wohltemperierte Klavier.

This example has characteristic two-note phrases often used by Bach (as well as by Mozart and other composers in their own way). Such a two-note phrase (in slow tempo) lends itself to a particular kind of ambiguity. It can be related to either the essentic form of grief or of love. As we have seen, these two forms have a degree of similarity, although they are quite distinct. One may suggest a sigh, the other a caress. Bach often uses such phrases in context of grief and sadness, as in the *St. Matthew Passion,* where the text makes the intent clear. However, the phrase may also be interpreted as a love acton. In fact, a proper combination of both modes, successively, may often be most meaningful.

In the sadness or grief interpretation, the grief acton starts on the first beat of the bar. The upbeat coincides with the "pick up phase" after the collapse (see Figure 37) which is characteristic of the grief

† A subject, the pianist Steven Manes, commented on how he experienced this: "It feels just like playing."

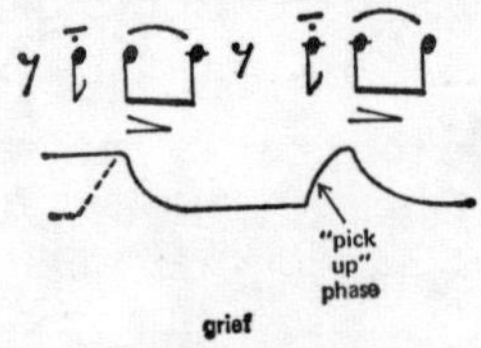

"pick up" phase

grief

Figure 37

acton. Consequently in such an interpretation the upbeat note is played in a slightly detached way (portamento). The last note of the phrase is considerably softer, and the beginning of the first note of the two-note phrase has a slight edge to it, as approximately indicated (see Figure 38).

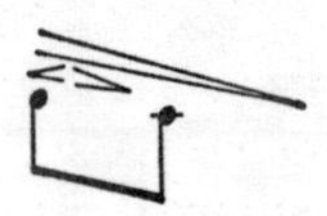

Figure 38

In the other mode of interpretation, the mode of love, the love E-acton begins earlier than the grief acton. The three notes are unified; there is a legato effect combining all three, the middle note falling near the bottom of the love E-acton. The last note would now only be slightly softer than the middle note (see Figure 39).

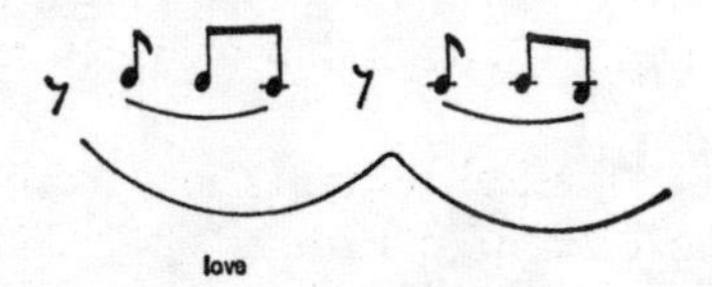

Figure 39

This interpretation lends itself here also in that the bass notes during the rest can be considered as coinciding with the preparatory upbeat for the love acton (inspiration). The breathing pattern implied here is more conjointed than in the grief mode (see Figure 40). In

Figure 40

each case expiration occurs on the first beat of the bar but in the grief interpretation the breathing rests at the end of expiration and is resumed with a kind of gasp, to be expelled again as a sigh. In the love mode, the breath alternates smoothly between expiration and inspiration. (For breathing patterns associated with love and grief see Chapter Nine.)

Thus in either case the particular E-actons act as a kind of template in which the musical parameters find their place. The detailed shape of the essentic form is inwardly implied by musical material but not completely filled. The imagination completes the form. Thus we tend to hear subtleties of inner forms, not all actually physically realized in the sound, but rather outlined. This is so even for realizations on bowed stringed instruments or the voice. With continuous sounding instruments, there may even be greater danger that the musician will provide actual sounds that conflict with the appropriate essentic form—for the listener such contrary produced sounds are difficult to think away.

In the example shown (see Plate 11 in insert) a particular interpretive solution there are grief actons for the first two phrases, the third one passing into more intense anguish, and the fourth one love. This progression is accorded appropriate meaning by the harmonic progression, and especially the B flat/B natural/C progression of the bass, the pull and harmonic resolution of which reinforce and guide the change in affect.

The nature of the musical meaning may be compared with the feeling tone of the Pietà (see Plate 5 in insert) on a much less grand scale.

EXAMPLE II

Chopin, Ballade No. 3 A Flat, Opus 47.

The main theme of this composition, given in the first four bars, has a unique magic of its own. (The ballade is composed after a poem "Ondine," the story of a fisherman enticed by a mermaid.)

The first half of this theme can be felt to embody longing, yearning, and ecstasy. It begins with a sense of being attracted, a pull, expanding, and at the second bar, there is a continuing sense of floating upward *after* the C is struck. This apparently limitless "being carried upward" is accompanied by a sense of ecstasy, lasting for a moment, till we are gently carried back to the ground by the following F–E flat phrase.

The inner form of this feeling and virtual body image may be illustrated graphically as follows (see Figure 41). There are several outstanding points to be made in connection with the expression of this.

First, this feeling is produced only if there is slight acceleration in the second half of the bar, and a corresponding lengthening of the first part of the second bar (rubato). The acceleration relates to the

Figure 41

feeling of being pulled, the attraction or surrender, the giving of one's self. The first part of the second bar is lengthened in turn and gives us that one extra moment (0.2 second) experienced as floating ecstasy. It is, as it were, an overabundance, a surfeit, and then one is gently returned, caress-like, to the earth, though still high up.

All this in the first two bars!

A second interesting point is the distinct inner form of the sound C one hears between the C and the F, *after* the C is struck in the second bar (an inner rising), which on the piano obviously cannot be realized. This inner sound, though only momentary, has to be supplied by the listener—it is sculptured out of his imagination—the essentic form forces him to think thus. Without this extra inner sound provided by the imagination, the phrase would be deprived of its magic power to lift one out of one's ordinary spheres of existence. This provides a good example of how a tone can be heard inwardly with a specific form, unlike its actual realizable physical sound. The sentographic representation of this will be evident (see Plate 12 in insert). Note also the reversal of the last pulse form on the horizontal trace, as well as a corresponding phase reversal on trace 4 indicating an inward movement, a caress ending the phrase.

(An analysis of the second part of the theme—bars 3 and 4—will not be given here, for reasons of space.)

EXAMPLE III

Mozart, Excerpt from Sonata in C Minor, K. 457, Second Mvt. (Bars 24-25), Adagio.

This theme of Mozart is note for note the same for the first five or six seconds as the theme of the slow movement of Beethoven's Pathétique Sonata. Op. 13, shown in Example IV. It is also in the same key and uses similar harmony. Yet the inner pulse is quite different. (If one were to substitute one for the other, one would necessarily stumble when conducting because of the different pulse forms and points of view implied; see pages 77–81).

The theme, repeated in the second bar, can be experienced to have a character akin to hope. The second part of the essentic form trace corresponds to a gentle, benign, Mozartean angelic smile which begins at the end of the "hope" phase. Note particularly that the hope form continues past the beginning of the third note of the melody—there is in fact a crescendo in intensity implied during the first half of the note—which of course the piano cannot provide. A bowed string instrument (or a singer) could supply what the "ear" demands here. Such a crescendo in intensity does not particularly mean an increase in total volume. Its tension can be expressed by a change in timbre, a greater and specific emphasis on the higher overtones as required in this example. Such refinements of tone production knowingly carried to the furthermost limits mark the power of the art of a Casals.

The hope of this Mozartean example is not an ego function, but is Hope, i.e. considered as an existence. The following "smile" acts as a kind of affirmation. The example represents an Apollonian point of view. (See Plate 13 in insert.)

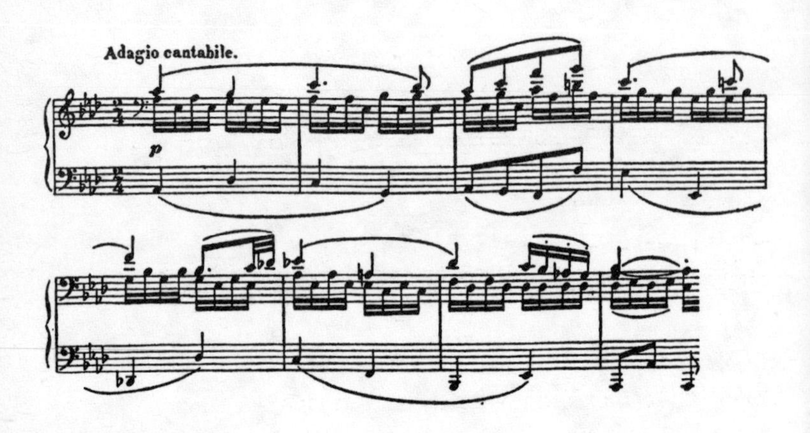

EXAMPLE IV

Beethoven, Sonata Op. 13 (Pathétique), Slow Movement.

This opening theme is note for note the same for the first two bars as the Mozart theme in the previous example. The pulse forms are different, however.

The world of this theme is noble, serene, and exalted. We find in it fulfillment, satisfaction, and at the end, especially, love and gratitude. The qualities of this theme on the whole are exalted so that it is difficult to find corresponding words to denote their character. Beethoven seems to be stretching the very fabric of our experience to let an unearthly, yet immediate light illumine and touch us. It would not be far wrong to say it has a holy quality.

The essentic forms are in part correspondingly unfamiliar, except where they suggest, as at the beginning, a particular kind of reverence, and at the end, love. Two different sentographic performances by the same artist are compared here. (See Plates 14 and 15 in insert; numbers on plates refer to the bars of the score.) The bottom trace is recorded from Sentograph I (right hand). The upper two traces are recorded from Sentograph II (left hand), representing essentic forms. (The horizontal trace contains a slight muscular tremor, invisible in the actual expression.)

EXAMPLE V

Schubert F minor Fantasy for Piano, 4 Hands

This example is chosen to illustrate transition from sadness to hope (bars 13–24).

The phrase of bar 23 illustrates how Schubert, by tying the three notes together (and by the harmonic content), implies the essentic form of hope. However, it is important to realize that it ends with the third tied note. (The essentic form of hope has a duration of about 3.3. seconds.) The following dotted rhythm is light, Schubertian, not a heavier march as if it were Beethoven. It is a good example of how the Schubertian point of view, implicit in the inner pulse form, constrains the particular phrasing. Through it, we are momentarily transported in thought to the future and view the fulfillment of hope with a particular joy. Variations of this juxtaposition of character—with faith, or triumph substituting for hope—give meaning and interest to the unfolding of the work. (See Plate 16 in insert.)

V. *References and Selected Bibliography*

Alland, A. "Cross cultural aspects of Clynes' sentic cycles," A.A.A.S. *Symposium, Biocybernetics of the Dynamic Communication of Emotions and Qualities.* Palisades, New York: American Sentic Association, 1970.

Allport, G. W., and Vernon, P. E. *Studies in Expressive Movement.* New York: Macmillan Co., 1933.

Arnold, M. B. "Brain function in emotion: A phenomenological analysis," *Physiological Correlates of Emotion,* P. Black, ed. Boston: Little, Brown, 1970.

Ax, A. F. "Physiological differentiation between fear and anger in humans," *Psychosom. Med.* 15: 433–442.

Barclay, A. "Innate releasing mechanism of aggression and sex in facial expression," A.A.A.S. *Symposium, Sentics, Brain Function and Human Values.* Palisades, New York: American Sentic Association, 1971.

Becking, G. *Der musikalische Rhythmus als Erkenntnisquelle.* Augsburg, Germany: B. Filser, 1928.

Bekesy, G. *Sensory Inhibition.* Princeton, New Jersey: Princeton University Press, 1967.

Bell, C. *Essays on the Anatomy and Philosophy of Expressions.* London: 1806.

Benson, H. "A review of Physiologic Changes in Meditation and Sentic Cycles," A.A.A.S. *Symposium, Sentics, Brain Function and Human Values.* Palisades, New York: American Sentic Association, 1971.

Benson, H., Beary, J. F., and Carro, Mark P. "The Relaxation Response," *Psychiatry* 37: 37–46, February 1974.

Bentley, D., and Hoy, R. R. "The Neurobiology of the Cricket Songs," *Scientific American* 231: 34–44, August 1974.

Bergleiter, H., et al. "The effects of awareness on cortical evoked potentials to conditional affective stimuli," *Psychophysiology* 5: (5) 517–529, 1969.

Bergson, H. *Le rive,* Paris, 1901.

Berkout, J., and Walter, E. O. "Temporal stability and individual differences in the human EEG: An analysis of variance of spectral values,"

EEG *Trans. Bio-Medical Engineering,* BME-15: 165–168, 1968.

Bindra, D. "Emotion and behavior theory: current research in historical perspective," *Physiological Correlates of Emotion,* P. Black, ed.: 3–18. Boston: Little, Brown, 1970.

Birdwhistell, R. I. "Communication as a multi-channel system," *International Encyclopedia of the Social Sciences.* New York: Macmillan Co., 1968.

Brown, B. L. "Paralinguistics: the tacit dimension in social interaction," *International Journal of the Sociology of Language.* In press.

Bruell, H. H. "Heritability of emotional behavior," *Physiologic Correlates of Emotion,* P. Black, ed. Boston: Little, Brown, 1970.

Bull, N., and Frank, L. "Emotions induced and studies in hypnotic subjects," *J. Nerv. Ment. Dis.* 3: 97–118, 1950.

Byers, P. "Anthropologic implications of sentic research," *A.A.A.S. Symposium, Sentics, Brain Function and Human Values.* Palisades, New York: American Sentic Association, 1971.

Cannon, W. B. *Bodily Changes in Pain, Hunger, Fear, and Rage.* 2nd ed. New York: Appleton, 1929.

Cattell, R. B., and Scheier, I. H. "The nature of anxiety: a review of thirteen multivariate analyses comprising 814 variables," *Psychol. Rep.* 4: 351–388, 1958.

Chase, R. A. "Recent contributions to the theory of innate ideas," *Synthese* 17: 1, 1967.

Clynes, M. "Communication and generation of emotion through essentic form," Karolinska Institute Symposium on "Parameters of Emotions." Proceedings published as *Emotions—Their Parameters and Measurement,* Lennart Levi, ed., 561–601. New York: Raven Press, 1975.

———. "The Biological Basis for Sharing Emotion," *Psychology Today,* July 1974: 51–55.

———. "A new laughter homologue, predicted by sentic theory," *Abstract, Society of Neuroscience.* New Orleans: October 1974.

———. "Essentic form: E-actons as programmed communication space time forms in the nervous system," *IFAC Congress.* Rochester, New York. *Regulation and Control in Physiologic Systems,* Iberall and Guyton, eds.: 604–607. Pittsburgh, Pennsylvania: Inst. Soc. America, 1973(a).

———. "Sentics: Biocybernetics of Emotion Communication," *Ann. N.Y. Acad. Sci.* 220: 55–131, 1973(b).

———. "Sentography: Dynamic forms of communication of emotion and qualities," *Comput. Biol. Med.* 3: 119–130, 1973(c).

———. "Sentography: dynamic measure of personal relationship profile," *Proceedings of 25th ACEMB Conference,* October 1–5, 1972.

———. "Sentics: Precision of direct emotion communication," in *A.A.A.S. Symposium, Sentics, Brain Function and Human Values.* Palisades, New York: American Sentic Association, 1971(a).

———. "Towards a theory of man, *Human Context* 3: No. 1, 1–75, March 1971(b).
———. "Dynamics of emotion communication in the present moment," *Proceedings, 9th International Conference of Medical Electronics and Biological Engineering*. Melbourne, Australia. August 1971(c).
———. "Biocybernetics of space-time forms in the genesis and communication of emotion," A.A.A.S. *Symposium, Biocybernetics of the Dynamic Communication of Emotion and Qualities*. Palisades, New York: American Sentic Association, 1970(a).
———. "Toward a view of man," *Biomedical Engineering Systems*, M. Clynes and J. H. Milsum, eds. 272–358. New York: McGraw-Hill, 1970(b).
———. "Biocybernetics of the dynamic communication of emotions and qualities," *Science* 170: 764–765, 1970(c).
———. "On being in order, *Zygon*, Vol. 5, No. 1, 63–84. Chicago: Chicago University Press: March, 1970(d).
———. "Towards a theory of man," *Human Context* 2: 367–449, December 1970(e).
———. "Sentics: The quantitative profiles of qualities and some human system applications," *54th Annual Meeting of the Federation of American Sociologists for Experimental Biology*. April 1970(f).
———. "Toward a theory of man: Precision of essentic form in living communication," *Information Processing in the Nervous System*, K. N. Leibovic and J. C. Eccles, eds. New York: Springer-Verlag, 1969(a).
———. "Cybernetic implications of rein control in perceptual and conceptual organization," *Ann. N.Y. Acad. Sci.* 156: 629–670, 1969(b).
———. ed. "Rein control or unidirectional rate sensitivity, a fundamental dynamic and organizing function in biology," *Ann. N.Y. Acad. Sci.* 156: 627–968, 1969(c).
———. "Speaker recognition by the central nervous system," Abstract, *The Society for Neuroscience*, November 1975.
———. "Doing Sentic Cycles by the Disabled and Paralyzed for Emotional Well-being," *Dis. Nerv. Syst.*, in press.
———. "A new form of laughter, predicted by theory," *Nature*, in press.
———. "After-image motion and the eye's kinesthetic sense," *Proceedings of the 21st Annual Conference on Engineering in Medicine and Biology*, Houston, Texas, November 1968.
———. "Computer analysis of reflex control and organization: respiratory sinum arhythmia," *Science* 131: 300–302, 1960.
———. "Respiratory control of heart rate: laws derived from analog computer simulation," *I. R. E. Transactions on Medical Electronics*, Vol. ME-7, 2–14, January 1960.
———. "Dynamics of vertex evoked potentials: the R-M brain func-

tion," *Average Evoked Potentials*, NASA, E. Donchin, ed., 177–206, 1969(d).

———. "Biocybernetic principles of dynamic asymmetry: Unidirectional rate sensitivity, rein control (or how to create opposites from a single measure)," *Biokybernetik* 1, H. Drischel and N. Tiedt, eds. Leipzig, 1968(a).

———. "Essentic form-aspects of control, function and measurement," *Proceedings of 21st ACEMB Conference*, 1968(c).

———. "Unidirectional rate sensitivity, a biocybernetic law of reflex and humoral systems as physiologic channels of control and communication," *Ann. N.Y. Acad. Sci.* 92: 946–969, 1961.

Clynes, M., and Kline, N. S. "Cyborgs and space," *Astronautics*, 26–27, 74–75. New York: American Rocket Society, September 1960.

Clynes, M., and Kohn, M. "Recognition of visual stimuli from the electric response of the Brain," *Computers and Electronic Devices in Psychiatry*, N. S. Kline and E. Laska, eds. New York: Grune and Stratton, Inc., 1968(b).

———. "Paradoxical pupil contraction to removal of colored light," *Proceedings of the 21st Annual Conference on Engineering in Medicine and Biology*, Houston, Texas, November 1968.

———. "Spatial visual evoked potentials as physiologic language elements of color and field structure," *Electroencephalogr. Clin. Neurophysiol.*, Suppl. 26, 82–96, 1967.

———. "Specific responses of the brain to color stimuli," *Proceedings of the 17th Annual Conference on Engineering in Medicine and Biology*. Cleveland, Ohio, November 16–18, 1964, pp. 22–23.

———. "Color responses of the pupil and brain of a monochromat," *Proceedings of the 21st Annual Conference on Engineering in Medicine and Biology*, Houston, Texas, November 1968.

Clynes, M., Kohn, M., and Gradijan, J. "Computer recognition of the brain's visual perception through learning the brain's physiologic language, *IEEE International Convention Record*, Part 9, 125–142. March 21, 1967.

Currier, R. "Sentic communication in a Greek island culture," A.A.A.S. *Symposium, Sentics, Brain Function and Human Values*. Palisades, New York: American Sentic Association, 1971.

Darwin, C. *The Expression of the Emotions in Man and Animals*. London: Murray, 1872.

Davitz, J. R. "A review of research concerned with facial and vocal expressions of emotion," *The Communication of Emotional Meaning*, J. R. Davitz, ed.: 13–29. New York: McGraw-Hill, 1964.

Davitz, J. R., and Davitz, L. "The communication of feelings by content-free speech," *J. Commun.* 9: 6–13, 1959.

Eastman, M. *Enjoyment of Laughter*. London: Hamish Hamilton, 1937.

Eccles, J. C. "The dynamic loop hypothesis of movement control," *In-*

formation Processing in the Nervous System, K. N. Leibovic and J. C. Eccles, eds. New York: Springer-Verlag, 1969.

Eibl-Eibesfeldt, I. *Ethology: The Biology of Behavior*. New York: Holt, Rinehart and Winston, 1970.

Einstein, A. "Autobiography," *Philosopher-Scientist*, P. A. Schlipp, ed.: 1–96. New York: Harper & Row, 1949.

Ekman, P., Sorenson, E. R., and Firensen, W. V. "Pan-cultural elements of facial display of emotions," *Science* 164: 86–88. 1969.

Engel, J. J. *Ideen zu einer Mimik*. 1785–86.

Ervin, F. R., and Sternbach, R. A. "Hereditary insensitivity to pain," *Trans. Amer. Neurol. Assn.* 85: 70–74.

French, A. P., Russell, P. L., and Tupin, J. P. "Subjective changes with the sentic cycles of Clynes," *Dis. Nerv. Syst.* 33: 598–602, 1972.

French, A. P., and Tupin, J. P. "Psychometric investigation of sentic cycles," *A.A.A.S. Symposium, Sentics, Brain Function and Human Values*. Palisades, New York: American Sentic Association, 1971.

Freud, S. *Civilization and Its Discontents*. London: Jonathan Cape & Harrison Smith, Inc., 1930, pp. 8–9.

———. "The Unconscious," *Collected Papers*, Vol. IV. London: Hogarth Press, 1949, pp. 109–111.

———. *The Moses of Michelangelo*. London: Hogarth Press and The Institute of Psychoanalysis, 1948, Vol. IV, pp. 257–258.

———. *The Poet and Day Dreaming*. London: Hogarth Press and The Institute of Psychoanalysis, 1948, Vol. IV, pp. 182–183.

———. *Wit and its Relation to the Unconscious*. London, 1916.

Gastaut, H., Regis, H., Lyagoubi, S., Mano, T., and Simon, L. "Comparison of the potentials recorded from the occipital, temporal and central regions of the human scalp, evoked by visual, auditory and somatosensory stimuli," *Electroencephalogr. Clin. Neurophysiol.*, Suppl. 16, 19–28, 1967.

Gelfand, S., Ullmann, L. P., and Krasner, L. "The placebo response: an experimental approach," *J. Nerv. Ment. Dis.* 136: 379–387, 1963.

Goethe, J. W. *Farbenlehre* (final version). 1817.

Graham, D. T. "Health, disease, and the mind-body problem: linguistic parallelism," *Psychosom. Med.* 29: 52–71, 1967.

Greenbie, B. B. "Sentics and biocybernetics in the search for an optimum human habitat," *A.A.A.S. Symposium, Sentics, Brain Function and Human Values*. Palisades, New York: American Sentic Association, 1971.

Grossman, S. P. "Modification of emotional behavior by intracranial administration of chemicals," *Physiological Correlates of Emotion*, P. Black, ed. Boston: Little, Brown, 1970, pp. 73–89.

Haber, W. B. "Observation on phantom-limb phenomena," *Arch. Neurol. Psychiat.* 57: 624–636, 1956.

Harlow, H. F., and Harlow, M. K. "Developmental aspects of emotional behavior," *Physiological Correlates of Emotion*, P. Black, ed. Boston: Little, Brown, 1970.

Hebb, D. O. *Introduction to K. S. Lashley, Brain Mechanism and Intelligence*. New York, 1963.

Hillman, James. *Emotion*. Evanston, Illinois: Northwestern Univ. Press, 1964.

Hohmann, G. W. "The effect of dysfunctions of the autonomic nervous system on experienced feelings and emotions," *Conference on Emotions and Feelings at New School for Social Research*, New York, 1962.

Hrbek, A. "Evoked responses of different sensory modalities in newborn infants," 6th Inter. Congress of Electroencephalography and Clinical Neurophysiology, San Diego, California, Sept. 13–19. *Electroencephalogr. Clin. Neurophysiol.* 27 (A), 1969.

Hubel, D. H., and Wiesel, T. N. "Shape and arrangement of column in cat's striate cortex," *J. Physiol.* 165: 559–568, 1963.

———. "Integrative activity in the cat's lateral geniculate," *J. Physiol.* 155: 385–398, 1961.

Huenergardt, D. "Relationship of essentic forms to facial communication of affect," A.A.A.S. *Symposium, Sentics, Brain Function and Human Values*. Palisades, New York: American Sentic Association, 1971.

Izard, C. *The Face of Emotion*. New York: Appleton-Century-Crofts, 1971.

Jakobsen, R. *Child Language, Aphasia and Phonological Universals*, A. R. Keiler, trans. The Hague, Netherlands, 1968.

James, W. *The Principles of Psychology*. New York: Holt, 1890.

John, E. R., et al. "Effects of visual form on the evoked response," *Science* 155, 1939–42, 1967.

Kandinsky, W. *Punkt und Linie zur Fläche*. Munich, Germany, 1926.

Kanizsa, G. "Subjective Contours," *Scientific American*, Vol. 234, No. 4, April 1976.

Kety, S. S. "Neurochemical aspects of emotional behavior," *Physiological Correlates of Emotion*, P. Black, ed. Boston: Little, Brown, 1970.

Klages, L. *Ausdrucksbewegung und Gestaltungskraft*. Leipzig: Barth, 1923.

———. *Grundlegung der Wissenschaft vom Ausdruck*. Bonn: Barth, 1950.

Kohler W. "Gestalt psychology today," *Amer. Psychol.* 14: 727–734, 1959.

———. "On the nature of association," *Proc. Amer. Phil. Soc.* 84: 489–502, 1941.

Kohn, M., and Clynes, M. "Color dynamics of the pupil," *Symposium on Rein Control, or Unidirectional Rate Sensitivity, a Fundamental Dynamic and Organizing Function in Biology*. M. Clynes, ed. Annals of the New York Academy of Sciences, Vol. 156, Art. 2, 351–950. April 21, 1969.

Laban, R. *Effort*. London: MacDonald and Evans, 1947.

———. *The Mastery of Movement*. London: MacDonald and Evans, 1958.

Lacey, J. I. "Psychophysiological approaches to the evaluation of psychotherapeutic progress and outcome," *Research in Psychotherapy*, E. A. Rubinstein and M. B. Parloff, eds. Washington, D.C., 1959, pp. 160–208.

———. *Some Autonomic-Central Nervous System Interrelationships in Physiological Correlates of Emotion*, P. Black, ed.: 205–226, 1970.

Lange, C. *Über Gemutsbewegungen*. 1887.

Lenneberg, E. H. *Biological Foundation of Language*. New York: John Wiley, 1967.

Levi, L. *Stress and Distress in Response to Psychosocial Stimuli*. New York: Pergamon, 1972.

Lewin, K. "Environmental forces in child development and behavior," *Handbook of Child Psychology*. Worcester, Massachusetts: Clark Univ. Press, 1931, pp. 94–127.

Lewitan, C. "Untersuchungen über das allgemeine psychomotorische Tempo," Z. *Psychol*. 101: 321–376, 1927.

Liberman, A. M., Cooper, F. S., Studdert-Kenedy, M., Harris K. S., and Shankweiler, D. P. "Some observations on the efficiency of speech sounds," *Haskins Lab. Report*. New York, 1966.

Lieberman, P. H., Klatt K. H., and Wilson, W. H. "Vocal tract laminations on the vowel repertories of Rhesus monkey and other non-human primates," *Science*, June 6, 1969.

Lindsley, D. B. "The role of nonspecific reticulo-thalamo-cortical systems in emotion," *Physiological Correlates of Emotion*, P. Black, ed. Boston: Little, Brown, 1970, pp. 147–184.

Lomax, Alan, "Song structure and social structure," *Ethnology* 1 (4): 425–451, 1962.

Longuet-Higgins, H. C. "The nonlocal storage and associative retrieval of spatio-temporal patterns," *Information Processing in the Nervous System*, K. N. Leibovic and J. C. Eccles, eds. New York: Springer-Verlag, 1969, pp. 37–46.

Luria, A. R. *Higher Cortical Functions in Man*, trans. from Russian by B. Haigh. New York, 1966.

MacLean, P. D. "Phylogenesis," *Expression of the Emotions in Man*, P. H. Knapp. New York: Internat. Univ. Press, Inc., 1963.

Maranon, G. *Rev. Fran. Endocrinol*. 2: 301–325, 1924.

———. "The psychology of gesture," *J. Nerv. Ment. Dis*. 112: 485–486, 1950.

Melcher, W. A. "Dual personality in handwriting," *J. Crim. Law and Criminol*. 2: 209–216.

Melzack, R., and Schecter, B. "Itch and vibration," *Science* 147: 1047–1048, 1965.

Melzack, R., and Wall, P. D. "Pain mechanisms: a new theory," *Science*, 150: 971–979, 1965.

Menuhin, Yehudi. *Theme and Variations*. London: Heineman, 1972.

Meyer, G. *Graphisch Fixierte Ausdrucksbewegungen*. 1898.

Meyer, L. B. *Emotion and Meaning in Music*. Chicago, Illinois: Chicago Univ. Press, 1956.

Minsky, M. *Computation: Finite and Infinite Machines*. Englewood Cliffs, New Jersey: Prentice-Hall, 1967.

Moles, A. *Information Theory and Aesthetic Perception*. Urbana, Illinois: Univ. of Illinois Press, 1966.

Morris, C. R. *Signs, Language and Behavior*. New York: Prentice-Hall, 1946.

Moses, P. *The Voice of Neuroses*. New York: Grune & Stratton, Inc., 1954.

Osgood, C. E., Suci, G. J., and Tannenbaum, P. *The Measurement of Meaning*. Urbana, Illinois: Univ. of Illinois Press, 1957.

Ostwald, P. F. *Soundmaking—the Acoustic Communication of Emotion*. Springfield, Illinois: Charles C. Thomas, 1963.

Pear, T. H. *Voice and Personality*. London: Chapman & Hall, 1931.

Piderit, T. *Mimik und Physiognomik*. 1858.

Ploog, D., Hopf, S., and Winter, P. "Ontogenese des Verhaltens von Totenkopf-Affen (Saimiri sciureus)," *Psychol. Forsch.* 31: 1–41, 1967.

Price, L. L. "Evoked response audiometry: some considerations," *J. Speech Hearing Dis.* 34: 137–141.

Rothschild, F. S. *Das Zentral Nerven System als Symbol des Erlebnis*. Basel, Switzerland: Karger, 1957.

Ruesch, Jurgen. *Therapeutic Communication*. New York: Norton, 1961.

Sapir, E. "Speech as a personality trait," *Amer. J. Sociol.* 32: 892–905, 1927.

Saudek, R. *Experiments with Handwriting*. New York: Morrow, 1928.

Schachter, S. *Advances in Experimental Social Psychology*, Vol 1, *The Interaction of Cognitive and Physiological Determinants of Emotional State*, 1962.

Schachter, S., and Singer, J. *Psychol. Rev.* 69: 379–399, 1962.

Schiller, F. *Über Anmut und Würde*. 1793.

Schnabel, A. *Music and the Line of Most Resistance*. Princeton, New Jersey: Princeton Univ. Press, 1942.

Schneider, G. E. "Two visual systems," *Science*, Feb. 28, 1969.

Schwangart, F. "Persönliches bei Tieren und tierisches Niveau," *Jahrb. Charakterologie* 5: 103–140, 1928.

Sebeok, T. A., ed. *Style in Language*. New York: John Wiley, 1960.

Seelig, E. "Die Registrierung unwillkürlicher Ausdrucksbewegungen als forensischpsychodiagnostische Methode," Z. *Psychol.* 28: 45–84, 1927.

Segal, S. J. ed. *Imagery: Current Cognitive Approaches*. New York: Academic Press, 1971.

Shagass, Ch. "Averaged somatosensory evoked responses in various psychiatry disorders," *Recent Advances Biol. Psychiat.* 10: 205–219, 1968.

Shevrin, H. "Forms of feeling: The role of idiologs in empathy and dream imagery," *A.A.A.S. Symposium, Sentics, Brain Function and Human Values*. Palisades, New York: American Sentic Association, 1971.

Sievers, Eduard. *Collected Works*. Stuttgart, Germany, 1875–1915.

Stanislavski, C. *Building a Character*. New York, 1949.

Starkweather, J. A. "Vocal communication of personality and human feelings," *J. Commun.* 11: 63–72, 1961.

Sternbach, R. A. "A comparative analysis of autonomic responses in startle," *Psychosom. Med.* 22: 204–210, 1960.

Stevens, K. N., and Halle, M. "Remarks on analysis by synthesis and distinctive features," *Models for the Perception of Speech and Visual Form*, W. Wather-Dunn, ed. Cambridge, Massachusetts, 1967.

Szasz, T. S. *Pain and Pleasure: A study of bodily feelings*. New York: Basic Books, 1957.

Tembrock, G. *Tierstimmen—Eine Einführung in die Bioakustik*. Lutherstadt: Wittenberg, 1959.

Thorpe, W. H. "Animal vocalization and communication," *Brain Mechanisms Underlying Speech and Language*, C. H. Milliken and F. L. Darley, eds. New York, 1957.

Tomkins, S. S., and McCarter, R. "What and where are the primary affects? Some evidence for a theory," *Percept. Mot. Skills* A.T. 119–158, 1964.

Valins, S. "The perception and labeling of bodily changes as determinants of emotional behavior," *Physiological Correlates of Emotion*, P. Black, ed. Boston: Little, Brown, 1970, pp. 229–242.

Vernon, P. E. "The personality of the composer," *Music and Letters* 11: 58–70, 1930.

Walter, W. G. "The analysis, synthesis and identification of evoked responses and contingent negative variation (CNV)," *Electroencephalogr. Clin. Neurophysiol.* 23: 489, 1967.

Wather-Dunn, W., ed. *Models for the Perception of Speech and Visual Form*. Cambridge, Massachusetts, 1967.

Wenger, M. A. "Emotion as visceral action: an extension of Lange's theory," *Feelings and Emotions*, M. L. Reymert, ed. New York: McGraw-Hill, 1950, pp. 3–10.

Wenger, M. A., Clemens, T. L., Darsie, M. L., Engel, B. T., Estess, F. M., and Sonnenschein, R. R., "Autonomic response patterns during intravenous infusion of epinephrine and nor-epinephrine," *Psychosom. Med.* 22: 294–307, 1960.

Wolff, W. "Gestaltidentität in der Charakterologie," *Psychol. Med.* 4: 32–44, 1929.

INDEX

New Publications by the Author since 1977

BOOKS

Clynes, M., and J. Panksepp, ed. 1988, *Emotions and Psychopathology*, Plenum Press, New York, 326pp.

Evans, J., Clynes, M., (ed.) 1986, *Rhythm in Psychological, Linguistic and Musical Processes*. Charles C. Thomas, Chicago, 291pp.

Clynes, M., (ed.) 1982, *Music, Mind and Brain: The Neuropsychology of Music*, Plenum Press, New York, 430pp.

ARTICLES

Clynes, M., 1988, *Generalized Emotion, its Production, and Sentic Cycle Therapy, in Emotions and Psychopathology,* M. Clynes and J. Panksepp, eds., Plenum Press, New York, pp107-170.

Clynes, M., 1987, What a musician can learn from newly discovered principles of musical thought, PM and PAM., in: *Action and Perception in Rhythm and Music.* A. Gabrielsson ed., Publication of The Royal Swedish Academy of Music. No. 55, Stockholm, pp201-233.

Clynes, M., 1986, Generative Principles of Musical Thought: Integration of Microstructure with Structure, CCAI, *The Journal for the Integrated Study of Artificial Intelligence, Cognitive Science and Applied Epistemology*, Vol. 3, No. 3, pp185-223.

Clynes, M., 1986, When Time is Music, in *Rhythm in Psychological, Linguistic and Musical Processes*, Evans and M. Clynes (eds.), C.C. Thomas, Chicago, pp169-224.

Clynes, M., and Walker, J., 1986, Music as Time's Measure, *Music Perception*, Vol. 4, No. 1, pp85-120.

Clynes, M., 1987, On Music and Healing, *Proceedings of the II International Symposium on Music and Medicine*, ed. R. Spintke and R. Droh, Springer Verlag, Berlin, Heidelberg, New York pp13-31.

Clynes, M., 1985, Secrets of Life in Music, in *Analytics*, Festschrift for Bengtsson, Royal Swedish Academy of Music, Publication No. 47, Stockholm, pp3-15.

Clynes, M., 1983, Expressive Microstructure in Music, linked to Living Qualities in *Studies of Music Performance*, J. Sundberg (ed.), Publication of Royal Swedish Academy of Music No. 39, pp79-181. Stockholm.

Clynes, M., and Nettheim, N., 1982. The Living Quality of Music: Neurobiologic Basis of Communicating Feeling, in *Music, Mind and Brain: The Neuropsychology of Music*, M. Clynes (ed.) pp47-82, Plenum Press, New York.

Clynes, M., and Walker, J., 1982, Neurobiologic Functions of Rhythm, Time and Pulse in Music in *Music, Mind and Brain: The Neuropsychology of Music*, M. Clynes (ed.) pp171-216, Plenum Press, New York.

Clynes, M., 1980, The communication of emotion: theory of sentics, in *Emotion: Theory, Research and Experience*, Vol. 1 Theories of Emotion, R. Plutchik, H, Kellerman (eds.) pp271-300, Academic Press, New York.

Clynes, M., 1979, The source of laughter and essentic form: Is evolution dis-covery? *Humanitas*, Vol. XV, 29-45, Duquesne University Press, Pittsburgh.

Clynes, M., 1979: Sentics: communication and generation of emotion through dynamic expression, in *Nonverbal Communication*, S. Weitz (ed.) 386-397, New York, Oxford University Press.

Since 1977 many thousands have benefited from Sentic Cycles. They can be learned in minutes. Having learned to do them, you can obtain their benefit whenever you wish, for the rest of your life. You can receive for your own use the following:

Sentic Cycles

A. STANDARD SENTIC CYCLE: set containing Sentic Cycle cassette audiotape with the sequence No Emotion, Anger, Hate, Grief, Love, Sex, Joy, Reverence (27 min.); a Finger Rest; and an illustrated Instruction Booklet.

B. ADVANCED SENTIC CYCLE: containing an Advanced Sentic Cycle audiotape, with only positive emotions, No Emotion, Love, Reverence, Bliss, Compassion, and Give Blessing (32 min.) with an illustrated Instruction Booklet (no finger rest required).

C. VIDEO OF ADVANCED SENTIC CYCLE: As B, but with this you can do the Advanced Cycle together with Dr. Manfred Clynes, and by yourself; contains visual information especially helpful for the Advanced Cycle (VHS, 70 min.).

Live Performances by Manfred Clynes

Cassette audiotapes of concerts by Manfred Clynes, recorded live, piano, 90 minutes each.

D. J.S. BACH Goldberg Variations

E. BEETHOVEN Diabelli Variations Op. 120, and
MOZART Adagio in B minor, and Sonata in B flat, K570.

These recordings have been regarded by some experts as arguably unsurpassed performances of these works.

To order:

	A	B	C	D or E
United States	$ 32.00	28.50	49.50	12.00
Australia	$A 32.50	28.50	49.50	12.00
Great Britain	£ 17.50	15.00	27.50	7.00

Please send cheque or money order to:
American Sentic Association, Box 2716, La Jolla, California, 92038
Australian Sentic Association, c/o Unity Press, 6a Ortona Road, Lindfield, N.S.W. 2070
European Sentic Association, c/o Prism Press, 2 South Street, Bridport, Dorset, DT6 3NQ, England.

You are cordially invited to become a Member of the American, European or Australian Sentic Association. Annual Membership fee is $25.00. Students and Senior Citizens, $10.00 (£14.00 and £6.00 for the European Association).